Student Edition

Bring Science Alive!®
Forces and Energy

 NEXT GENERATION SCIENCE STANDARDS For States, By States

Co-Chief Executive Officer
Bert Bower

Co-Chief Executive Officer
Amy Larson

Chief Operating Officer
Ellen Hardy

Director of Product Development
Maria Favata

Strategic Product Manager
Nathan Wellborne

Managing Editor
Ariel Stein

Senior Science Editor
Rebecca Ou

Senior Strategic Editor
Kim Merlino

***Forces and Energy* Lead Editor**
Ariel Stein

Science Content Developers
Karin Akre
Tanya Dewey
Mantissa Johnston
Suzanne Lyons
Abigail Pillitteri
Clay Walton
Jennifer Yeh

Editors
Helene Engler
Sally Isaacs
Lauren Kent
Marlene Martzke
Tylar Pendgraft
Alex White
Ginger Wu

Writers
Sarah Martin
Linda Blumenthal
Sabre Duren
Rebecca Mikulec
Laura Prescott
Molly Wetterschneider

Illustrator/Graphic Artists
Andrew Dakhil
Martha Iserman
Aki Ruiz

Production and Design
Jodi Forrest
Jen Valenzuela
Michelle Vella

Web and Print Designer
Sarah Osentowski

Video Developer
Dominic Mercurio

Director of Operations
Marsha Ifurung

Investigation UX Testing
Davin Kunovsky

Software
Morris Thai
Christopher Ching
Robert Julius
Gabriel Redig

Software Quality Assurance
Mrudula Sarode

Art Direction
Julia Foug

Teachers' Curriculum Institute
PO Box 1327
Rancho Cordova, CA 95741

Customer Service: 800-497-6138
www.teachtci.com

ISBN 978-1-58371-079-1

1 2 3 4 5 6 7 8 9 10 -WC- 23 22 21 20 19 18

Manufactured by Webcrafters, Inc., Madison, WI
United States of America, March 2018, Job # 134705

Welcome to *Bring Science Alive!*

Welcome to *Bring Science Alive! Forces and Energy*. We've created this program to help you understand the science and engineering ideas in the Next Generation Science Standards (NGSS). Believe it or not, forces and energy are involved in everything you see and do, from the way the planets orbit the sun to how you brush your teeth. But, understanding how we are affected by forces and energy can lead to a lot of perplexed head scratching and shoulder shrugging. No fear—*Bring Science Alive!* is here with a host of amazing investigations to make the baffling world of forces and energy fun and (relatively) easy to understand.

Get ready to experience forces and energy right in your own classroom. You'll be using a simulation to see how energy affects the motion of skateboarders in a virtual skate park. You'll design model go-carts and test how they hold up to collisions. You'll build and test a model zip-line system. You'll use the principles of electromagnetism to build a tiny motor that really works. And you'll figure out the best materials for keeping cool on a hot day and for warming up when the weather turns cold.

You'll finish this program with a newfound understanding for the often-mystifying world of forces and energy. And, believe me, the next time you and your friends ride a roller coaster or bundle up on a cold day, they aren't going to be able to keep you quiet. You'll be explaining those events with the enthusiasm of a true scientist. THAT'S what *Bring Science Alive!* will do for you.

Enjoy your adventure!

Bert Bower
TCI Co-CEO and Founder

Science Advisory Board

Science Content Scholars

David Begun, Ph.D.
Professor, Population Biology and Evolution and Ecology
University of California, Davis

Gillian Bowser, Ph.D.
Research Scientist, Natural Resource Ecology Laboratory
Colorado State University

John Czworkowski, Ph.D.
Chemistry Instructor
Grossmont College
El Cajon, California

Tanya Dewey, Ph.D.
Research Scientist, Biology Department
Colorado State University

Brian W. Holmes, Ph.D.
Professor, Physics and Astronomy
San José State University
San José, California

Ehsan Khatami, Ph.D.
Assistant Professor, Physics and Astronomy
San José State University
San José, California

Charles Liu, Ph.D.
Professor, Astrophysics
The College of Staten Island
City University of New York

Michael J. Passow, Ed.D.
Adjunct Associate Research Scientist, Lamont-Doherty Earth Observatory
Columbia University

Lesilee Rose, Ph.D.
Professor, Department of Molecular and Cellular Biology
College of Biological Sciences
University of California, Davis

Paul Ruscher, Ph.D.
Dean, Science Division
Lane Community College
Eugene, Oregon
Fellow, *American Meteorological Society*

Science Teacher Consultants

Kenneth Amunrud
Science Teacher
Joseph George Middle School
Alum Rock Union Elementary School District
San José, California

Nancy Anderson
Middle School Science Teacher
Mannington Township School
Mannington Township, New Jersey

Amy Argento
Science Teacher
Jefferson Middle School
Torrance Unified School District
Torrance, California

Noel Berghout
Math and Science Teacher
Jane Lathrop Stanford Middle School
Palo Alto Unified School District
Palo Alto, California

Carla Dalfonso
Science Specialist
Joe Serna Jr. Charter School
Lodi Unified School District
Lodi, California

Nora Haddad
Science Teacher
San Martin/Gwinn Environmental Science Academy
Morgan Hill Unified School District
Santa Clara County, California

Marsenne Kendall
Chemistry Teacher
Half Moon Bay High School
Cabrillo Unified School District
Half Moon Bay, California

Ann M. Lorey
Science Department Supervisor and Instructional Coach
Jane Lathrop Stanford Middle School
Palo Alto Unified School District
Palo Alto, California

Kevin Lynch
Science Teacher
J.L. Stanford Middle School
Palo Alto Unified School District
Palo Alto, California

Michael Passow
Earth Science Teacher (ret.)
White Plains Middle School
White Plains, New York

Stephanie Ruzicka
Science Teacher
Horner Junior High School
Fremont Unified School District
Fremont, California

Michelle Serrano
Secondary Science Curriculum Specialist
Hemet Unified School District
Hemet, California

Mathematics Teacher Consultant

Kenneth Amunrud
Mathematics Teacher
Joseph George Middle School
Alum Rock Union Elementary School District
San José, California

Reading Consultant

Marilyn Chambliss, Ph.D.
Associate Professor of Education Emerita
University of Maryland

How to Read the Table of Contents

The table of contents is your guide to *Bring Science Alive! Forces and Energy*. In addition to showing parts of your Student Text, it shows the exciting science and engineering investigations you will be doing in class.

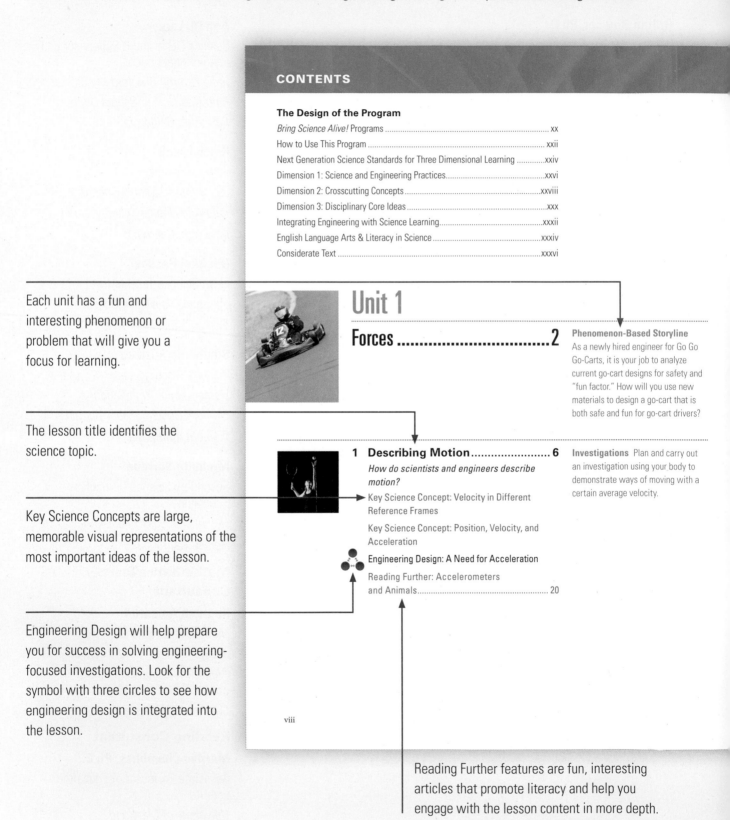

Each unit has a fun and interesting phenomenon or problem that will give you a focus for learning.

The lesson title identifies the science topic.

Key Science Concepts are large, memorable visual representations of the most important ideas of the lesson.

Engineering Design will help prepare you for success in solving engineering-focused investigations. Look for the symbol with three circles to see how engineering design is integrated into the lesson.

CONTENTS

Unit 1

Phenomenon-Based Storyline
As a newly hired engineer for Go Go Go-Carts, it is your job to analyze current go-cart designs for safety and "fun factor." How will you use new materials to design a go-cart that is both safe and fun for go-cart drivers?

How do scientists and engineers describe motion?

Key Science Concept: Velocity in Different Reference Frames

Key Science Concept: Position, Velocity, and Acceleration

Engineering Design: A Need for Acceleration

Investigations Plan and carry out an investigation using your body to demonstrate ways of moving with a certain average velocity.

viii

Reading Further features are fun, interesting articles that promote literacy and help you engage with the lesson content in more depth.

An essential question prepares you for inquiry—and for using evidence to explain how the natural world works.

Investigations Define force and its units. Apply Newton's third law of motion to different interactions in order to design a model for a zipline return system.

Investigations integrate:

- science and engineering practices,
- crosscutting concepts,
- and disciplinary core ideas.

Investigations Construct explanations for the effects of forces using Newton's first and second laws of motion, and then apply those laws to a shuffleboard-style game.

Engineering Challenge Using Newton's Laws, design a safe model go-cart that can withstand collisions from any side.

Engineering Challenge investigations invite you to apply science concepts and the engineering design process to solving relevant and engaging problems.

Performance Assessment Evaluate the safety of modern go-carts. Determine how the mass and speed of a cart affect the forces involved in collisions, and consider how the structure and materials of the go-carts keep riders safe.

A Performance Assessment related to the unit's storyline inspires you to use science and engineering practices, crosscutting concepts, and disciplinary core ideas.

 Engineering Design will help prepare you for success in solving engineering-focused investigations. Look for this symbol to see how engineering design is integrated into the lesson.

CONTENTS

The Design of the Program

Unit 1

Forces 2

How do scientists and engineers describe motion?

Key Science Concept: Velocity in Different Reference Frames

Key Science Concept: Position, Velocity, and Acceleration

 Engineering Design: A Need for Acceleration

Phenomenon-Based Storyline
As a newly hired engineer for Go Go Go-Carts, it is your job to analyze current go-cart designs for safety and "fun factor." How will you use new materials to design a go-cart that is both safe and fun for go-cart drivers?

Investigations Plan and carry out an investigation using your body to demonstrate ways of moving with a certain average velocity.

Investigations Define force and its units. Apply Newton's third law of motion to different interactions in order to design a model for a zipline return system.

Investigations Construct explanations for the effects of forces using Newton's first and second laws of motion, and then apply those laws to a shuffleboard-style game.

Engineering Challenge Using Newton's Laws, design a safe model go-cart that can withstand collisions from any side.

Performance Assessment Evaluate the safety of modern go-carts. Determine how the mass and speed of a cart affect the forces involved in collisions, and consider how the structure and materials of the go-carts keep riders safe.

 Engineering Design will help prepare you for success in solving engineering-focused investigations. Look for this symbol to see how engineering design is integrated into the lesson.

Unit 2

Phenomenon-Based Storyline
A drone hovers in the air and seems to defy gravity. You have access to an engineer's plans for the drone's motor. Can you piece together how electromagnetism powers the drone's propellers and allows it to fly?

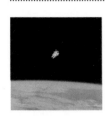

Investigations Investigate how mass affects gravitational force using simulations and drawings that demonstrate gravitational forces and fields.

Investigations Ask questions about electric charges and investigate the forces involved in static electricity by modeling electric fields using simulations and drawings.

Investigations Observe magnetic forces and fields by conducting a hands-on investigation to see how motors and generators work.

Performance Assessment
A drone's motors use properties of electromagnetism to power the propellers so the drone can fly. Analyze the parts of a drone's motor and then describe how drones can defy gravity and fly.

Unit 3

Kinetic and Potential Energy 110

Phenomenon-Based Storyline
One small action in a Rube Goldberg machine causes a chain reaction of effects. How can you use the ideas of kinetic and potential energy to figure out how the machine works?

Investigations Model potential and kinetic energy conversions with a 3-D bar graph. Then, construct an argument about the energy conversions in hands-on experiments.

Investigations Observe and graph relationships between kinetic energy, mass, and speed by constructing pendulums.

Investigations Model gravitational potential energy, and other types of potential energy, by using a skateboarding simulation.

Engineering Challenge Design musical instruments based on principles of energy conversion, transfer, and transformation.

Performance Assessment
Analyze parts of a Rube Goldberg machine in a video to understand the transfers and transformations of energy involved in chain reactions.

Unit 4

Phenomenon-Based Storyline
Temperatures in the desert vary greatly between daytime highs and nighttime lows. How do people and other animals minimize or maximize thermal energy transfer to survive these temperature swings?

Investigations Plan and carry out an investigation to determine how temperature change depends on the masses and types of matter involved. Design posters to explain conduction, convection, and radiation.

Investigations Investigate thermal conductivity and analyze data about temperature changes of ice. Compare the heat capacities of sand and water.

Performance Assessment
Design and test a device that either minimizes or maximizes thermal energy transfer, to be used in a desert situation.

Key Science Concepts

Figures

Interdisciplinary Science makes the connections between the life, earth, and physical sciences.

Interdisciplinary Science

Mathematics Connections integrate mathematical and scientific learning.

Mathematics Connections

Primary Sources

Bring Science Alive! Programs

Bring Science Alive! is a collection of nine middle school science programs that are 100 percent aligned to NGSS. These programs can be organized into three year-long courses for either integrated-science or discipline-specific learning progressions. Programs are well coordinated to crosscutting concepts such as patterns, energy and matter, and structure and function. Science and engineering practices are integrated with disciplinary core ideas and crosscutting concepts in engaging and challenging investigations.

Weather and Climate

Investigate the atmosphere and energy transfer, the water cycle, air pressure and air masses, weather prediction, climate factors and patterns, and Earth's changing climate.

Planet Earth

Construct explanations about Earth's natural resources, the rock and water cycles, rock layers, fossils, geologic time, plate tectonics, and natural hazards using varied time scales.

Space

Model cause and effect relationships involving Earth's rotation, revolution, and tilted axis; lunar phases and eclipses, the solar system, galaxies, and the universe.

Bring Science Alive! integrates Science and Engineering Practices, Crosscutting Concepts, and Disciplinary Core Ideas to result in Three Dimensional Learning.

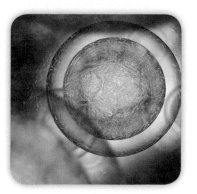

Cells and Genetics

Use evidence to explore traits, survival, and reproduction; the structure and functions of body systems and cells; genes and inheritance of traits, mutations, and engineering and genetics.

Ecosystems

Model interdependency in ecosystems, photosynthesis and cellular respiration, energy flow and cycling of matter, biodiversity, and explore the human impacts on ecosystems and biodiversity.

Adaptations

Identify cause and effect relationships between Earth's history and the fossil record, natural selection and changes in species, genes and patterns of inheritance; and humans, evolution, and heredity.

Matter

Apply the concepts of conservation of matter and energy transfer to model atoms, molecules, particle motion, state changes, and chemical reactions; and explore engineering solutions involving chemical reactions.

Forces and Energy

Solve engineering problems and plan investigations about forces, Newton's Laws of Motion; kinetic and potential energy; thermal energy, heat, and the thermal properties of matter.

Waves

Explore mechanical waves and their properties by looking at patterns in data, waves in different mediums, the wave model of light, properties of light waves, and technologies using waves to transfer information.

How to Use this Program

The components of *Bring Science Alive!* provide the tools needed for a complete learning system that integrates science and engineering practices, crosscutting concepts, and disciplinary core ideas. Designed for deep learning, *Bring Science Alive!* lessons use research-based learning strategies to reach all students.

1 Each new lesson begins with a **Lesson Guide** preview activity that teachers access through their online subscriptions. Lesson guides are the interactive guides at the heart of every TCI lesson.

2 Guided by the Lesson Guide and using the **Science Materials Kits** and their **Interactive Student Notebooks**, students conduct one or more investigations that powerfully integrate the three dimensions of NGSS. While investigating, students build understandings that they will need in order to complete the end-of-unit performance assessment.

4 The lesson concludes with students demonstrating their mastery of the science and engineering practices, crosscutting concepts, and disciplinary core ideas through a variety of paper and online **assessment tools**.

3 In their online student subscriptions, students expand their understanding by engaging with their dynamic **Student Text** and working through an **Interactive Tutorial**. Then they process what they have learned in their online **Interactive Student Notebook**.

Alternatively, students can read from the hardcover Student Edition and process their learning in a consumable Interactive Student Notebook.

Next Generation Science Standards for Three Dimensional Learning

The Next Generation Science Standards (NGSS) were written to change the way science is taught in K–12 classrooms and reflect recent advances in science, technology, and the understanding of how students learn. NGSS aims to help students prepare for college, 21st-century careers, scientific literacy needed as citizens, and competition in an increasingly global economy.

Performance Expectations

NGSS standards are called *performance expectations* and are worded to explain what students should be able to do in assessments at the completion of a unit of study. The performance expectations are built on the foundation provided by *A Framework for K-12 Science Education* (2012). Every performance expectation integrates the three dimensions described in the Framework: science and engineering practices, crosscutting concepts, and disciplinary core ideas. Also included in the performance expectations are clarification statements providing examples and other details, and assessment boundaries to guide test development. The graphic shows an example of how all the pieces result in a coherent standard to guide instruction.

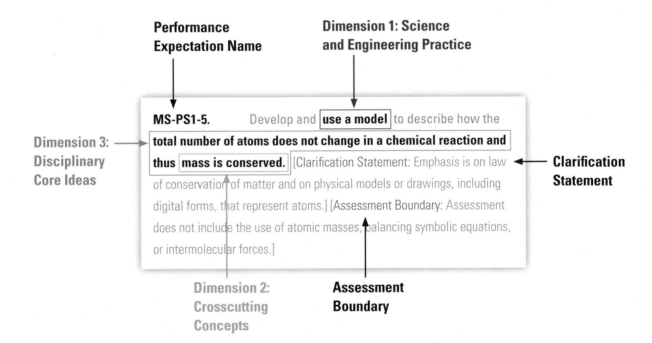

Dimension 1: Science and Engineering Practices

Science and Engineering Practices, such as developing and using models, describe what actual scientists and engineers do. Students develop the ability to use these practices through investigating the natural and designed worlds. While engaged in practices, students develop understandings described by the disciplinary core ideas and crosscutting concepts. The eight practices involve ways of thinking about investigations and engineering problems, the integration of mathematics, and social interactions. Without any particular order implied, these eight practices help define what has been called "scientific inquiry" and "engineering processes."

Bring Science Alive! investigations guide students to develop and reflect on their use of science and engineering practices.

Dimension 2: Crosscutting Concepts

Crosscutting Concepts, such as patterns and cause and effect, are the themes that organize students' understanding of science and engineering in the same way that scientists and engineers do. They can also be thought of as lenses all students should use as they explore and describe phenomena related to physical, earth and space, and life sciences. These "big picture" concepts are important in helping students make connections across all disciplines of science and engineering.

Each lesson focuses on a crosscutting concept that is explained in the lesson introduction and developed through the lesson.

Dimension 3: Disciplinary Core Ideas

Disciplinary Core Ideas are focused statements of content specific to the physical, earth and space, life sciences, or engineering. There are a limited number of core ideas, avoiding "mile wide, inch deep" curricula. The purpose of limiting the number of science concepts is to allow students the time they need for learning science and engineering practices through investigations. NGSS core ideas assume that students have mastered the content of previous grades and are ready for more advanced learning.

Students learn disciplinary core ideas by collecting evidence and building arguments through investigations, research, reading, and using multimedia tools.

Science and Engineering Practices | Dimension 1

The Next Generation Science Standards (NGSS) emphasize learning by investigating the natural world through the practices of scientific inquiry. Being able to use science understandings and practices allows students to investigate further questions about the natural world and solve meaningful engineering problems. NGSS identifies eight practices of science and engineering. Each lesson of *Bring Science Alive!* provides scaffolded instruction and reflection of one or more of these practices.

Asking Questions and Defining Problems

Science often begins by asking meaningful questions that can be answered by explanations supported by evidence. Similarly, engineering may begin with a question but always involves defining a problem that can be solved by carefully-tested solutions. Students learn to ask supporting questions that clarify and move them forward in investigations and solving engineering problems.

Developing and Using Models

Science and engineering use models to represent very large, very small, or very complicated systems. Using models helps scientists and engineers develop questions and explanations, gather data and make predictions, and communicate ideas to others. Students learn to develop, interpret, and modify models to describe scientific phenomena and test their engineering solutions.

Planning and Carrying Out Investigations

Scientific investigations are planned and carried out to describe a phenomena, test a hypothesis, or model how the world works. They are also used to test engineering solutions. Students design investigations that generate data for evidence to support their claims and learn how to be systematic in their methods so that they can obtain the most precise results.

Analyzing and Interpreting Data

All the data in the world is meaningless unless it can be presented in a form that reveals patterns and relationships and allows results to be communicated. Students analyze and interpret data by organizing their data into tables and graphs to identify overall trends and specific patterns.

Using Mathematics and Computational Thinking

Scientists and engineers use mathematics to represent physical variables and their relationships and to make quantitative descriptions and predictions. Students use mathematics aligned to the Common Core State Standards to analyze data for patterns and answer scientific questions. They also use mathematics to test and compare scientific arguments and engineering solutions.

Constructing Explanations and Designing Solutions

The goal of scientific inquiry is to construct explanations for why things happen. Likewise, the goal of engineering is to design solutions to people's problems. Students engage in constructing explanations when they make sense of the data they collect during investigations and when they propose solutions to engineering problems.

Engaging in Argument from Evidence

Argument is a process for comparing different explanations and solutions, and determining which is best. Reasoning and argument based on evidence are important for identifying the best explanation or the best solution to a design problem. Students engage in critical discussions to practice listening to, comparing, and evaluating competing explanations and solutions.

Obtaining, Evaluating, and Communicating Information

Researching, reading, interpreting, and producing scientific and technical text is an important part of science and engineering. Students learn to recognize key ideas, identify bias, distinguish observations from inferences, arguments from explanations, and claims from evidence. They communicate their findings orally, in writing, and through extended discussions.

The Next Generation Science Standards (NGSS) underscore the importance of making connections between the life, earth, physical sciences, and engineering. The seven crosscutting concepts are designed to do just this. While the seven overarching concepts are the same from kindergarten through twelfth grade, the details increase in complexity as students progress. *Bring Science Alive!* develops crosscutting concepts in conjunction with appropriate disciplinary core ideas and science and engineering practices throughout the Student Text, Lesson Guide activities and investigations, and assessments.

Patterns

Middle school students relate macroscopic patterns to microscopic structures, identify relationships that show patterns in rates of change, analyze numerical data on graphs and charts for patterns, and identify patterns that lead to understanding cause-and-effect relationships.

Cause and Effect

Through investigations and discussion, students come to appreciate that a phenomenon may have more than one cause, that the likelihood of certain types of outcomes must be expressed in terms of probability, and that by recognizing cause-and-effect relationships they can make predictions in science and engineering. They also discover how relationships can be causal or correlational but that not all correlational relationships are causal.

Scale, Proportion, and Quantity

Phenomena involving time, space, or energy can be observed at different scales. The function of a system may change, depending on the scale at which it is observed. Students learn that some natural systems are either too large or too small to be directly observed, but they can explored using models of various scales. Mathematical reasoning becomes increasingly important to understanding and communicating scientific ideas as students learn that certain relationships can be represented as expressions or equations and that proportional relationships are useful for describing relationships between many scientific quantities.

Systems and System Models

The concept of a system as an organized group of parts is essential in all science disciplines and, certainly, for designing, building, and testing solutions to engineering problems. Throughout their investigations, students use the concept of systems to show how parts interact both within and outside a system, as well as how systems have sub-systems. Models are essential for understanding inputs and outputs and that energy and matter flow through many systems.

Energy and Matter

Energy and matter flow into, out of, and within both natural systems and designed systems. Students learn to track energy flow through both natural and designed systems. They use that understanding to describe the role energy plays in cycling of matter, and in describing the many forms energy takes as it is transferred from one part of a system to another.

Structure and Function

This crosscutting concept is closely related to systems and system models. Students learn to analyze the functions of all parts of a system by examining their shapes, properties, and their relationships to each other. Designing and building structures for particular functions also requires consideration of the parts' shapes and the materials from which they are made.

Stability and Change

Like structure and function, stability and change is a concept that directly supports the understanding of systems. Students' explanations of stability and change in systems include how changes to one part affect other parts of the system, how change can be gradual or sudden, and how equilibrium is maintained through feedback mechanisms.

Disciplinary Core Ideas | Dimension 3

The Next Generation Science Standards include a limited number of compelling scientific and engineering ideas to ensure that K–12 students learn and engage in the practices of science and engineering. Every *Bring Science Alive!* lesson allows students to build understanding of the disciplinary core ideas through the uses of these practices and the crosscutting concepts.

Core Idea ESS1: Earth's Place in the Universe

Planet Earth is part of a vast universe that has developed over a huge expanse of time and can be understood using observation, physics, and chemistry. Middle school students learn how gravitational forces hold the solar system together; explain patterns that result in lunar phases, eclipses, and seasons; and explore Earth's history by understanding rock strata and the fossil record.

Core Idea ESS2: Earth's Systems

Earth is made up of a set of dynamic systems whose interactions and processes determine how Earth changes over time. Students study the effects of energy flows and the cycling of matter in many of these systems, such as plate tectonics, the water cycle, weather systems, and changes due to weathering and erosion.

Core Idea ESS3: Earth and Human Activity

Humans depend on, are affected by, and cause changes to Earth's systems. Students learn how many natural resources are limited in quantity or distribution, the causes of natural hazards and likelihood that they will occur, and how humans impact the biosphere and can design solutions to lessen their impacts.

Core Idea LS1: From Molecules to Organisms: Structures and Processes

The functioning of all organisms is closely related to the structures that make them up, on scales ranging from individual molecules to whole body systems. Middle school students study structures such as cells, tissue, organs, and organ systems; and functions like behaviors, photosynthesis, cellular respiration, and sensory responses.

Core Idea LS2: Ecosystems: Interactions, Energy, and Dynamics

Ecosystems are dynamic systems in which organisms interact with one another and nonliving resources. They can be described by the flow of energy and cycling of matter. Students study patterns of interdependency; producers, consumers, and decomposers; and the effects of disruptions to ecosystems.

Core Idea LS3: Heredity: Inheritance and Variation of Traits

Heredity is the mechanism by which traits are passed via genes from parents to offspring. Middle school students learn that

genes control the production of proteins that affect traits, how sexual reproduction results in variation in inherited genetic information, and about the effects of mutations on traits.

Core Idea LS4: Biological Evolution: Unity and Diversity

Biological evolution explains both the similarities and differences among species and their history on Earth. Students learn how the fossil record and embryological development indicate that species are related, how natural and artificial selection result in changes to species over time, and how changes in biodiversity can affect humans.

Core Idea PS1: Matter and Its Interactions

The existence of atoms is fundamental to understanding the characteristics and behavior of matter. Middle school students apply the concepts of atoms and molecules to explain the existence of different substances, properties of matter, changes in state, and conservation of matter in chemical reactions.

Core Idea PS2: Motion and Stability: Forces and Interactions

Forces are a tool for describing the interactions between objects and for explaining and predicting the effects of those interactions. In middle school, students begin to quantitatively describe the effects of forces and learn to describe forces that act at a distance using fields.

Core Idea PS3: Energy

Energy is a tool for explaining and predicting interactions between objects. In middle school, students learn that systems often involve kinetic and potential energy. Energy concepts are extended to explain more complex interactions, such as those involved in chemical reactions, living things, and Earth systems.

Core Idea PS4: Waves and Their Applications in Technologies for Information Transfer

Waves are repeating patterns of motion that transfer energy from place to place without overall displacement of matter. Students use properties, such as wavelength, frequency, and amplitude, to understand the behaviors of wave-like phenomena, including light, sound, and water waves. Scientists and engineers also use wave properties to encode information as digitized signals for communication.

Core Idea ETS1: Engineering Design

Engineers solve problems using a design process involving specific practices and knowledge. Students in the middle grades learn the importance of defining criteria and constraints with precision, testing solutions, and using test results to improve solutions iteratively to achieve optimal designs.

Integrating Engineering with Science Learning

The Next Generation Science Standards describe engineering as a process similar to, and just as important as, scientific inquiry. The four engineering design performance expectations for middle school require students to understand how to define criteria and constraints, evaluate competing design solutions, analyze data to combine several designs, and develop models to test and refine proposed designs.

Student Text

In *Bring Science Alive!* student texts, engineering design is well integrated with the scientific core ideas of the lesson, including all the same support as other parts of the lesson: interactive tutorials, vocabulary development, and assessments.

Engineering design sections are identified by the symbol with three circles.

Engineering Design

5. A Need for Acceleration

One day, while flipping through TV channels you see an odd car race. The cars have long, narrow front ends, big engines in the back, and fat tires. The cars speed down a short stretch of track and parachutes pop out of the backs of the cars after they cross the finish line. What kind of race is this and why are the cars so funny looking?

The race with the odd-looking cars is a drag race, and the odd-looking cars are called *dragsters*. During a drag race, two cars travel as fast as they can on a track that is only 0.25 miles long. Since the track is so short and because the cars start the race standing still, a dragster has to be able to reach a high velocity very quickly. In other words, a good dragster has to have a high acceleration.

Drag racing started in the 1930s when teenagers and young adults met on country roads and dry lakebeds to see who had the fastest car. The early dragsters were simply regular cars that were "souped up" to go faster. By the 1950s, drag racing became more organized with official racetracks and rules.

As the sport's popularity grew, dragster engineers began to develop designs to improve the cars' performance. Although the designs varied, they all had to conform to meet the criteria and constraints that the engineers had agreed. **Criteria** are the requirements that must be met for an engineering solution to be successful. On the other hand, **constraints** are limitations on an engineering solution.

Some of the criteria for a dragster are that it must accelerate quickly, be easily controlled, and carry a driver. The biggest constraint on a dragster is that it must be safe. Dragsters are large, powerful machines and any crash could be deadly for the drivers and anyone watching near the track.

During a drag race, cars called *dragsters* move from a standing start over a course that is only 0.25 miles long. To be successful, a dragster has to accelerate very quickly. Engineers work on ways to increase dragsters' acceleration while still keeping the cars safe for their drivers.

Engineers experimented with engine placement as a way to get more acceleration out of the dragsters on test tracks. For example, a popular design called the *slingshot* placed the engine in front of the driver. The driver sat at the very back of the car behind the dragster's rear wheels. The slingshot design had great acceleration and good control. The design's great acceleration made it a good fit for the main criteria of dragster design. But constraints on the design prevented it from widespread use. The design was too dangerous for the driver.

Another design put the engine behind the driver and turned it 90 degrees from its normal placement in dragsters. Because the engine was turned sideways, these cars were called *sidewinders*. Engineers thought that turning the engine sideways would increase the traction of rear tires and give the car better acceleration. But, the sidewinder's acceleration was not as great as hoped. So, the sidewinder design did not meet the criteria for dragster design.

Another design put four engines in one dragster! The engines gave the dragster a lot of power, but they were heavy. Furthermore, controlling four engines at once was tricky. They also produced so much smoke and exhaust that the driver often could not see the track for the beginning of the race. So, dragsters with four engines did not meet the criteria or fit within the constraints.

The successes and failures of the various designs eventually led to the design that is in use today. Today's dragsters have a similar shape to the slingshot, but the engine is placed behind the driver. They have a single engine, which is not turned sideways. Although the overall design of dragsters is not changing much, engineers are still working on ways to increase their acceleration.

Today's dragsters have similar design elements. For example, the engine is placed behind the driver for safety reasons.

LESSON SUMMARY
Describing Motion

Position An object's motion is described in terms of its distance and direction from a reference point.

Speed and Velocity Speed and velocity describe how fast an object changes position. Velocity also describes the direction an object is moving.

Reference Frames A reference frame is a point of view used to describe the motion of objects.

Acceleration An object accelerates when it changes speed, changes direction, or both.

A Need for Acceleration Engineers design and test drag racing cars to maximize acceleration while also maintaining safety.

Engineering vocabulary is developed in the same ways as science vocabulary.

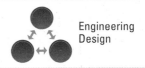
Investigations

In *Bring Science Alive!*'s engineering challenges, students use science and
engineering practices to solve fun, interesting problems that have the potential
to help answer scientific questions, improve lives, protect the environment,
entertain, and delight.

The consistent engineering design process
in *Bring Science Alive!*'s engineering
challenges provides a clear road map for
approaching design problems. Using it,
students will decide when to define the
problem, develop possible solutions, and
optimize their designs.

Each engineering challenge focuses on one
or two easy-to-learn engineering skills.
By the time they complete the program,
students will have a full set of tools for
tackling any design problem.

English Language Arts & Literacy in Science

Bring Science Alive! is aligned with the Common Core State Standards for English Language Arts & Literacy (CCELA). Literacy instruction is built into the online Student Text, Interactive Student Notebook, and the Lesson Guides. The following six key points are from the grades 6–8 CCELA Standards for Literacy in History/Social Studies, Science, and Technical Subjects. They are particularly important in science instruction.

Reading Standards for Literacy

✓ **Main Ideas and Details** Identifying key ideas and details applies to reading science text, following multistep procedures for experiments, and using scientific tools and other technology.

When using the *Bring Science Alive!* online text, students have the option to see the main idea of each section highlighted. Additionally, every lesson includes one or more multistep investigations that students must follow to carry out science experiments, analyze data, and solve engineering problems.

✓ **Craft and Structure** In the middle grades, mastering new vocabulary includes understanding the meaning of scientific and mathematical symbols as well as domain-specific terms, words, and phrases.

Learning of scientific symbols and mathematical representations is scaffolded in *Bring Science Alive!* First, the concept is presented in words and phrases. Next, symbols are shown alongside these words and phrases. Finally, the symbolic notation is shown on its own.

✓ **Integration of Knowledge and Ideas** Students should be able to integrate their learning on a topic using experiments, multimedia materials, and the text.

Each *Bring Science Alive!* lesson concludes with a processing task that requires students to demonstrate their understanding of science and engineering practices, crosscutting concepts, and disciplinary core ideas as a result of carrying out investigations, manipulating simulations, and reading the text.

Writing Standards for Literacy

✓ **Purposes for Writing** The writing standards stress the use of certain conventions of good writing, including the use of previews, supporting details, appropriate transitions, domain-specific vocabulary, and an objective tone.

Bring Science Alive! students write for different purposes, including to explain scientific concepts and to record investigation procedures and results so that others can replicate and test them. Students are asked to construct written arguments to persuade others to accept an engineering design solution. They also write accounts of their investigations using precise language, scientific vocabulary, and minimal bias.

✓ **Production and Distribution of Writing** Routine writing of clear and coherent content that is appropriate to its purpose is central throughout the writing standards.

Bring Science Alive! includes regular writing opportunities in the Lesson Guides and Interactive Student Notebook. Writing, peer review, and editing are essential tools in guiding students to develop arguments and explanations that result in three dimensional learning.

✓ **Research to Build and Present Knowledge** Short research projects, using a variety of print and digital sources appropriately, should be carried out to answer broad questions that generate more specific questions.

Students build research skills using print and digital sources, including the Internet. Unit problems require students to gather and assess relevant information and to integrate this information with what they learn during hands-on investigations.

Considerate Text

Literacy is fundamental for success in science. *Bring Science Alive!* is both engaging and helps students read text that is more complex and at a higher level than other text they read. That's because our writers wrote it as "considerate text," which is another way to say that it makes readers want to read it. Considerate text is well written and well-organized. Here are some ways this Student Text is considerate of all levels of readers.

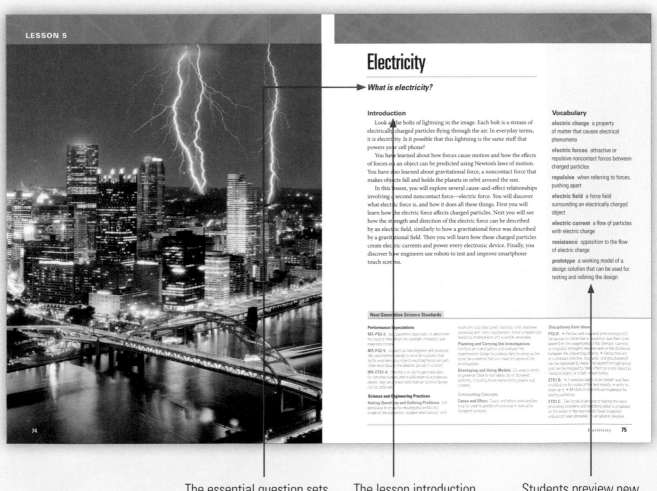

The essential question sets a purpose for reading.

The lesson introduction clearly explains the purpose and carefully-crafted organization of the lesson.

Students preview new science terms and their definitions before they read the lesson.

Short sections, each with an informative title, make it easier for readers to understand and remember the main ideas.

The paragraph that begins each section orients and engages the reader.

Single-column text makes the lesson easier to read.

1. Electric Charge and Forces

You and your friends are decorating the school gym for a dance. As you blow up balloons, you decide to do a magic trick. You rub a balloon on your hair and then place the balloon on the wall where it sticks. How could you explain this trick?

The explanation for the sticking balloon starts with charged particles. All matter is made of particles that are too small to see. Some of these particles have electric charge. Electric charge is a property of matter that causes electrical phenomena. Particles with electric charge interact with other particles with electric charge.

Two kinds of electric charge exist. These kinds of charges are called *positive* and *negative*, names chosen to show that the charges have opposite effects.

As demonstrated in Figure 5.1A, objects may have either equal or unequal numbers of positively charged particles and negatively charged particles. Objects that have equal numbers of positively charged particles and negatively charged particles are called *neutral* because they have no overall charge. Most objects you regularly encounter are neutral.

Most of the time, your hair and a balloon have equal numbers of positively charged and negatively charged particles and are neutral. However, when you rub a balloon on your hair, negatively charged particles from your hair are transferred to the balloon. Your hair now has more positively charged particles than negatively charged particles, and has an overall positive charge. The balloon, on the other hand, has more negatively charged particles and has an overall negative charge.

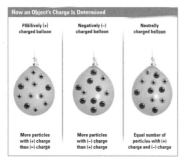

Balloons will stick to a wall after you rub them on your hair.

How an Object's Charge Is Determined

Positively (+) charged balloon	Negatively (–) charged balloon	Neutrally charged balloon
More particles with (+) charge than (–) charge	More particles with (–) charge than (+) charge	Equal number of particles with (+) charge and (–) charge

Figure 5.1A
All objects contain positively charged particles and negatively charged particles. If an object has equal numbers of positively and negatively charged particles, the object is neutral. If an object has unequal numbers of positively and negatively charged particles, the object has an overall charge.

Charged objects can interact through electric forces. Electric forces are attractive or repulsive noncontact forces between charged particles. Recall that an attractive force pulls objects together. On the other hand, a repulsive force pushes objects apart. Whether an electric force is attractive or repulsive depends on the charges of the objects. You can investigate this in an experiment similar to the one shown in Figure 5.1B. It shows two balloons hanging side by side on strings to explore the cause-and-effect relationships involved. Neutral objects, such as the first pair of balloons, do not experience electric forces.

The electric forces between two objects are repulsive when they have the same kind of charge. In Figure 5.1B, pairs of balloons with the same kind of charge are pushed apart. In another example, when your friend pulls a wool sweater over his head, negatively charged particles from the sweater transfer to each hair on his head. As a result, each strand of hair has more negatively charged particles and therefore, is negatively charged. Because all strands of hair have the same charge, the electric force between them is repulsive. The strands of hair push each other away.

On the other hand, when two objects have opposite charges, the electric forces between them are attractive. Figure 5.1B shows how pairs of balloons will behave. Now recall the balloons for the school dance. Rubbing a balloon on your hair will give the balloon a negative charge. When you hold the balloon close to the wall, the negatively charged balloon pushes the negatively charged particles in the wall away, giving the area near the balloon a positive charge. The balloon and the area of wall near the balloon have opposite charges, so the electric force between them is attractive. As a result, the balloon and the wall pull together and the balloon sticks to the wall.

Figure 5.1B
The electric force is an attractive or repulsive force between charged objects. The electric force pushes objects apart if they have the same charge, but pulls objects together if they have opposite charges. No electric force exists between neutral objects.

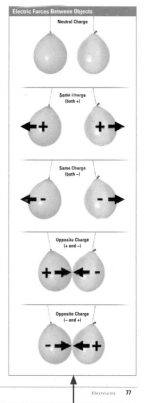

Electric Forces Between Objects

Neutral Charge

Same Charge (both +)

Same Charge (both –)

Opposite Charge (+ and –)

Opposite Charge (– and +)

Captions reinforce the main idea of the section and provide supporting details.

Important new science and engineering vocabulary is in bold type, defined in the same sentence, and used throughout the rest of the text.

Scientific illustrations are carefully labeled and titled.

UNIT 1

Forces

OVERVIEW

As this go-cart rolls downhill, it picks up speed. What causes the cart to pick up speed? And how can the driver slow down, stop, or change the direction of the go-cart? In this unit, you will learn about the motion of objects and how this motion can change. You will also learn about the forces involved when objects in motion interact. You will then propose a plan to test design improvements for go-carts that will increase their safety during collisions.

Phenomenon-Based Storyline
As a newly hired engineer for Go Go Go-Carts, it is your job to analyze current go-cart designs for safety and "fun factor." How will you use new materials to design a go-cart that is both safe and fun for go-cart drivers?

Investigations Plan and carry out an investigation using your body to demonstrate ways of moving with a certain average velocity.

Investigations Define force and its units. Apply Newton's third law of motion to different interactions in order to design a model for a zipline return system.

Investigations Construct explanations for the effects of forces using Newton's first and second laws of motion, and then apply those laws to a shuffleboard-style game.

Engineering Challenge Using Newton's Laws, design a safe model go-cart that can withstand collisions from any side.

Performance Assessment
Evaluate the safety of modern go-carts. Determine how the mass and speed of a cart affect the forces involved in collisions, and consider how the structure and materials of the go-carts keep riders safe.

Performance Expectations

MS-PS2-1. Apply Newton's Third Law to design a solution to a problem involving the motion of two colliding objects.

MS-PS2-2. Plan an investigation to provide evidence that the change in an object's motion depends on the sum of the forces on the object and the mass of the object.

MS-ETS1-1. Define the criteria and constraints of a design problem with sufficient precision to ensure a successful solution, taking into account relevant scientific principles and potential impacts on people and the natural environment that may limit possible solutions.

MS-ETS1-2. Evaluate competing design solutions using a systematic process to determine how well they meet the criteria and constraints of the problem.

Science and Engineering Practices

Planning and Carrying Out Investigations
Plan an investigation individually and collaboratively, and in the design: identify independent and dependent variables and controls, what tools are needed to do the gathering, how measurements will be recorded, and how many data are needed to support a claim.

Engaging in Argument from Evidence
Evaluate competing design solutions based on jointly developed and agreed-upon design criteria.

Constructing Explanations and Designing Solutions
Apply scientific ideas or principles to design an object, tool, process or system.

Asking Questions and Defining Problems
Define a design problem that can be solved through the development of an object, tool, process or system and includes multiple criteria and constraints, including scientific knowledge that may limit possible solutions.

Connections to Engineering, Technology, and Applications of Science: Influence of Science, Engineering, and Technology on Society and the Natural World
• All human activity draws on natural resources and has both short- and long-term consequences, positive as well as negative, for the health of people and the natural environment. • The uses of technologies and any limitations on their use are driven by individual or societal needs, desires, and values; by the findings of scientific research; and by differences in such factors as climate, natural resources, and economic conditions.

Crosscutting Concepts

Stability and Change
Explanations of stability and change in natural and designed systems can be constructed by examining the changes over time and forces at different scales.

Systems and System Models
Models can be used to represent systems and their interactions—such as inputs, processes, and outputs—and energy and matter flows within systems.

Disciplinary Core Ideas

PS2.A: Forces and Motion
• All positions of objects and the directions of forces and motions must be described in an arbitrarily chosen reference frame and arbitrarily chosen units of size. In order to share information with other people, these choices must also be shared. • For any pair of interacting objects, the force exerted by the first object on the second object is equal in strength to the force that the second object exerts on the first, but in the opposite direction (Newton's third law). • The motion of an object is determined by the sum of the forces acting on it; if the total force on the object is not zero, its motion will change. The greater the mass of the object, the greater the force needed to achieve the same change in motion. For any given object, a larger force causes a larger change in motion.

ETS1.A: Defining and Delimiting Engineering Problems
The more precisely a design task's criteria and constraints can be defined, the more likely it is that the designed solution will be successful. Specification of constraints includes consideration of scientific principles and other relevant knowledge that are likely to limit possible solutions.

ETS1.B: Developing Possible Solutions
There are systematic processes for evaluating solutions with respect to how well they meet the criteria and constraints of a problem.

Connect Your Learning

Every day you interact with and are surrounded by objects in motion. From nonliving things such as automobiles to living things such as yourself, objects in motion are influenced by forces. These forces also determine how objects interact with each other. By coming to understand how forces affect living and nonliving objects, you can explain many different phenomena in a world in motion.

A swimmer in motion pivots and pushes off the concrete wall of a pool. How can you use forces to explain why and how the wall also pushes against the swimmer?

A moving car appears to be still, while the scenery outside seems to be moving at a rapid pace. How is it that objects that are stationary look like they are moving, while objects in motion look like they are completely still?

Forces

The least weasel has one of the strongest bite forces ever recorded. How can scientists use forces to understand how such a small animal can have such a strong bite?

Describing Motion

How do scientists and engineers describe motion?

Introduction

It's the final match of the tennis tournament. The defending champion awaits the serve from the challenger. All eyes are on the challenger as she throws the tennis ball high in the air and raises her racket. *Thwack!* The racket hits the ball and sends it flying to the other side of the court. Suppose that you are talking to a friend on the phone while watching the game. How would you describe what you see?

Tennis, like all sports, involves a lot of motion. The ball soars and bounces, rackets are swung in large arcs, and each player runs around on his or her side of the court. A tennis game is a system that includes two people, two rackets, a ball, a net, and a court. What parts of the system never change and what parts are changing constantly? The net and the court do not move—they never change. The people, the rackets, and the ball are in motion most of the time. Although these parts change, the system as a whole is stable because the parts within it stay the same.

In this lesson, you will first learn to describe the motion of an object, including its current position and how it is moving. This includes describing that motion from different points of view. Then, you will learn to describe changes in the motion, including speeding up, slowing down, and changing direction. Using the terminology you just learned, you will explore how engineers design drag cars for maximum acceleration while maintaining safety.

Vocabulary

position the distance and direction that an object is from a reference point

reference point an object or place you use to describe the locations of other objects

rate an amount of something measured per unit of something else; many rates describe changes or events that happen over time

speed the rate that describes how far an object moves over time

velocity an object's speed and direction of motion

reference frame a point of view on the speed and direction that objects are moving and what reference point they are moving relative to

acceleration the rate of change of an object's velocity; acceleration can be speeding up, slowing down, or changing direction

criteria the requirements that must be met for an engineering solution to be successful

constraints limitations on an engineering solution

Next Generation Science Standards

Performance Expectations

MS-PS2-2. Plan an investigation to provide evidence that the change in an object's motion depends on the sum of the forces on the object and the mass of the object.

MS-ETS1-2. Evaluate competing design solutions using a systematic process to determine how well they meet the criteria and constraints of the problem.

Science and Engineering Practices

Planning and Carrying Out Investigations Plan an investigation individually and collaboratively, and in the design: identify independent and dependent variables and controls, what tools are needed to do the gathering, how measurements will be recorded, and how many data are needed to support a claim.

Engaging in Argument from Evidence Evaluate competing design solutions based on jointly developed and agreed-upon design criteria.

Crosscutting Concepts

Stability and Change Explanations of stability and change in natural and designed systems can be constructed by examining the changes over time and forces at different scales.

Disciplinary Core Ideas

PS2.A. All positions of objects and the directions of forces and motions must be described in an arbitrarily chosen reference frame and arbitrarily chosen units of size. In order to share information with other people, these choices must also be shared.

ETS1.B. There are systematic processes for evaluating solutions with respect to how well they meet the criteria and constraints of a problem.

1. Position

Suppose that you are learning to drive. As you drive the instructor's black car down the road, your instructor asks where the white van is. "The white van is about four car-lengths behind us," you say.

When you describe the distance and direction to the white van, you are describing its position. An object's **position** is its current distance and direction from a reference point.

A **reference point** is an object or place you use to describe the locations of other objects. The reference point that you used to describe the location of the white van was your black car. Observe Figure 1.1. When you describe the distance from a reference point, you can think of the reference point as the 0 point on an imaginary number line. The number line extends from the reference point to the object whose position you are describing. You described the position of the white van as four car-lengths behind your car. "Four car-lengths" is the distance measured from the reference point (your car). "Behind" is the direction from the reference point.

Car-lengths is a useful unit when you are driving a car, but it is not as useful in other situations, such as if you were trying to describe how far a tennis ball traveled. Most of the time, the distance part of position is given using standard units of length, such as meters (m).

You can use positive or negative numbers to indicate the direction an object is in when describing its position. For example, the red car is +15 m from the black car, meaning it is 15 m in front of the car. On the other hand, the white van is −21 m away from the black car, meaning it is 21 m behind the black car.

Figure 1.1

The position of an object is described as distance and direction away from a reference point. If the front of the black car is used as a reference point, an imaginary number line extends in front of and behind that point on the black car. Using this number line, you see that the front of the red car is 15 m away from the front of the black car, and the front of the white van is −21 m away from the front of the black car.

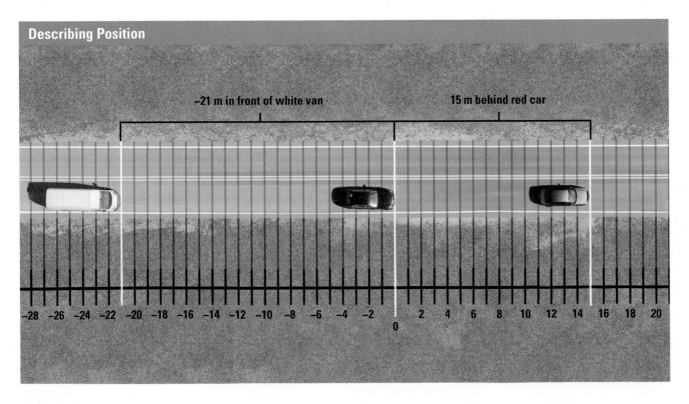

Describing Position

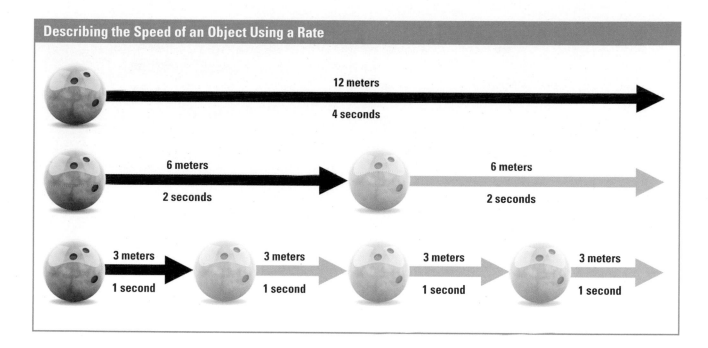

Describing the Speed of an Object Using a Rate

12 meters
4 seconds

6 meters
2 seconds

6 meters
2 seconds

3 meters
1 second

3 meters
1 second

3 meters
1 second

3 meters
1 second

2. Speed and Velocity

The red car in front of you exits the highway, and the road ahead is clear. You press on the gas pedal to go faster. "It can be tempting to drive too fast when no one is in front of you," says your instructor. "How fast are you going?"

When your instructor asks how fast you are going, he wants to know how quickly the position of the car is changing. In other words, he wants to know how far the car moves in a given amount of time, such as a second or an hour. How far the car moves in a given amount of time is an example of a rate. A **rate** is an amount of something measured per unit of something else.

Many rates describe changes or events that happen over time. Suppose that a man in an eating contest eats 60 hot dogs in 10 minutes. His rate of eating is 6 hot dogs per minute. However, not all rates involve time. A grocery store may sell watermelon at a rate of $0.70 per pound, which means that a 10-pound watermelon costs $7.00.

Speed The rate that describes the distance an object moves over time is that object's **speed**. Speed is one way that the motion of an object can be described. Speeds can be measured in various units, but all speeds are measured in units of distance per a unit of time. For example, a car's speed is often measured in kilometers per hour (km/h) or miles per hour (mi/h or mph). Scientists often describe speeds using meters per second (m/s).

Figure 1.2A shows you how the same speed can be represented different ways. In 1 second, the bowling ball rolls 3 meters. In 2 seconds it rolls 6 meters, and in 4 seconds it rolls 12 meters. In all of these cases, its speed is 3 m/s.

Figure 1.2A

The speed of an object is a rate that describes how far the object moves in a certain amount of time. Arrows can be used to illustrate rates. Each arrow represents an object traveling 3 m in 1 s. So, the object's speed is 3 m/s. After 4 s, the object travels a total of 12 m.

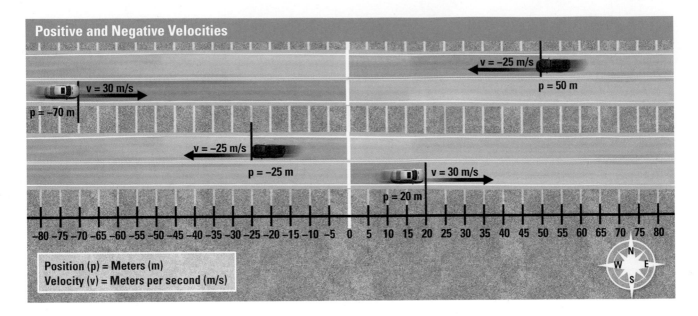

Positive and Negative Velocities

v = −25 m/s
p = 50 m

v = 30 m/s
p = −70 m

v = −25 m/s
p = −25 m

v = 30 m/s
p = 20 m

−80 −75 −70 −65 −60 −55 −50 −45 −40 −35 −30 −25 −20 −15 −10 −5   0   5   10   15   20   25   30   35   40   45   50   55   60   65   70   75   80

Position (p) = Meters (m)
Velocity (v) = Meters per second (m/s)

Figure 1.2B

The velocity of an object is the object's speed and direction of motion. The yellow car's speed is 30 m/s, and its direction of motion is east. Therefore, the yellow car's velocity is 30 m/s east. The red car's speed is 25 m/s, and its direction of motion is west. Therefore, the red car's velocity is 25 m/s west.

Velocity Speed is one way of describing how fast an object is going, but it does not tell you what direction the object is moving in. **Velocity** is an object's speed and direction of motion.

Like speed, velocity can be measured in different units. Car velocity is usually expressed as kilometers per hour (km/h) in a given direction. You could describe velocity of a runner as 4 m/s *toward the finish line*, and the velocity of a snail is about 1.5 cm/min *to the east*.

An object's velocity can change from moment to moment. Instead of trying to calculate an object's velocity at a given moment, you can calculate the object's average velocity. You calculate the average velocity of an object by dividing the distance it traveled by time needed to travel that distance. To find the distance an object traveled, you subtract the object's starting position from its ending position. So, the equation for average velocity is:

$$average\ velocity = \frac{end\ position - start\ position}{time}$$

In Figure 1.2B, the yellow car moves from −70 m to 20 m from the white line in 3 seconds. Additionally, the yellow car is moving in the positive direction along the number line to the east. Using the equation above, you can calculate its average velocity as:

$$average\ velocity = \frac{20\ m - -70\ m}{3\ s} = 30\ m/s\ east$$

To fully describe the velocity of the car, you have to look at a situation to find and name the direction the car is going. Whether the velocity is positive or negative tells you if the object is moving forward or backward. In the same amount of time, the red car moves from 50 m to −25 m from the white line in 3 seconds. It is moving in the negative direction to the west. Its average velocity is:

$$average\ velocity = \frac{-25\ m - 50\ m}{3\ s} = -25\ m/s\ west$$

3. Reference Frames

After completing your driving practice for the day, you switch places with one of the other students in your driver's education class. She gets into the driver's seat, and you climb into the back seat and start to read your driver's manual. After riding for a while, you feel a touch of motion sickness. To get rid of the queasy feeling, you look out the window and watch the scenery go by. Why did you feel woozy when you were looking down, but not when you looked outside?

Motion sickness often happens when what you feel does not match with what you see. As the car moved, your body vibrated with the engine, swayed during turns, and bounced when going over bumps. When you looked down at the book, the book and everything you could see inside the car stayed in place. Your eyes told your brain that you were not moving because you could not see anything changing positions. Your body felt like it was moving, but your eyes did not see any motion, and you got motion sickness.

When you looked out the car window, you could see trees and buildings go by. The inside of the car still looked stationary, but you saw objects outside moving relative to the car. Your eyes saw that you were moving, which matched with what your body was feeling, and the motion sickness went away.

Without changing your position, you saw the car in two different reference frames. A **reference frame** is a point of view on the speed and direction that objects are moving and what reference point they are moving relative to. When you sit inside the car, the car seems still. So the speed of the car is 0 km/h from your point of view. The road, buildings, and trees might be moving at −90 km/h, zipping by backwards. You might call this the "car reference frame." When you stand on the road, the road does not seem to be moving. So the road, buildings, and trees are all moving at 0 km/h, while the car is zipping by forward at 90 km/h. You might call this the "road reference frame."

Motion looks different when viewed from different reference frames. In the car reference frame on the left, the bushes are moving backward and the car mirror is not moving. In the road reference frame on the right, the car is moving forward and the bushes are not moving.

Reference frames are arbitrary, which means that you are free to choose which reference frame you use to describe position or motion. But you have to stick to that reference frame if you want to describe the motion of multiple objects together. Most often, you likely use a reference frame where you are not moving, because it makes it easy to describe things as you see it. However, other people tend to use their own point of view as reference frames, so they describe position and motion differently.

For example, suppose that your teacher is walking from the front of the room to the back as shown in Figure 1.3. You and your classmates all see him move, but you see different things. Why?

The reference frame you use can determine how you describe position or motion. Your friend in the back of the room sees the teacher walking in front of her and toward her. From her reference frame, the teacher is moving in a forward direction and has speed of 1 m/s. But from the front row, you see the teacher walking away from you and behind you. From your reference frame, the teacher is walking with a velocity of −1 m/s. Your teacher is not moving in a different way, but you and your friend describe it differently because you are describing it using different reference frames.

Because reference frames are arbitrary, you have to specify which reference frame you are using to share information about position or motion with other people. For example, suppose you and your friend are facing each other and you want him to look at a car nearby. You could say either "look at the car to my right" or "look at the car to your left." When you say "my right" or "your left" you are stating which reference frame you are using to describe the car's position.

Figure 1.3

Your reference frame determines how you describe position or motion. Depending on where you sit in the classroom, you will see a different perspective on Mr. Garcia's motion.

Velocity in Different Reference Frames

How you see and measure motion depends on your reference frame. People can have different reference frames, which means that they may measure motion differently. When people want to share information about an object's motion, they must also share the reference frame that they are using to measure the motion. Suppose that you and your friend are observing the scene shown. You observe from the train platform and your friend observes from the inside the train. Each of you talks about what you see over the phone.

Ground Reference Frame

You say to your friend:

> In my reference frame from the train platform, I see the train traveling 25 m/s west and the plane traveling 250 m/s east.

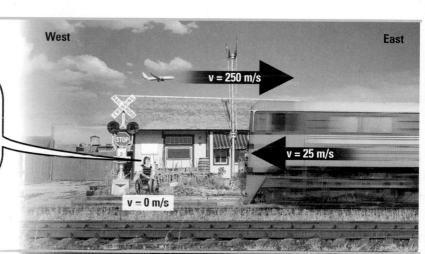

Train Reference Frame

Your friend says:

> From my reference frame inside the train, the train station is traveling 25 m/s east, and the plane is traveling 275 m/s east.

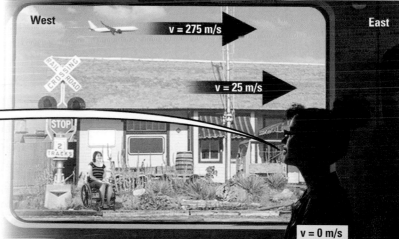

Plane Reference Frame

If you could talk to a passenger on the plane, that passenger might say:

> From my reference frame inside the plane, the train station is traveling 250 m/s west, and the train is traveling 275 m/s west.

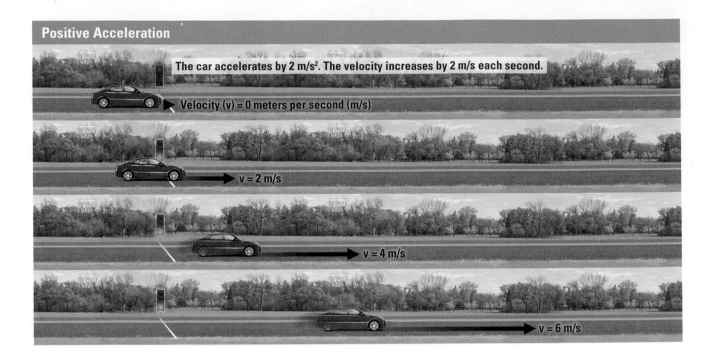

Positive Acceleration

The car accelerates by 2 m/s². The velocity increases by 2 m/s each second.

Velocity (v) = 0 meters per second (m/s)

v = 2 m/s

v = 4 m/s

v = 6 m/s

Figure 1.4A
Acceleration is the rate of change of an object's velocity. This car is accelerating because its velocity is increasing over time. As each second passes, its velocity increases by 2 m/s, so the rate that the car's velocity changes is 2 m/s per second.

This multiple exposure image shows that a ball accelerates as it rolls down a ramp. The exposures were taken 0.025 seconds apart, and the ball moves farther during each time interval. It moves farther because its velocity keeps increasing.

4. Acceleration

Car ads sometimes brag that a car can go "from 0 to 60" in just a few seconds. What does that mean? Why is it better for a car to go from 0 to 60 in 5 seconds than for it to go from 0 to 60 in 10 seconds?

The phrase "from 0 to 60" is a statement about a car's acceleration. **Acceleration** is the rate of change of an object's velocity. When the speed of a car increases from 0 mph to 60 mph, its velocity is changing, so it is accelerating. An object accelerates whenever its velocity changes. Recall that velocity is the speed and direction that an object travels. So, acceleration can take three forms.

Speed Increasing When the speed of an object increases over time, the object accelerates. For example, when a car moves after stopping at a stop sign such as in Figure 1.4A, it accelerates. A runner that starts sprinting at the end of a long race also accelerates by increasing her speed.

Speed Decreasing Any change in speed is a change in velocity, so an object that is slowing down is also accelerating. You might think it is weird to say that a car accelerates to stop at a stoplight, as shown in Figure 1.4B, but that statement is true! Sometimes people call slowing down *deceleration*.

Changing Direction Because velocity includes the direction that an object travels, an object accelerates when it changes direction. So, a car turning a corner while keeping the same speed is accelerating. An object can also accelerate by changing direction and speed at the same time, such as a car slowing down while turning.

Acceleration as a Rate Acceleration is more than just changing velocity. It is a rate that measures the change in velocity per unit of time. This rate tells you how quickly (or how slowly) an object's velocity changes over time. The more quickly an object changes speed or direction, the greater its acceleration.

An object's acceleration can change from moment to moment, just like its velocity can. However, you can calculate an object's average acceleration. First subtract its starting velocity from its ending velocity. Then divide that result by the time over which the change in velocity happened. Written as an equation, acceleration is:

$$average\ acceleration = \frac{ending\ velocity - starting\ velocity}{time}$$

When you look at the equation, you can see that acceleration has units of velocity divided by units of time. A common unit of velocity is meters per second (m/s) and a common unit of time is seconds (s). Thus, a common unit of acceleration is meters per second per second ((m/s)/s), which is also written as meters per second squared (m/s^2).

The car in Figure 1.4A starts with a velocity of 0 m/s and reaches a velocity of 6 m/s in 3 seconds. Its acceleration is:

$$average\ acceleration = \frac{6\ m/s - 0\ m/s}{3\ s} = 2\ m/s^2$$

The car's speed increases by 2 m/s every second.

The car in Figure 1.4B starts with a velocity of 6 m/s and slows to a velocity of 0 m/s in 3 seconds. So the second car's acceleration is:

$$average\ acceleration = \frac{0\ m/s - 6\ m/s}{3\ s} = -2\ m/s^2$$

The car's speed decreases by 2 m/s every second until it comes to a complete stop.

Figure 1.4B

When an object slows down, it has negative acceleration. The velocity of this car decreases by 2 m/s as each second passes. Its acceleration is –2 m/s^2.

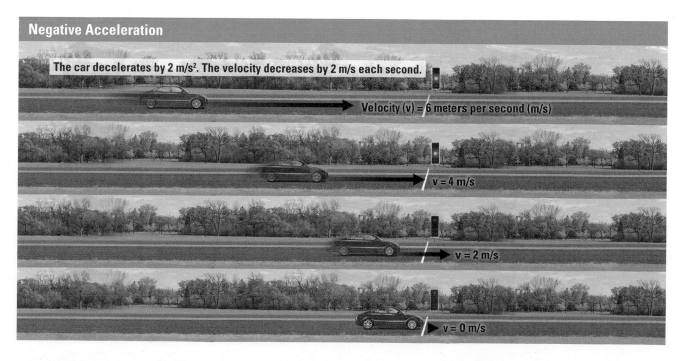

Negative Acceleration

The car decelerates by 2 m/s^2. The velocity decreases by 2 m/s each second.

Velocity (v) = 6 meters per second (m/s)

v = 4 m/s

v = 2 m/s

v = 0 m/s

Position, Velocity, and Acceleration

The position, velocity, and acceleration of a horse changes many times during a horse show. In this scenario, all motion is described from the horse's reference frame. So the direction in front of the horse is the positive direction, and the direction behind the horse is the negative direction. Can you describe the horse's motion?

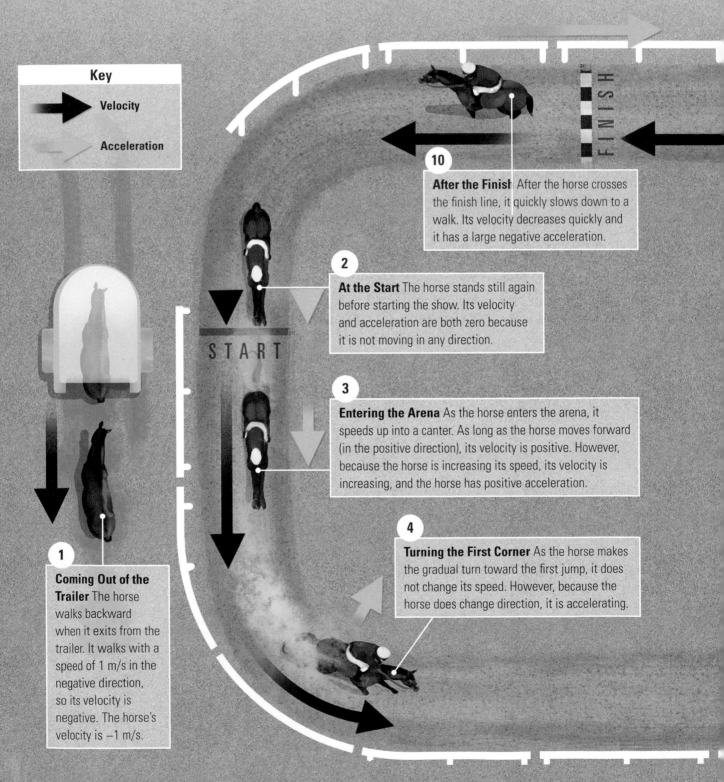

Key

→ **Velocity**

Acceleration

10 After the Finish After the horse crosses the finish line, it quickly slows down to a walk. Its velocity decreases quickly and it has a large negative acceleration.

2 At the Start The horse stands still again before starting the show. Its velocity and acceleration are both zero because it is not moving in any direction.

3 Entering the Arena As the horse enters the arena, it speeds up into a canter. As long as the horse moves forward (in the positive direction), its velocity is positive. However, because the horse is increasing its speed, its velocity is increasing, and the horse has positive acceleration.

4 Turning the First Corner As the horse makes the gradual turn toward the first jump, it does not change its speed. However, because the horse does change direction, it is accelerating.

1 Coming Out of the Trailer The horse walks backward when it exits from the trailer. It walks with a speed of 1 m/s in the negative direction, so its velocity is negative. The horse's velocity is −1 m/s.

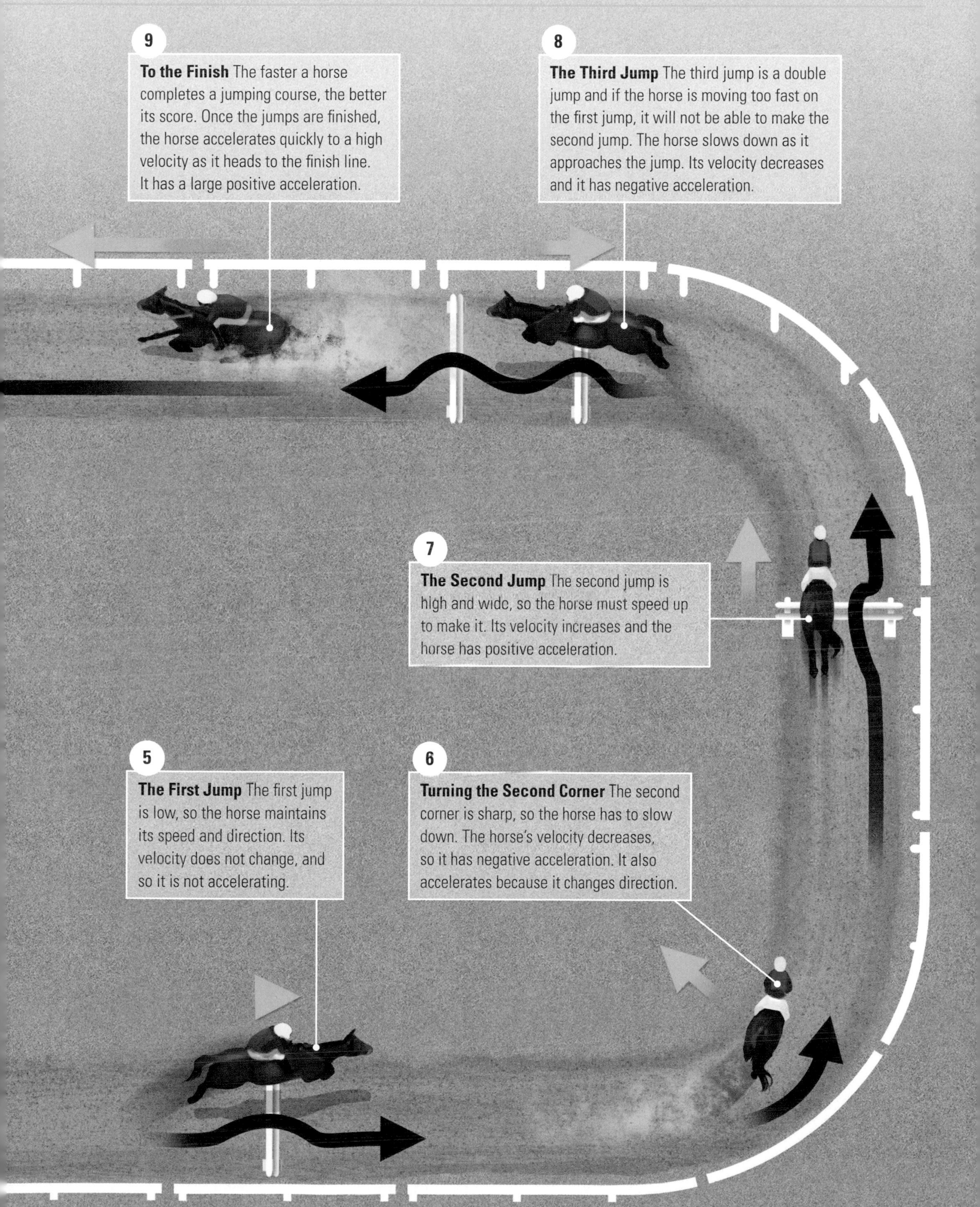

9

To the Finish The faster a horse completes a jumping course, the better its score. Once the jumps are finished, the horse accelerates quickly to a high velocity as it heads to the finish line. It has a large positive acceleration.

8

The Third Jump The third jump is a double jump and if the horse is moving too fast on the first jump, it will not be able to make the second jump. The horse slows down as it approaches the jump. Its velocity decreases and it has negative acceleration.

7

The Second Jump The second jump is high and wide, so the horse must speed up to make it. Its velocity increases and the horse has positive acceleration.

5

The First Jump The first jump is low, so the horse maintains its speed and direction. Its velocity does not change, and so it is not accelerating.

6

Turning the Second Corner The second corner is sharp, so the horse has to slow down. The horse's velocity decreases, so it has negative acceleration. It also accelerates because it changes direction.

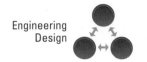
5. A Need for Acceleration

One day, while flipping through TV channels you see an odd car race. The cars have long, narrow front ends, big engines in the back, and fat tires. The cars speed down a short stretch of track and parachutes pop out of the backs of the cars after they cross the finish line. What kind of race is this and why are the cars so funny looking?

The race with the odd-looking cars is a drag race, and the odd-looking cars are called *dragsters*. During a drag race, two cars travel as fast as they can on a track that is only 0.25 miles long. Since the track is so short and because the cars start the race standing still, a dragster has to be able to reach a high velocity very quickly. In other words, a good dragster has to have a high acceleration.

Drag racing started in the 1930s when teenagers and young adults met on country roads and dry lakebeds to see who had the fastest car. The early dragsters were simply regular cars that were "souped up" to go faster. By the 1950s, drag racing became more organized with official racetracks and rules.

As the sport's popularity grew, dragster engineers began to develop designs to improve the cars' performance. Although the designs varied, they all had to conform to meet the criteria and constraints that the engineers had agreed on. **Criteria** are the requirements that must be met for an engineering solution to be successful. On the other hand, **constraints** are limitations on an engineering solution.

Some of the criteria for a dragster are that it must accelerate quickly, be easily controlled, and carry a driver. The biggest constraint on a dragster is that it must be safe. Dragsters are large, powerful machines and any crash could be deadly for the drivers and anyone watching near the track.

During a drag race, cars called *dragsters* move from a standing start over a course that is only 0.25 miles long. To be successful, a dragster has to accelerate very quickly. Engineers work on ways to increase dragsters' acceleration while still keeping the cars safe for their drivers.

Engineers experimented with engine placement as a way to get more acceleration out of the dragsters on test tracks. For example, a popular design called the *slingshot* placed the engine in front of the driver. The driver sat at the very back of the car behind the dragster's rear wheels. The slingshot design had great acceleration and good control. The design's great acceleration made it a good fit for the main criteria of dragster design. But constraints on the design prevented it from widespread use. The design was too dangerous for the driver.

Another design put the engine behind the driver and turned it 90 degrees from its normal placement in dragsters. Because the engine was turned sideways, these cars were called *sidewinders*. Engineers thought that turning the engine sideways would increase the traction of rear tires and give the car better acceleration. But, the sidewinder's acceleration was not as great as hoped. So, the sidewinder design did not meet the criteria for dragster design.

Another design put four engines in one dragster! The engines gave the dragster a lot of power, but they were heavy. Furthermore, controlling four engines at once was tricky. They also produced so much smoke and exhaust that the driver often could not see the track for the beginning of the race. So, dragsters with four engines did not meet the criteria or fit within the constraints.

The successes and failures of the various designs eventually led to the design that is in use today. Today's dragsters have a similar shape to the slingshot, but the engine is placed behind the driver. They have a single engine, which is not turned sideways. Although the overall design of dragsters is not changing much, engineers are still working on ways to increase their acceleration.

Today's dragsters have similar design elements. For example, the engine is placed behind the driver for safety reasons.

LESSON SUMMARY

Describing Motion

Position An object's motion is described in terms of its distance and direction from a reference point.

Speed and Velocity Speed and velocity describe how fast an object changes position. Velocity also describes the direction an object is moving.

Reference Frames A reference frame is a point of view used to describe the motion of objects.

Acceleration An object accelerates when it changes speed, changes direction, or both.

A Need for Acceleration Engineers design and test drag racing cars to maximize acceleration while also maintaining safety.

Accelerometers and Animals

The competitors are waiting to start the race that will determine the fastest animal in the world. The cheetah represents the running animals, the peregrine falcon represents the flying animals, and the sailfish represents the swimming animals. And, a complimentary entry was given to humans for organizing the event. Who will win?

Who is the fastest of them all? If you use acceleration to measure how fast something is, a mantis shrimp is faster than a cheetah, a peregrine falcon, and a sailfish.

Before the race starts, an unexpected contestant comes forward: the mantis shrimp. The mantis shrimp's human manager announces, "This animal cannot run as fast as the cheetah or swim as fast as the sailfish, but it is the fastest animal here!"

"How is it possible?" inquires the human racer.

The shrimp's manager explains, "Fast can mean high speed or high acceleration. The acceleration of the mantis shrimp's hammer-like legs is higher than the acceleration of any of the other animals in this competition."

Scientists collect animal motion data in different ways. The acceleration of cheetahs was measured using accelerometers attached to collars.

Data Collection on the Go

As entertaining as it would be, a race like the one described could not happen in real life. A peregrine falcon is fastest when it is diving down through the air, and a sailfish is fastest when it is jumping out of a water wave. So scientists studying animal movement have to measure animals' acceleration in different ways.

Recall that acceleration is the rate of change of an object's velocity. Data about an object's position can be used to calculate the object's velocity at different points in time. Then, acceleration is determined using the calculated velocities. One way that scientists measure animal acceleration is to attach an accelerometer on the animal. An accelerometer is a device that calculates acceleration by measuring changes in position.

The accelerometer collects data that can be used to find the animal's speed and acceleration. Scientists used accelerometers to measure the acceleration of cheetahs by attaching accelerometers to the cheetahs with collars. In one study, scientists found that cheetahs have accelerations as high as 13 m/s^2. By comparison, Olympic gold medalist Usain Bolt has an acceleration of around 9.5 m/s^2 and a good sports car has an acceleration of 9–10 m/s^2.

Small accelerometer devices do not interfere with an animal's motion. For example, a tiny accelerometer won't cause much drag in the water when a sailfish swims. Scientists studying sailfish found a sailfish's acceleration to be almost 32 m/s^2.

An accelerometer is a tiny electronic device that measures motion. It can be attached directly to animals such as fish and birds without interfering with the animals' movement.

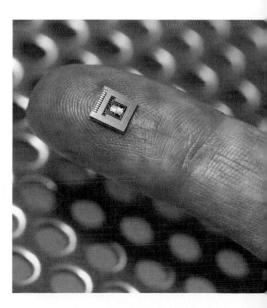

Smile! You're on High-Speed Camera!

Sometimes, attaching an accelerometer to an animal is difficult or not practical. Luckily, scientists have another tool that they can use to measure accelerations of animals without attaching anything to them. That tool is a high-speed camera. A high-speed camera is a video camera that can take a lot of images in a short period of time. Some cameras can take more than 1 million images each second!

To measure an animal's motion with a high-speed camera, scientists video the animal and then analyze the images to measure the distance that the animal moves. Because the scientists know how many photos are taken each second, they know how much time elapses as the animal moves. They can use the distance and time data to calculate the animal's speed and acceleration.

Scientists studying the diving flight of peregrine falcons used a high-speed camera to collect data. The scientists used a camera because they were interested in the shape of the falcons' dives and the birds' body shape during flight. But they also found that during part of the dives, the falcons reached accelerations of 11.5 m/s^2.

Mantis shrimp have hammer-like legs that they swing very quickly to smash the shells of clams, crabs, and other sea creatures. Because the legs swing so quickly, scientists had to use high-speed cameras to study their motion. They found that those legs have accelerations of around 104,000 m/s^2! Compared to mantis shrimp, peregrine falcons, sailfish, and cheetahs are very slow.

The mantis shrimp's hammer-like legs have a powerful punch. The acceleration of the legs is one of the fastest motions in the animal kingdom.

Hammer-like legs

Some athletes use accelerometers and other motion tracking devices. These devices can help them perform better during training and competition.

Tracking Humans

Accelerometers are not only tools that scientists use to study how fast animals can move. Accelerometers can also be used to track different types of movement. People use accelerometers all the time, sometimes without even knowing it.

Most cell phones contain accelerometers that are used to track how the phone moves. Phone apps use the motion information in different ways. For example, some games are controlled by tilting the phone in various directions, and the tilt of the phone is measured by the phone's accelerometer. Star and planet finder apps can tell which way the phone is pointing so you can figure out what stars or planets you are looking at. The apps work thanks to the accelerometer and other sensors in the phone.

Many fitness trackers work because of accelerometers. People wear these fitness trackers on their wrists or waists. When people walk or run, their arms swing and their hips move. Accelerometers in fitness trackers detect the motions of the arms or hips and use these data to measure how many steps a person takes. Some people use fitness trackers to improve their running. But no matter how much a person uses an accelerometer to train, he or she will never move as fast as a mantis shrimp's leg! ◆

People often wear accelerometers to track their own activity. Many fitness trackers use accelerometers to record the number of steps a person takes each day.

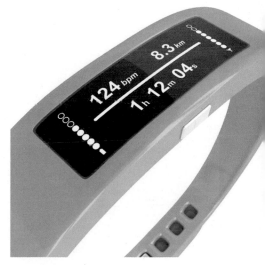

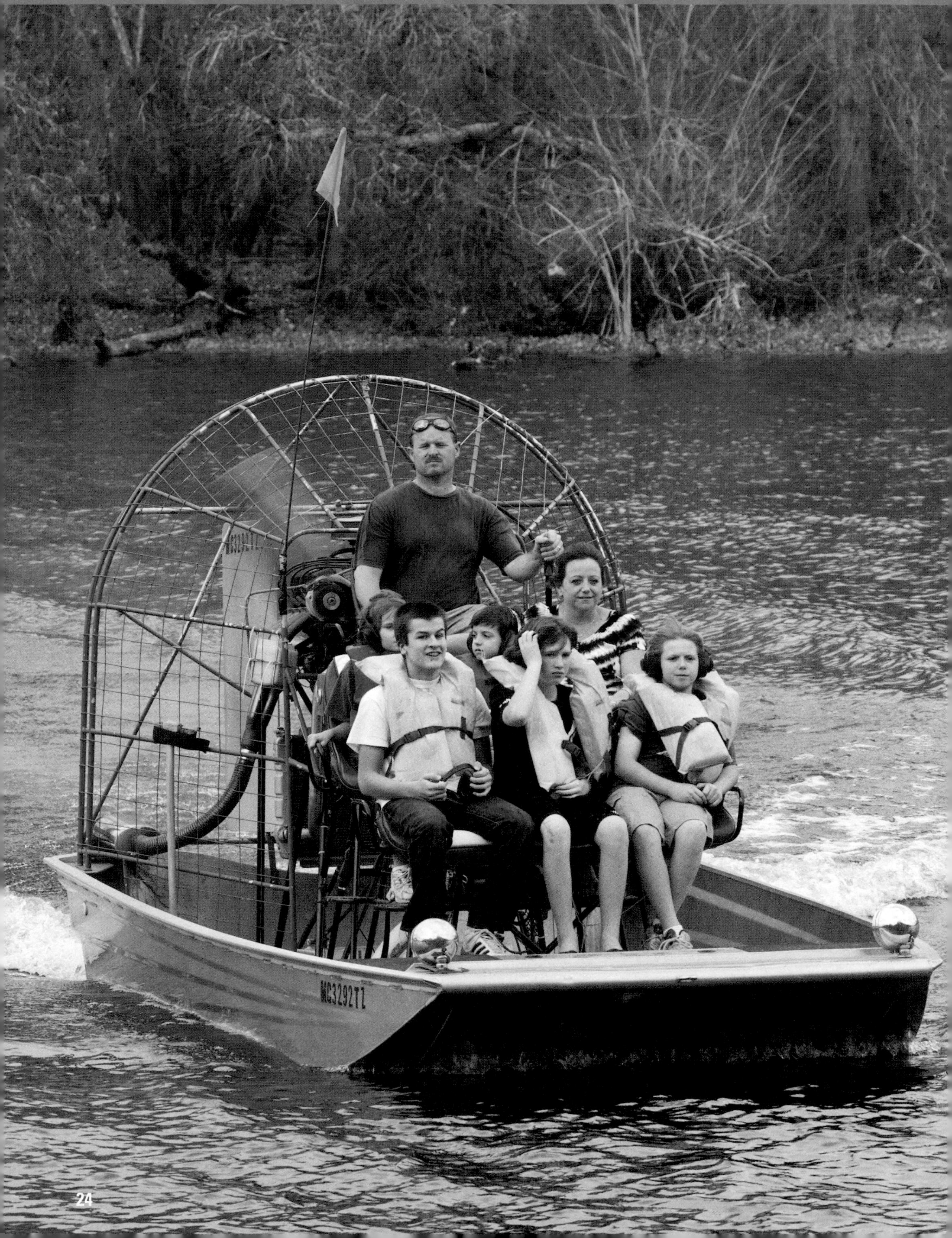

Forces in Interactions

What forces exist between interacting objects?

Introduction

The photo shows someone driving an airboat in a river. Behind the pilot is a giant fan that blows air backward and makes the boat move. How does blowing air backward make the boat move forward?

How the interaction between the fan and the air makes the boat move can be explained using Newton's laws of motion. Newton's laws of motion were developed by Isaac Newton in the 1600s. The laws are general descriptions of interactions between objects, including the interaction between the fan and the air. The laws are related, but you will learn about each one separately.

In this lesson, you will begin by learning about Newton's third law because it describes the forces that happen when objects, such as the giant fan and the air, interact. You will learn about Newton's life and will learn to identify the forces referred to in the third law. You will then read about how the effects of the third law led to problems during spacewalks and what engineers did to solve those problems.

In the next lesson, you will learn the first and second laws of motion. These laws describe how forces cause acceleration, which changes the motion of the objects.

Vocabulary

scientific law a set of verbal or mathematical rules to describe a natural phenomenon; unlike scientific theories, scientific laws do not explain the phenomenon

force a push or a pull on an object

newton a unit used to measure the strength of a force

Newton's third law of motion states that when an object exerts a force on a second object, the second object exerts a force on the first object with equal strength, but in the opposite direction

Next Generation Science Standards

Performance Expectations

MS-PS2-1. Apply Newton's Third Law to design a solution to a problem involving the motion of two colliding objects.

MS-ETS1-1. Define the criteria and constraints of a design problem with sufficient precision to ensure a successful solution, taking into account relevant scientific principles and potential impacts on people and the natural environment that may limit possible solutions.

Science and Engineering Practices

Constructing Explanations and Designing Solutions Apply scientific ideas or principles to design an object, tool, process or system.

Asking Questions and Defining Problems Define a design problem that can be solved through the development of an object, tool, process or system and includes multiple criteria and constraints, including scientific knowledge that may limit possible solutions.

Crosscutting Concepts

Systems and System Models Models can be used to represent systems and their interactions—such as inputs, processes, and outputs—and energy and matter flows within systems.

Influence of Science, Engineering, and Technology on Society and the Natural World

Disciplinary Core Ideas

PS2.A. For any pair of interacting objects, the force exerted by the first object on the second object is equal in strength to the force that the second object exerts on the first, but in the opposite direction (Newton's third law).

ETS1.A. The more precisely a design task's criteria and constraints can be defined, the more likely it is that the designed solution will be successful. Specification of constraints includes consideration of scientific principles and other relevant knowledge that are likely to limit possible solutions.

1. Sir Isaac Newton and His Laws of Motion

What would you do if school were closed for two years? You probably would not do what Isaac Newton did when his college closed for two years. He developed a new kind of math, figured out what light was, and began work on the scientific laws that are now named after him. Who was Isaac Newton, and how did he come up with his laws of motion?

Newton's Early Life Isaac Newton was an English scientist and mathematician. He was born on a farm in 1643. His father died before he was born, and he was raised by his grandmother after his mother remarried. When Newton was a teenager, his mother took him out of school so that he could manage the family farm. But Newton was not very good at farming and was not interested in it either.

Newton was allowed to return to school and was ready to start college when he was 18. He attended Trinity College in Cambridge University. In 1665, Newton received his college degree and won a scholarship to continue his studies.

However, soon after he received his degree, the university closed because a contagious disease called the bubonic plague was spreading across England. The school was closed for two years, so Newton went home and spent his time studying math and science on his own.

Sir Isaac Newton was an English scientist who lived from 1643 to 1727. His mother hoped that he would become a farmer, but he disliked the work and went to college instead. Newton learned old ideas in college, but studied new ideas on his own.

Newton's Studies and Influences

When Newton was in college, he learned ideas that would not be taught in schools today. Some of these ideas were once thought to be true, but are no longer considered to be accurate. Newton was taught that Earth was the center of the solar system and that the sun traveled around Earth. This was accepted because it appears true from Earth's reference frame.

Not all people in Newton's time believed these "old" ideas. In 1543, Polish astronomer Nicolaus Copernicus published a book explaining his theory that all the planets moved around the sun. Then in the early 1600s, German astronomer Johannes Kepler announced three laws that described the math behind the planets' motion around the sun. Newton studied the work of Copernicus, Kepler, Galileo Galilei, and others on his own. During the plague years, Newton was able to spend a lot of time thinking about the "new" ideas and trying to make sense of them.

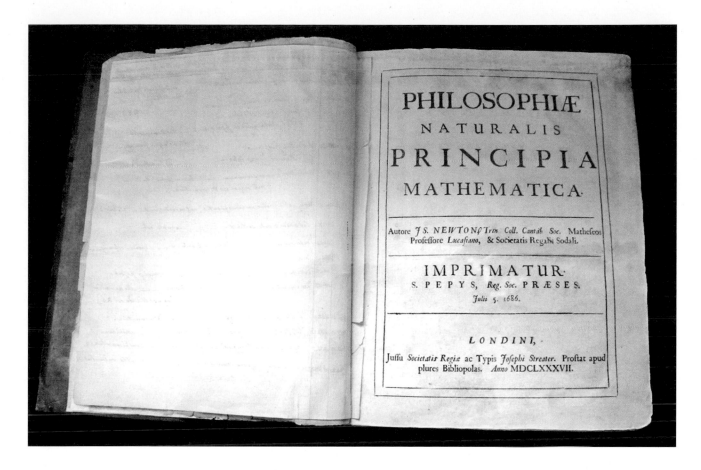

Newton's Masterpiece In 1687, Newton published books that are still recognized as some of the greatest scientific works. The books were called *Philosophiae Naturalis Principia Mathematica*, which is Latin for *Mathematical Principles of Natural Philosophy*. They are usually called just *Principia*. Newton was 44 years old when the books was published.

Newton presented four scientific laws in *Principia*. A **scientific law** is a statement or mathematical description of a natural phenomenon. Unlike scientific theories, scientific laws do not explain the phenomenon. Newton developed his laws by combining the ideas and observations of many other scientists. Copernicus, Kepler, Galileo, and others studied the motion of the planets. By combining their work, Newton was trying to develop a mathematical model to describe the planets' motion. As Newton worked on this model, he found that it could also describe the motion of all objects. The four laws in *Principia* make up this model.

One of the laws in *Principia* is the universal law of gravitation. This law describes the factors that affect gravity, which is the force that determines the motion of the planets. The other three laws describe the relationship between forces and motion. They are now called *Newton's laws of motion*. Although Newton's laws of motion are related to one another and to the universal law of gravitation, they are easier to understand when studied separately. But first, you need to learn what scientists mean by *force*.

Newton published his masterpiece, a set of books called *Principia*, in 1687. The books were written in Latin, and they contain four scientific laws that Newton developed. Three of those laws are now known as Newton's laws of motion.

2. Forces

The word *force* is used in different ways in everyday language. A storm may have a lot of force, someone may speak forcefully, and a door may be forced open. In science, the word *force* has a specific meaning. What is the scientific meaning of *force*, and what do forces do?

In science, a **force** is a push or a pull on an object. When a force is exerted on an object, the force can cause the object to accelerate. The word *exert* means "to put forth" or "to apply." You push on a soccer ball when you kick it, so your foot exerts a force on the ball. That force can make the ball start moving or can make it change directions. You can even exert a force to stop the ball. Forces can cause other changes, too. The shape of a sponge changes when you exert a force on it by squeezing it.

Forces always occur when two objects interact. Look at Figure 2.2. When you kick a soccer ball, your foot is only exerting a force on the ball while it is touching the ball. Your foot is not exerting a force on the ball before you touch it, and it stops exerting a force on the ball as soon as the ball leaves your foot.

Forces are described using both strength and direction. The strength of a force is how strong or weak the push or pull is. The strength of forces is measured in a unit called the **newton** (N), which was named in honor of Isaac Newton. To lift a banana, you need an upward force of about 2 N to lift. You would need about 120 N of upward force to lift a 27-pound, 2-year-old child.

Forces can be modeled using arrows. The length of the arrow represents the strength of the force. An arrow modeling a 100 N force would be twice as long as an arrow modeling a 50 N force. The direction that an arrow points models the direction of the force.

Figure 2.2

A force is a push or a pull by one object on another object. A force can cause an object to accelerate. When a person exerts a force on the ball, the ball accelerates in the direction of his or her force.

Forces on Objects in a System with a Soccer Ball

Foot exerts no force on the ball

Foot exerts 50 newton force on the ball

50 N

Foot no longer exerts a force on the ball

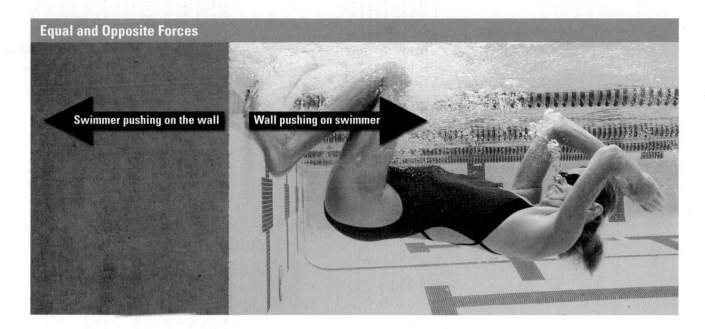

Equal and Opposite Forces

Swimmer pushing on the wall

Wall pushing on swimmer

3. Newton's Third Law of Motion

A swimmer turns around in a pool. You, and many people, may recognize that this swimmer is exerting a force on the pool wall with her feet. But Newton would identify a force that a lot of people don't realize exists. What force is that?

Newton would identify a force exerted by the wall on the swimmer, which is described by Newton's third law of motion. **Newton's third law of motion** states that when an object exerts a force on a second object, the second object exerts a force with equal strength on the first object, but in the opposite direction. The third law describes a system of interacting objects in which each object exerts a force on the other object. When two objects interact, two forces are exerted on different objects. The third law is sometimes stated as, "For every action there is an equal and opposite reaction." However, that phrase does not mention that the forces act on different objects.

Because each force acts on different objects, each force affects the motion of only one object. Figure 2.3A shows that the swimmer exerts a force on the wall; the wall is much heavier than the swimmer, so it does not move. At the same time, the wall exerts a force of the same strength on the swimmer; the swimmer is much lighter than the wall, so the force accelerates her away from the wall. In this system, two forces were exerted and they were exerted on different objects.

Newton's third law of motion also explains what happens when a car collides with a wall. The moving car exerts a force on the nonmoving wall, while the wall exerts a force of equal strength on the car. The force of the car on the wall damages the wall, and the force of the wall on the car stops the car from moving forward which causes the car to crumple. In this system, both interacting objects were affected by the same amount of force, but the car got the worst of it!

Figure 2.3A

Newton's third law states that when an object exerts a force on a second object, the second object exerts a force with equal strength on the first object, but in the opposite direction. So, when a swimmer pushes against a pool wall, the wall pushes against the swimmer with an equal and opposite force.

When a car strikes a wall, the car exerts a force on the wall and the wall exerts an equal force in the opposite direction on the car. The force on the wall dents the wall, and the force on the car crumples its front end.

The two interacting forces described by Newton's third law are sometimes called a *force pair*. The forces in every force pair act on different objects. Often, one force of a force pair is easy to identify because its effect is easily seen. The other force of the force pair can be more difficult to identify because it may not have a great effect. Recall the airboat at the beginning of this lesson. The fan on the airboat is pushing a lot of air backward. At the same time, the air is pushing the fan forward. Because the fan is attached to the boat, the fan and the boat move forward.

In certain situations, however, the effects of both forces in a force pair can be seen. For example, think about two identical pendulums hanging side by side. If you move each pendulum outward by the same amount and let go, the pendulums will collide as shown in Figure 2.3B. When they collide, the blue pendulum will exert a force on the gold pendulum, and the gold pendulum will exert a force on the blue pendulum. The forces obey Newton's third law and are equal in strength and opposite in direction. The force exerted by the blue pendulum pushes the gold pendulum to the right. At the same time, the force exerted by the gold pendulum pushes the blue pendulum to the left. The two forces cause the pendulums to swing away from each other in the same way and at the same time.

This experiment with pendulums is similar to experiments that Newton used to verify that his third law of motion was correct. Newton collided pendulums of different sizes and made of different materials. Knowing how far the pendulums moved was evidence that allowed Newton to measure the force on each pendulum. The evidence showed that the size of the force on one pendulum was always the same as the size of the force on the other pendulum.

Figure 2.3B

Newton's third law of motion can be observed using two pendulums. When the pendulums collide, the pendulums exert forces on each other. The two pendulums move outward by the same amount because the forces on them are equal in strength.

Collisions of Pendulums

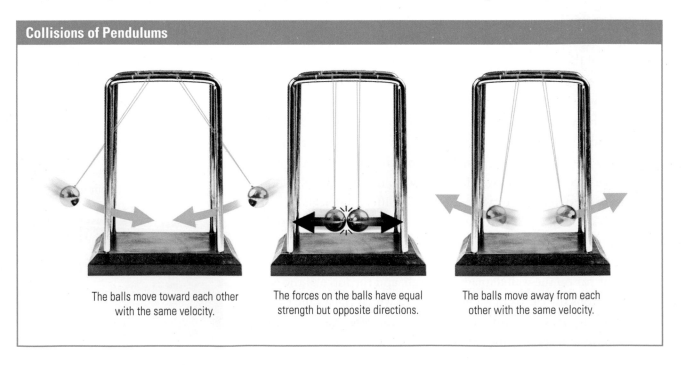

The balls move toward each other with the same velocity.

The forces on the balls have equal strength but opposite directions.

The balls move away from each other with the same velocity.

Forces on Interacting Objects

When two objects touch, they form a system described by Newton's third law of motion. In the system, each object exerts an equal and opposite force on the other object. Using the numbers on and the direction of the force arrows, identify the equal and opposite forces in each image. How do those forces change the motion of the objects?

When two moving cars collide, they exert equal and opposite forces on each other. Those forces cause the cars to stop moving.

When a person skates on a skateboard, the person's foot pushes back on the ground. The ground pushes forward on the foot. Since the ground is unmoving, the skateboard moves forward.

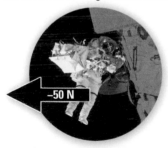 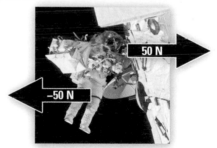 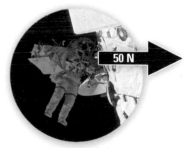

In a spacewalk, the astronaut pushes on the spacecraft. The spacecraft pushes back on the astronaut.

 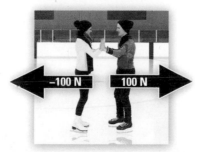 

When the male ice skater exerts a force on the female ice skater, the female ice skater exerts an equal and opposite force on the male ice skater. Both skaters move backward away from each other.

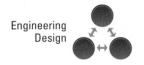
4. Engineering for EVAs

On June 5, 1966, Eugene Cernan exited the Gemini 9 spacecraft as it was in orbit around Earth to do an *extravehicular activity* (EVA), otherwise known as a spacewalk. He was the second American astronaut to walk in space and the first to try to do work during an EVA. Cernan quickly discovered tasks that were easy on Earth were nearly impossible while floating in space. When he tried to turn a knob, his body would spin instead! He spent most of the EVA trying to keep his body stable in space and could not complete his job. How did Cernan's experience make NASA's engineers rethink and redesign tools and equipment for use during EVAs?

Cernan's problems happened because NASA engineers had not predicted how Newton's third law of motion would affect his stability. The engineers examined the forces acting on Cernan during his EVA to find the problem. They learned that some of the effects of the third law that are not noticeable on Earth are very much noticeable in space. For example, when you push a button, the button pushes back. But on Earth, you do not move backward because gravity pulls you down and keeps you stable on the ground. If an astronaut floating in space pushes a button, no gravitational force keeps the astronaut stable. So when the button pushes back on the astronaut, the astronaut floats backward. When Cernan applied a twisting force to turn the knob, the knob exerted an opposite twisting force on Cernan, which made him spin.

EVAs are such unusual situations that they present design problems that have interesting criteria and constraints. Ever since Cernan's failed EVA, NASA engineers have worked to define the criteria and constraints for every piece of equipment that astronauts use during EVAs. Even the tasks astronauts do while spacewalking are designed with criteria and constraints.

An extravehicular activity (EVA) is when an astronaut goes outside of a spacecraft or a space station. Astronauts doing EVAs have to deal with the effects of Newton's third law of motion because gravity does not keep them stable.

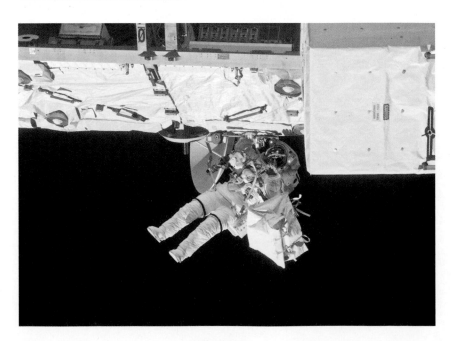

Many EVA design problems start with constraints rather than criteria. The main constraint on any EVA tool or task is the spacesuits that the astronauts have to wear. The suits are big and bulky, and are made of stiff material that is hard to move in. Furthermore, the gloves on the suits cover each finger with thick material, which interferes with the astronauts' ability to feel things and make precise movements.

The effects of Newton's third law are another constraint in EVA design. Engineers realized that astronauts needed a way to keep their bodies steady while working. They added handholds to the outside of spacecraft, but to use them, astronauts had to keep one hand on a handhold while working. This means that astronauts had to be able to use EVA tools with only one hand.

With these constraints in mind, NASA engineers added criteria to increase the success of EVAs. For example, one criterion is that, when possible, EVA tasks and equipment should be designed so that astronauts use as few tools as possible. That way, astronauts do not have to carry or keep track of too many tools. However, if tools are needed for a task, it is preferred that the task must be designed to use the standard tools kept on spacecraft.

Today, astronauts train for these EVAs by practicing their tasks underwater. Floating underwater is similar to floating in space. This way, the astronauts can learn how the effects of Newton's third law might push them around before they actually step out of a spacecraft to do some spacewalking!

Astronauts train for EVAs in different ways. This astronaut hangs from a partial gravity simulator, which helps him learn what low gravity feels like. He uses the simulator to practice tasks that he will do in space.

LESSON SUMMARY

Forces in Interactions

Sir Isaac Newton and His Laws of Motion When Isaac Newton's university was closed due to plague in the 1600s, Newton had plenty of free time to think. During this time, he began to develop four important scientific laws, including the laws of motion.

Forces Forces are pushes or pulls that act on objects and cause changes, such as changes in motion. Forces are often measured in newtons (N).

Newton's Third Law of Motion The third law of motion states that all forces act in equal and opposite pairs and that each force in a pair acts on a different object. Newton's third law can be observed in action by experimenting with two pendulums hanging side by side.

Engineering for EVAs The first time a NASA astronaut tried to work on a spacewalk, there were problems related to Newton's third law. To maintain astronaut stability in space, NASA engineers had to design tools and tasks that considered how the third law affected people in low gravity.

The Urge to Fly

People dream about flying all the time. Little kids stretch out their arms and imagine that they are soaring through the sky. Movie makers and comic book artists often give superheroes the ability to fly. But humans can't fly without help. How have people become airborne, and how are forces involved in human flight?

The force responsible for keeping people on the ground is gravity. Gravity pulls people down toward the center of Earth. So to fly or glide, a person needs a way to overcome the force of gravity.

One of the earliest inventions that allowed people to partly overcome the force of gravity was the parachute. Parachutes work by increasing air resistance. Air resistance is a force that opposes the motion of an object moving through air. When an object falls downward through the air, air resistance pushes up on the object.

Parachutes increase the air resistance on a person falling through the sky because the air resistance on an object depends partly on the surface area of the object. The larger the surface area of an object, the greater the air resistance on the object. Parachutes are made of large pieces of cloth that open up like umbrellas. The cloth greatly increases the surface area of a falling person, and thus greatly increases the air resistance pushing up on the person. Because air resistance acts in the opposite direction as gravity, combining the two forces means that the overall force pulling the person down is weaker. So, the person does not fall as fast and instead gently floats to the ground.

People have not found a way to overcome the force of gravity without help. A parachute uses air resistance to oppose the downward pull of gravity so that a person falls more slowly.

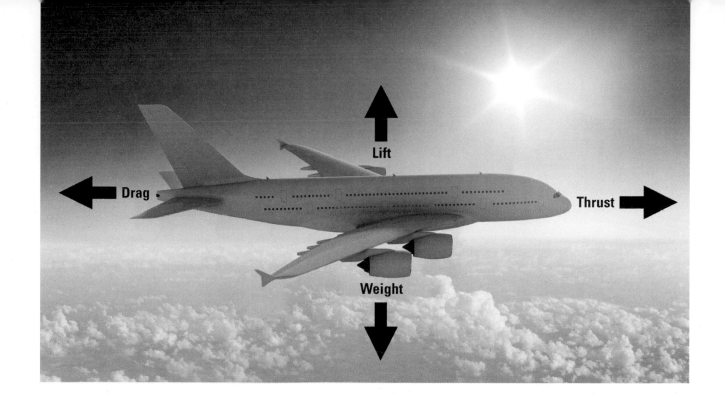

Four forces act on all flying objects. Lift is an upward force, thrust is a forward force, weight is a downward force, and drag is a backward force.

Forces and Flying Machines

When you use a parachute, you are not really flying—you are simply falling more slowly than normal. When something flies, it moves forward through the air and can stay up on its own. Birds and insects can fly, and people can fly when they are in an airplane.

When an object flies, four forces act on the object. The first force is the downward force of gravity. The strength of the force of gravity on an object is the object's weight. So although the downward force on all objects is called *gravity*, the downward force of a particular object is called its *weight*.

For an object to fly, it needs a force pushing it up to act against its weight. The second force is the upward force called *lift*. Planes and birds get lift from the way air travels around their wings.

An object in flight also needs a force to move it forward through the air. The third force is a forward force on a flying object, called *thrust*. Birds and insects get thrust by beating their wings, and airplanes get thrust from their engines or propellers.

As you learned, objects moving through air experience air resistance, which is the fourth force. As a flying object moves forward, air resistance pushes it backward. The backward force of air resistance on a flying object is called its *drag*.

The four forces of weight, lift, thrust, and drag determine how a flying object moves through the air. When a plane takes off, its lift is greater than its weight. When a plane descends to land, its weight is greater than its lift. If the plane's thrust is greater than its drag, it accelerates, and if its drag is greater than its thrust, it decelerates.

Build a Glider

The four forces of flight act on every flying object. They act on airplanes, helicopters, birds, and bees. They also act on flying toys such as drones and paper airplanes. How would these four forces act on a glider made of two paper hoops and a straw?

To build a hoop glider, you need a 21.6 cm by 27.9 cm (8 1/2 by 11-inch) sheet of cardstock, a metric ruler, a pen or pencil, a pair of scissors, tape, and a drinking straw. You will not need the entire sheet of cardstock, so you can share it with a few classmates.

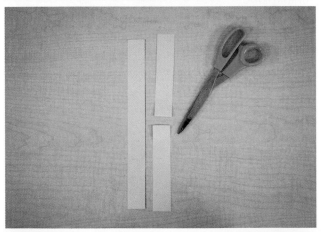

Use the ruler to draw a line 3 cm away from one long edge of the cardstock. Use the ruler to draw another line that is 3 cm away from the first line that you drew.

Use the scissors to cut along each of the lines that you drew to make two long strips of cardstock. Fold one strip in half by lining up the two narrow edges. Crease the strip at the fold; then open it back up. Use the scissors to cut this strip of cardstock in half at the crease to make two short strips of cardstock. You only need one short strip; the other can be given to a classmate.

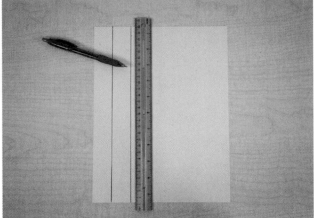

Form a hoop with the short strip of cardstock and use tape to hold the ends together. Repeat this process with the long strip of cardstock. You will have two hoops of two different sizes.

Use the tape to attach one hoop to each end of the straw. Your completed glider should look like the one shown in the photo.

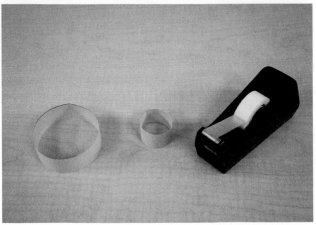

A hoop glider is a flying toy that you can make from cardstock and a straw. To construct your own glider, gather the materials shown in the picture, and follow the directions in the text.

Glider Games

Once you have made your glider, you can test it. Find an open area away from other people, hold your glider by the straw so that the smaller hoop is pointing away from you, and gently toss it forward. You may have to practice a few times to learn the best way to throw the glider.

As you watch your glider in flight, try to discover how the four forces of flight affect the motion of the glider? Can you figure out where the glider's lift and thrust come from?

Design and conduct several experiments using your glider. For example, you could have contests with your classmates to see whose glider travels the farthest. You could also calculate the average speed of your glider by dividing the distance traveled by the time needed to travel that distance. You could even modify your glider and find out how the modification affects its flight. Does adding additional hoops help or hurt the glider's performance? What happens if you make bigger hoops or use a shorter straw? Remember to collect your data in an organized manner so that you can analyze them to find the results of your experiment.

A hoop glider has a simple design, but you will find that it can fly very well. Do you think a hoop glider could be built that could carry a person? It would have to be a pretty big glider! ◆

A hand-crafted hoop glider, like the one shown here, is a simple flying machine. The forces that act on a hoop glider in flight are the same as the forces that act on an airplane.

Effects of Forces

How do forces affect motion?

Introduction

The Iditarod is a dog sled race held every year in Alaska. The racers (called *mushers*) and their dog teams travel more than 1,500 km from Anchorage to Nome with the dogs pulling the sled the entire distance. Winning mushers finish the race in around 10 days, while other mushers may need two or more weeks to finish. Why do some mushers finish the race much faster than others?

All modes of transportation, including dog sleds, involve making something move. But bicycles, cars, and dog sleds do not start moving on their own. A force is needed to make any object move. Unlike a bike or a car, a dog sled is a relatively simple system to understand. As a result, a dog sled is an ideal system for learning how forces cause stability and change in an object's motion.

In this lesson, you will learn about Newton's first and second laws of motion. These two laws describe how the forces acting on an object will change the object's motion. You will learn about how these laws helped engineers design effective seatbelts. Along the way, you will also learn a little more about the Iditarod and read about the effects of forces in your everyday life.

Vocabulary

net force the sum of all forces acting on an object

balanced forces forces that have a net force equal to 0 N

unbalanced forces forces that have a net force not equal to 0 N

Newton's first law of motion states that an object at rest stays at rest, and an object in motion stays in motion with a constant velocity unless acted on by unbalanced forces

Newton's second law of motion states that an object's acceleration is equal to the net force on the object divided by its mass

friction a force that opposes motion between two surfaces that are touching

Next Generation Science Standards

Performance Expectations

MS-PS2-2. Plan an investigation to provide evidence that the change in an object's motion depends on the sum of the forces on the object and the mass of the object.

MS-ETS1-1. Define the criteria and constraints of a design problem with sufficient precision to ensure a successful solution, taking into account relevant scientific principles and potential impacts on people and the natural environment that may limit possible solutions.

Science and Engineering Practices

Planning and Carrying Out Investigations Plan an investigation individually and collaboratively, and in the design: identify independent and dependent variables and controls, what tools are needed to do the gathering, how measurements will be recorded, and how many data are needed to support a claim.

Asking Questions and Defining Problems Define a design problem that can be solved through the development of an object, tool, process or system and includes multiple criteria and constraints, including scientific knowledge that may limit possible solutions.

Influence of Science, Engineering, and Technology on Society and the Natural World

Crosscutting Concepts

Stability and Change Explanations of stability and change in natural and designed systems can be constructed by examining the changes over time and forces at different scales.

Disciplinary Core Ideas

PS2.A. The motion of an object is determined by the sum of the forces acting on it; if the total force on the object is not zero, its motion will change. The greater the mass of the object, the greater force needed to achieve the same change in motion. For any given object, a larger force causes a larger change in motion.

ETS1.A. The more precisely a design task's criteria and constraints can be defined, the more likely it is that the designed solution will be successful. Specification of constraints includes consideration of scientific principles and other relevant knowledge that are likely to limit possible solutions.

1. Net Force

Iditarod mushers have constraints on the number of dogs they can use. Each musher can start the race with as many as 16 dogs pulling the sled and must finish the race with at least five dogs pulling the sled. Mushers take very good care of their dogs to keep them from becoming ill or injured during the race. If a dog gets sick or is injured during the race, mushers can leave their dogs with veterinarians and continue the race with their remaining dogs. Why do mushers want to finish the race with as many dogs as possible?

Each dog in a dog sled team exerts a force on the sled. A musher wants as many dogs as possible because the forces exerted by the dogs add up to a large force on the sled. In fact, when more than one force acts on any object, the effect of those forces can be found by adding the forces. The sum of all forces acting on an object is the **net force** on the object.

The net force is found by combining all the forces on an object. Recall that forces have both strength and direction. Whether you add or subtract forces depends on the directions that the forces act. If the forces on an object act in the same direction, the strengths of the forces are added. For example, when three people push a van that has run out of gas, they all push in the forward direction. If the people push with forces of 100 N, 125 N, and 200 N, the net force is:

$$100 \text{ N} + 125 \text{ N} + 200 \text{ N} = 425 \text{ N}$$

Because all the forces on the van are in the forward direction, the net force is also in the forward direction.

The net force on an object is the combination of all forces acting on that object. If the forces act in the same direction, the strengths of the forces are added together. The net force on the van is 425 N because the strengths of the forward forces on the van add up to 425 N.

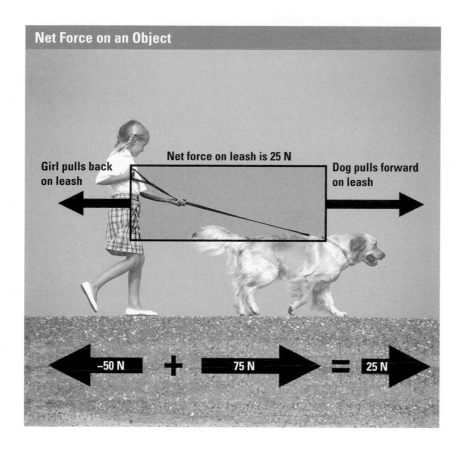

Net Force on an Object

Girl pulls back on leash

Net force on leash is 25 N

Dog pulls forward on leash

−50 N + 75 N = 25 N

Figure 3.1

When forces act in opposite directions, the net force is found by subtracting the strengths of the forces. The dog pulls the leash with a force of 75 N in the forward direction, and the girl pulls the leash with a force of 50 N in the backward direction. Thus, the net force is 25 N in the forward direction.

On the other hand, forces are subtracted to find the net force if the forces act in opposite directions. The leash in Figure 3.1 has forces acting on it in opposite directions. The dog jumps forward, pulling the leash with him. The girl pulls back on the leash, but is dragged forward by the dog. If the dog pulls with a force of 75 N and the girl pulls with a force of 50 N, the net force on the leash is:

$$75 \text{ N} - 50 \text{ N} = 25 \text{ N}$$

When forces are subtracted to find the net force, the direction of the net force is the same direction as the larger force. So the force on the leash is 25 N in the forward direction. As a result the leash, along with the dog and the girl, accelerate forward.

Sometimes the net force on an object is simply equal to one force on the object. Think about a train of cars on a roller coaster car coming to a stop at the end of a ride. Brakes are applied to slow the train down. The brakes exert a backward force on the train. Because all forward or backward forces on the train are very small, the net force on the train is, practically, just the force of the brakes. If the direction the train is traveling is positive, then the force of the brakes is in the negative direction. So, the net force on the train is negative, the train's acceleration is negative, and the train slows down.

Finding the net force is useful because you can use the net force to predict the effect of all the forces on an object at once. Once you find the net force you can predict if and how the object's motion will change.

Sometimes the net force on an object is equal to a single force acting on the object. At the end of a roller coaster ride, the only force acting on the car is the backward force of the brakes. This backward force causes the car to slow to a stop.

2. Newton's First Law

Suppose that you are pushing a luggage cart in an airport or a train station. By pushing with different strengths, you can make the cart speed up, slow down, or move at a constant velocity. How can net force and Newton's first law of motion be used to predict how the luggage cart—or any object—will move?

An object's motion is determined by the net force on it. When you find the net force, you also find whether the forces are balanced or unbalanced. **Balanced forces** are forces that have a net force equal to 0 N. **Unbalanced forces** are forces that have a net force not equal to 0 N. Newton's first law of motion describes what happens to an object when the forces on it are balanced.

Newton's first law of motion states that an object at rest stays at rest, and an object in motion stays in motion with a constant velocity unless acted on by unbalanced forces. This means that an object is stable, or does not change its behavior, unless an unbalanced force acts on it. The statement of the first law is long, but you can separate it into parts to fully understand the law.

"An Object at Rest" The first part of the first law of motion says that an object at rest stays at rest if the forces on it are balanced. When an object is "at rest" it is stationary, or not moving. So the first part of the first law says that, if the forces on a stationary object are balanced, the object will not move. This makes sense. If a luggage cart is standing still, and the net force on it is 0 N, such as in Figure 3.2A, the cart will stay still.

Figure 3.2A

Newton's first law of motion describes the motion of an object when the forces on it are balanced. If the forces on a stationary cart are balanced, the cart will stay still. Also, if the cart is already moving and the forces on it are balanced, the cart will keep moving with the same velocity—that is, at the same speed and in the same direction.

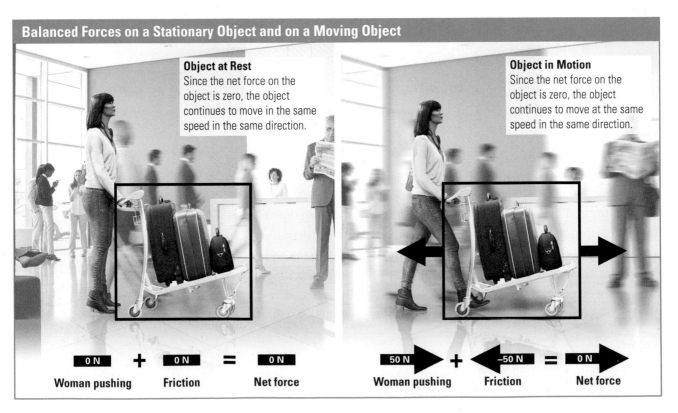

Balanced Forces on a Stationary Object and on a Moving Object

Object at Rest
Since the net force on the object is zero, the object continues to move in the same speed in the same direction.

Object in Motion
Since the net force on the object is zero, the object continues to move at the same speed in the same direction.

| 0 N | + | 0 N | = | 0 N |
| Woman pushing | | Friction | | Net force |

| 50 N | + | −50 N | = | 0 N |
| Woman pushing | | Friction | | Net force |

"An Object in Motion" The second part of the first law of motion says that an object in motion will stay in motion with a constant velocity if the forces on it are balanced. This means that, if the net force on a moving object is 0 N, the object will keep moving with the same speed and in the same direction. In other words, the object's motion will not change.

When a luggage cart moves forward, friction between the wheels and the floor push backward on the cart. If you push the moving cart forward with a force equal in strength to the force of friction pushing backward, the forces on the cart are balanced. As a result, the cart will continue moving at a constant velocity.

"Unless Acted on by an Unbalanced Force" The first law describes what happens to the motion of an object when the forces on it are balanced, but it only hints at what happens when the forces on an object are unbalanced. When an unbalanced force acts on an object, the object will accelerate, which means that the object will change its speed and/or direction.

For example, if you push the luggage cart with a force stronger than the force of friction, the net force on the cart will be greater than 0 N and in the forward direction. This unbalanced force will cause the cart to speed up. On the other hand, if you pull back on the cart, your pulling force and friction will be in the same direction, so the net force will be greater than 0 N in the opposite direction. In this case, the cart slows down.

Figure 3.2B
If the forces on an object are unbalanced, the object will accelerate. If the net force on a moving cart acts in the direction that the cart is moving, the cart will speed up. If the net force on a moving cart is in the direction opposite to the cart's motion, the cart will slow down.

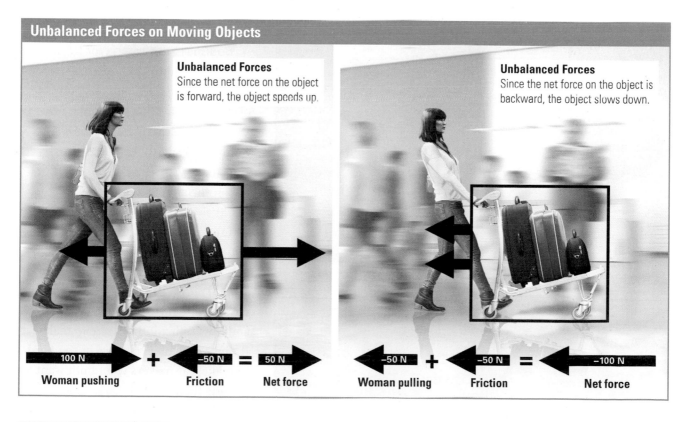

Unbalanced Forces on Moving Objects

Unbalanced Forces
Since the net force on the object is forward, the object speeds up.

Unbalanced Forces
Since the net force on the object is backward, the object slows down.

| 100 N | + | −50 N | = | 50 N |
| Woman pushing | | Friction | | Net force |

| −50 N | + | −50 N | = | −100 N |
| Woman pulling | | Friction | | Net force |

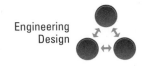

Engineering
Design

3. Designing a Better Seatbelt

Cars have changed a lot since the 1970s. Cars look sleeker, they have more computer-controlled functions, and they have a lot more cup holders. But one design element in all American cars has not changed much in more than 40 years: the seatbelt.

Cars had seatbelts before 1970, but the belts were usually one strap that went around a person's waist and buckled near a person's stomach. Those belts held a person's lower half in place, but they could cause injuries when a body was pushed forward into the buckle during a collision. In 1958, a Swedish engineer named Nils Bohlin set out to solve this problem by designing a better seatbelt.

Defining Criteria and Constraints An important step in any engineering design is to precisely state the problem to be solved. To do this, engineers describe the criteria and constraints of the design solution.

The three-point seatbelt was designed to meet precisely defined criteria. The seatbelt was designed to hold a person's upper and lower body in place during a collision. It was also designed to be comfortable and easy to use.

Bohlin knew that, according to Newton's first law of motion, a person's body will keep moving forward during a head-on collision. Before the collision, the car and the body are both moving forward with the same velocity. The force of the collision makes the car stop abruptly. If nothing exerts a force on a person inside the car, the person will keep moving forward and may hit the dashboard, the window, or the seat in front of him or her.

Bohlin set the criteria for the new seatbelt: it had to hold both the upper and lower parts of a person's body in place during a collision. Bohlin also knew that ease of use and comfort were important to seatbelt design. If seatbelts were difficult to secure or uncomfortable to wear, people were not likely to use them. Bohlin set additional criteria: the seatbelt had to be comfortable and should be able to be secured using only one hand. Several constraints on the seatbelt design were the cost to make them and how difficult they were to make. If they were too expensive or too hard to make, car makers would not want to include them in their cars.

The Three-Point Solution To meet his first criterion, Bohlin knew that he needed two straps. One strap would hold the upper body and the other strap would hold the lower body. To meet his second criterion, Bohlin came up with a system in which the two straps were joined and attached to the car in three places. The top strap attached above a person's shoulder, the bottom strap attached near one hip, and both straps attached near the other hip. With this design, a person could grab the seatbelt with one hand and draw it across his or her body to buckle it. The simple three-point design met all of the design criteria.

The seatbelt design also stayed within the design constraints. Each seatbelt is made of a few simple parts, such as a single strap, a two-piece buckle, and some gears. The parts could be made with inexpensive materials and were simple to assemble.

Bohlin's three-point seatbelt design was first used in cars in 1959. The design was so successful in preventing injury and saving lives, that American car makers have been required to include three-point seatbelts in all cars made since 1968. The societal desire for safety has further resulted in laws that require people to wear seatbelts in moving cars.

Bohlin's original design has been improved over the years, but its main features remain the same. The overall design is unchanged because Bohlin did an excellent job by setting good criteria and producing a design that met all of them.

Prior to Bohlin's invention, cars like this did not have adequate safety restraints. To determine a successful solution, Bohlin had to precisely define the criteria and constraints of his problem. Bohlin listed several criteria and several constraints that he kept in mind as he created a solution.

4. Newton's Second Law

When a musher wants the sled to go faster, the musher might yell a command to encourage the dogs to pull harder. The stronger pull of the dogs will make the sled accelerate. However, this is not the only way a musher can account for acceleration. What else determines how much the sled will accelerate?

Newton's second law of motion describes the factors that determine an object's acceleration. **Newton's second law of motion** states that an object's acceleration is equal to the net force on the object divided by its mass. This law is easier to understand by looking at the different relationships between acceleration, force, and mass.

Acceleration and Force One factor that determines how much an object accelerates is the strength of the net force on the object. For an object with a given mass, the greater the net force acting on the object is, the greater the acceleration of the object is.

The net force on a dog sled depends on the number of dogs pulling the sled, and the net force affects the acceleration of the sled. Observe Figure 3.4A, where each sled dog pulls with a force of 50 N. If three dogs pull on a sled, the net force on the sled will be 150 N in the forward direction. If six dogs pull the sled, the net force will be 300 N in the forward direction. Six dogs pull the sled with twice the net force as three dogs do. So the sled will have twice the acceleration as when the sled is pulled by three dogs. This explains why Iditarod mushers want to have as many dogs as possible pulling their sleds. More dogs mean a greater net force, which means a greater acceleration. A greater acceleration on the sled means that the musher will finish the race faster.

Figure 3.4A

Newton's second law of motion says that the acceleration of an object increases as the net force on that object increases. The net force of six dogs pulling a sled is twice as strong as the net force of three dogs pulling the sled. So, the acceleration of the sled pulled by six dogs is twice the acceleration of the sled pulled by three dogs.

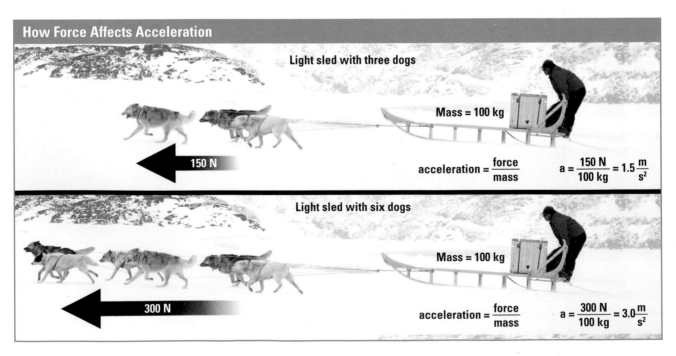

How Force Affects Acceleration

Light sled with three dogs

Mass = 100 kg

150 N

$$\text{acceleration} = \frac{\text{force}}{\text{mass}} \qquad a = \frac{150 \text{ N}}{100 \text{ kg}} = 1.5 \frac{\text{m}}{\text{s}^2}$$

Light sled with six dogs

Mass = 100 kg

300 N

$$\text{acceleration} = \frac{\text{force}}{\text{mass}} \qquad a = \frac{300 \text{ N}}{100 \text{ kg}} = 3.0 \frac{\text{m}}{\text{s}^2}$$

Acceleration and Mass The other factor that affects how much an object accelerates is the object's mass. If identical net forces act on two objects that have different masses, the object that has the larger mass will have a smaller acceleration.

The mass of an Iditarod sled depends on the amount of supplies carried on the sled, and the mass of the sled affects its acceleration. Iditarod mushers have to carry enough food and water to survive between checkpoints. However, supplies increase the mass of the sled. A heavier sled has a smaller acceleration when pulled by the same number of dogs than a lighter sled. For example, a sled with a mass of 300 kg will have half the acceleration of a sled with a mass of 150 kg when both sleds are pulled by the same net force.

The Second Law Equation Newton's second law allows the relationships between acceleration (a), force (F), and mass (m) to be written as an equation. The equation for the second law is:

$$a = \frac{F}{m}$$

Figures 3.4A and 3.4B show how the second law equation is used to calculate acceleration in different situations. When mass stays the same, any change in force will result in a proportional change in acceleration. Six dogs pull a sled with twice the force of three dogs. The force doubles, so the acceleration of the sled also doubles.

When force stays the same, any change in mass will result in an inverse change in acceleration. If a sled has 2 times the mass of another sled, the heavier sled will have 1/2 the acceleration of the lighter sled. If a sled has 3 times the mass of another sled, the heavier sled will have 1/3 the acceleration.

Figure 3.4B

Newton's second law of motion also says that the acceleration of an object decreases as the mass of the object increases. The mass of the heavy sled is twice the mass of the light sled, and both sleds are pulled by the same net force. As a result, the acceleration of the heavy sled is half the acceleration of the light sled.

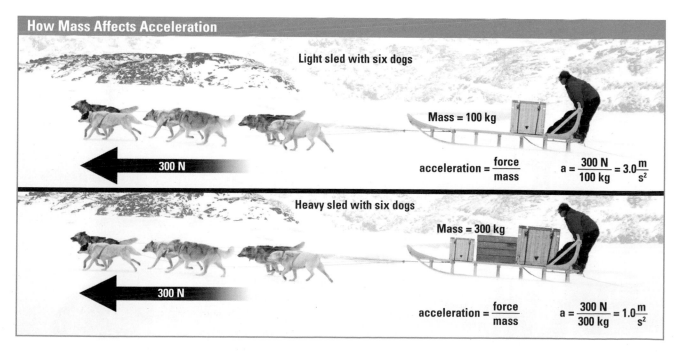

How Mass Affects Acceleration

Light sled with six dogs

300 N

Mass = 100 kg

$$\text{acceleration} = \frac{\text{force}}{\text{mass}} \qquad a = \frac{300 \text{ N}}{100 \text{ kg}} = 3.0 \frac{\text{m}}{\text{s}^2}$$

Heavy sled with six dogs

300 N

Mass = 300 kg

$$\text{acceleration} = \frac{\text{force}}{\text{mass}} \qquad a = \frac{300 \text{ N}}{300 \text{ kg}} = 1.0 \frac{\text{m}}{\text{s}^2}$$

Newton's Laws of Motion

Whether or not an object accelerates depends on if balanced or unbalanced forces act on it. If unbalanced forces act on an object, its acceleration depends on its mass and the net force acting on it. If Newton were alive today, how would he use his first and second laws of motion to explain the forces and motion in a volleyball game?

Net Force
The force of the girl pushing up on the ball is stronger than the force of gravity pulling it down. To find the net force, subtract the force of gravity from the upward force. There is a net force pushing the ball upward.

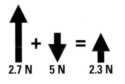

2.7 N   5 N   2.3 N

Balanced Forces
Two people both push the ball right above the net. They push on the ball with equal force, so the net force on the ball is zero newtons. The ball continues to move at the same speed, and in the same direction.

No net force

Unbalanced Forces
There is a positive net force on the ball, so the ball accelerates. The girl pushing on the ball causes it to slow down, change direction, and then speed up and sail back over the net.

Positive net force

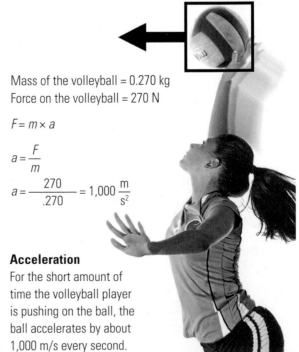

Mass of the volleyball = 0.270 kg
Force on the volleyball = 270 N

$F = m \times a$

$a = \dfrac{F}{m}$

$a = \dfrac{270}{.270} = 1,000 \dfrac{m}{s^2}$

Acceleration
For the short amount of time the volleyball player is pushing on the ball, the ball accelerates by about 1,000 m/s every second.

5. Forces Around You

If you slide a coin across a table, you know that it will slow down and stop. That observation seems to go against the first law of motion. That law says that an object in motion will stay in motion at the same velocity unless acted on by an unbalanced force. Shouldn't the coin keep sliding at the same velocity until someone exerts a force on it?

The coin does not keep sliding because an unbalanced force *does* act on it, but that force is not exerted by a person. The coin, like most objects, has many forces acting on it all the time. One of those forces has to do with the rubbing of the coin against the table as it slides.

Friction is a force that opposes the motion between two surfaces that are touching. As the coin slides forward on the table, a force of friction between the table and the coin acts in the backward direction. Because the force of friction is in the opposite direction of the coin's motion, friction causes the coin to have a negative acceleration, which means that its velocity decreases.

Friction is often useful. Friction between your feet and the ground keep your feet from slipping when you walk. Softball players take advantage of friction to stop them when they slide into bases. In softball, a player often wants to get to base as quickly as possible. But if she runs as fast as she can all the way to the base, she could accidentally run past it and risk getting tagged out by the opposing team. So a player runs as fast as she can until the last moment, and then drops into a slide. During the slide, the friction between the player and the ground slows the player's motion so she stops right at the base.

Friction is a force that opposes the motion between two surfaces that are touching. Softball players take advantage of friction when they slide. The friction quickly stops their motion so that they do not go past the base.

LESSON SUMMARY

Effects of Forces

Net Force The net force on an object is found by combining all the forces acting on the object.

Newton's First Law Newton's first law of motion states that the motion of an object does not change unless unbalanced forces act on the object.

Designing a Better Seatbelt The inventor of the modern car seatbelt successfully met the criteria and constraints that he set for his seatbelt design.

Newton's Second Law Newton's second law of motion states that the acceleration of an object is equal to the net force on the object divided by its mass.

Forces Around You Friction is a force that opposes motion between touching surfaces and can be helpful or harmful depending on the situation.

Amazing Animal Forces

Picture an epic battle between a dinosaur predator called a *Tyrannosaurs rex* and a prehistoric shark called a *megalodon*. Fossils of these two creatures show that each was huge, strong, and had very large, sharp teeth. Although such a fight could not have really happened, it is fun to imagine it. Who would win?

Because both the *T. rex* and the megalodon are extinct and did not live on Earth at the same time, we will never know who would win the battle. However, scientists can draw conclusions about the behavior of extinct animals by comparing them to living animals. Some of those behaviors can help determine the winner of the fight.

One behavior that scientists study is biting. Specifically, scientists try to determine how much force animals exert when they bite down on a tool that measures force. Getting a human or a small lizard to bite down on a tool is not very difficult or dangerous, but think about trying to measure the bite force of a crocodile! Despite the danger involved, Dr. Gregory Erickson and his team at Florida State University have measured the bite force of every crocodile species alive. They found that the saltwater crocodile has the strongest bite force of all living animals that can be measured directly.

Scientists study different kinds of animal behavior including biting. In this photo, Dr. Erickson uses a tool designed to measure the bite force of an alligator.

Virtual Bites

Obviously, scientists cannot directly measure the bite force of extinct animals—there aren't any alive to test! So how do scientists find the bite force of a *T. rex* or a megalodon? They use computer models. A computer model estimates bite force by comparing animals that have unknown bite forces with animals that have known bite forces. For example, it might compare the size and shape of a *T. rex* skull with the size and shape of the skull of a large living lizard, such as a crocodile, that has a known bite force. Then the model will scale up the bite force of the lizard to estimate the bite force of the *T. rex*.

Scientists also use computer models to estimate the bite force of living animals. To get these estimates, scientists analyze the size and shape of skulls and jaw bones. Bigger jaws and thicker bones often mean that an animal has a strong bite force. The shape of the skull also affects bite force. Animals with shorter snouts tend to have stronger bite forces. They also analyze the muscle structure around the mouth. The more muscles an animal has around its mouth, the stronger its bite force is. The computer uses these data to calculate probable bite forces.

The graph compares the bite force of living and extinct animals. The values for humans and saltwater crocodiles are measured, and the rest of the values are estimated.

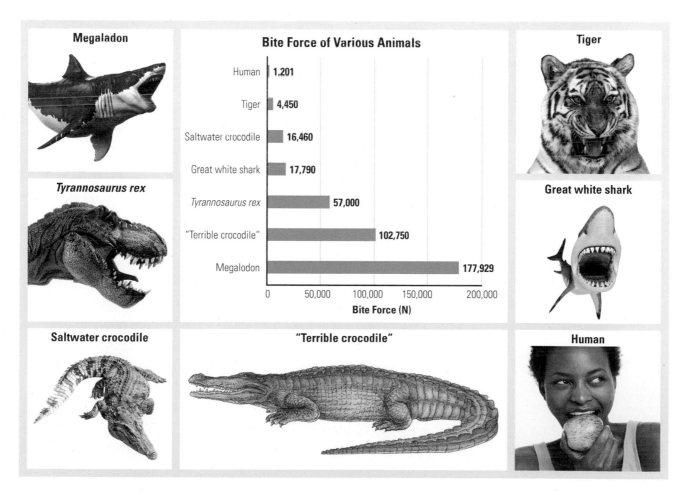

Megaladon

Tyrannosaurus rex

Saltwater crocodile

"Terrible crocodile"

Tiger

Great white shark

Human

Bite Force of Various Animals

Animal	Bite Force (N)
Human	1,201
Tiger	4,450
Saltwater crocodile	16,460
Great white shark	17,790
Tyrannosaurus rex	57,000
"Terrible crocodile"	102,750
Megalodon	177,929

The least weasel is a tiny but powerful predator. Its bite force quotient is one of the highest measured.

An animal's bite force quotient is its bite force divided by its mass. Bite force quotients are used to compare the relative strength of the bites of animals that vary greatly in size.

Bite Force Quotients of Various Animals

Animal	Bite Force Quotient (N/kg)
Tasmanian devil	181
Least weasel	164
Lion	124
Giant panda	151
Black bear	64

It's All Relative

In the graph comparing bite forces, all the animals shown (except for humans) are large predators. This makes sense because you would expect a predator to have a strong bite to easily kill its prey. However, predators and their prey come in many sizes, and the bite force of small predators is not nearly as strong as the bite force of large predators. So scientists studying predators came up with a different way to compare their biting abilities.

An animal's bite force quotient describes how powerful the animal's bite is *for its size*. Bite force quotient is equal to an animal's bite force (measured in newtons) divided by its mass (measured in kilograms). A bite force quotient greater than 100 means that an animal has a stronger bite than expected.

A group of scientists calculated the bite force quotient of several living and extinct predators and found a surprising result. Of all the predators they examined, the one with the second highest bite force quotient was a tiny predator called a *least weasel*. The least weasel is only about 20 cm long with a mass of up to only 70 grams! Least weasels hunt mice, voles, and other small rodents, but those rodents are about the same size as the weasel. So the weasel has to pack a powerful bite to kill them.

Ouch!

Why do scientists calculate bite forces and bite force quotients? Scientists use bite force data and bite force quotients to learn about or draw conclusions about various animals' predatory behavior. For example, they might use the data to determine if an extinct giant piranha had a bite strong enough to break through turtle shells or break the bones of large prey.

Engineers can also use bite force data to solve problems in their work. Communication equipment, such as Internet cables, are placed underwater in the oceans. For some reason, sharks like to chew on these cables. Engineers can use shark bite force data to design better protection for the cables.

Bite force data and bite force quotients are also interesting to some people. These people like to debate the outcomes of imaginary animal fights using data and information that they find on the Internet. Some may try to find the odds of a wildebeest escaping from the jaws of a crocodile. And some have even tried to decide the winner of the battle between a *T. rex* and a megalodon. Knowing what you now know about bite forces, who do you think would win? ◆

A crocodile can take down a wildebeest with its strong bite. Bite force data and bite force quotients help scientists studying predators.

Noncontact Forces

OVERVIEW

This drone hovers quietly in the air for several moments before taking off. What forces allow this drone to lift off for flight? In this unit, you will learn about the forces of gravity, electricity, and magnetism. You will also learn about how these forces interact with objects to cause many familiar effects and patterns you see in your everyday life. You will then analyze a drone's motor in order to explain how electromagnetism helps it maintain flight.

Phenomenon-Based Storyline
A drone hovers in the air and seems to defy gravity. You have access to an engineer's plans for the drone's motor. Can you piece together how electromagnetism powers the drone's propellers and allows it to fly?

UNIT CONTENTS

4 Gravity

What is gravity?

Reading Further: Sci-Fi: Putting the Science in Fiction

Investigations Investigate how mass affects gravitational force using simulations and drawings that demonstrate gravitational forces and fields.

5 Electricity

What is electricity?

Engineering Design: Testing Touch Screens

Reading Further: Lightning Strikes!

Investigations Ask questions about electric charges and investigate the forces involved in static electricity by modeling electric fields using simulations and drawings.

6 Magnetism and Electromagnetism

What are magnets?

Engineering Design: Optimizing Wind Turbine Designs

Reading Further: Louder! The Electric Guitar

Investigations Observe magnetic forces and fields by conducting a hands-on investigation to see how motors and generators work.

Performance Assessment A drone's motors use properties of electromagnetism to power the propellers so the drone can fly. Analyze the parts of a drone's motor and then describe how drones can defy gravity and fly.

UNIT 2

Next Generation Science Standards

Performance Expectations

MS-PS2-3. Ask questions about data to determine the factors that affect the strength of electric and magnetic forces.

MS-PS2-4. Construct and present arguments using evidence to support the claim that gravitational interactions are attractive and depend on the masses of interacting objects.

MS-PS2-5. Conduct an investigation and evaluate the experimental design to provide evidence that fields exist between objects exerting forces on each other even though the objects are not in contact.

MS-ETS1-4. Develop a model to generate data for iterative testing and modification of a proposed object, tool, or process such that an optimal design can be achieved.

Science and Engineering Practices

Asking Questions and Defining Problems
Ask questions that can be investigated within the scope of the classroom, outdoor environment, and museums and other public facilities with available resources and, when appropriate, frame a hypothesis based on observations and scientific principles.

Planning and Carrying Out Investigations
Conduct an investigation and evaluate the experimental design to produce data to serve as the basis for evidence that can meet the goals of the investigation.

Engaging in Argument from Evidence
Construct and present oral and written arguments supported by empirical evidence and scientific reasoning to support or refute an explanation or a model for a phenomenon or a solution to a problem.

Developing and Using Models
Develop a model to generate data to test ideas about designed systems, including those representing inputs and outputs.

Connections to Nature of Science: Scientific Knowledge is Based on Empirical Evidence
Science knowledge is based upon logical and conceptual connections between evidence and explanations.

Crosscutting Concepts

Cause and Effect
Cause and effect relationships may be used to predict phenomena in natural or designed systems.

Systems and System Models
Models can be used to represent systems and their interactions—such as inputs, processes and outputs—and energy and matter flows within systems.

Disciplinary Core Ideas

PS2.B: Types of Interactions
• Gravitational forces are always attractive. There is a gravitational force between any two masses, but it is very small except when one or both of the objects have large mass—e.g., Earth and the sun. • Forces that act at a distance (electric, magnetic, and gravitational) can be explained by fields that extend through space and can be mapped by their effect on a test object (a charged object, or a ball, respectively). • Electric and magnetic (electromagnetic) forces can be attractive or repulsive, and their sizes depend on the magnitudes of the charges, currents, or magnetic strengths involved and on the distances between the interacting objects. • Forces that act at a distance (electric, magnetic, and gravitational) can be explained by fields that extend through space and can be mapped by their effect on a test object (a charged object, or a ball, respectively).

ETS1.B: Developing Possible Solutions
A solution needs to be tested, and then modified on the basis of the test results, in order to improve it. • Models of all kinds are important for testing solutions.

ETS1.C: Optimizing the Design Solution
The iterative process of testing the most promising solutions and modifying what is proposed on the basis of the test results leads to greater refinement and ultimately to an optimal solution.

Connect Your Learning

There are forces that act on everyone and everything around you, but you cannot see them. These forces cause Earth to revolve around the sun, as well as the motors on school buses to run. These forces are called noncontact forces because they do not need to make contact with any objects in order to affect them. You can design simple experiments to explain how these phenomena are present in all kinds of interactions.

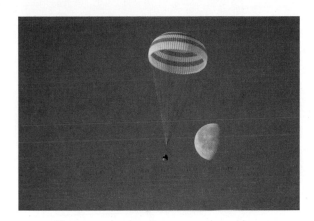

Noncontact Forces

The moon and the object attached to this parachute are both falling toward the center of Earth. However, the person will land safely on the ground, but the moon will stay where it is. How can the same force that causes this person to land also keep the moon safely where it is in the sky?

These balloons are sticking to the wall, but it is not because of glue! How can the same force that causes these balloons to stick to the wall also cause a computer to turn on?

Wind farms such as these use the wind to turn turbines that generate electricity. How do these windmills use motion to generate electromagnetic forces?

Gravity

What is gravity?

Introduction

The photo shows an astronaut on a spacewalk above Earth's surface. There is no tether connecting him to his spacecraft, but he does have a jetpack that can move him in any direction. What would happen to his motion without the tether or jetpack? Would he float off into the depths of space beyond Earth? Would he fall back to Earth's surface? How do you know?

In the last lesson, you learned what forces are and how they affect the motion of objects. In this lesson, you will learn about gravity, a word that is shorthand for all of the effects in the universe related to objects having mass.

As you explore this lesson, you will find out that some of the things you observe and experience every day are caused by gravity. You will learn what affects the gravity between objects, and about tools scientists use to describe and predict gravity. You will also discover how gravity affects astronauts and objects in space. Throughout the lesson, you will see how Newton's laws of motion describe various effects of gravity.

Vocabulary

gravitational forces always attractive, noncontact forces between objects that have mass

attractive when referring to forces, pulling together

orbit the path that an object in space follows around another object due to gravitational forces between the objects

gravitational field a map of a force field that can be used to predict which way gravitational forces will pull an object

force field a model that describes what the force on an object would be if the object were placed in any location in space; usually used to predict the strength and direction of noncontact forces

weight the amount of gravitational force on an object; weight is measured in newtons

mass the amount of matter in an object; mass is measured in kilograms

Next Generation Science Standards

Performance Expectations

MS-PS2-4. Construct and present arguments using evidence to support the claim that gravitational interactions are attractive and depend on the masses of interacting objects.

MS-PS2-5. Conduct an investigation and evaluate the experimental design to provide evidence that fields exist between objects exerting forces on each other even though the objects are not in contact.

Science and Engineering Practices

Planning and Carrying Out Investigations Conduct an investigation and evaluate the experimental design to produce data to serve as the basis for evidence that can meet the goals of the investigation.

Engaging in Argument from Evidence Construct and present oral and written arguments supported by empirical evidence and scientific reasoning to support or refute an explanation or a model for a phenomenon or a solution to a problem.

Scientific Knowledge is Based on Empirical Evidence

Crosscutting Concepts

Cause and Effect Cause and effect relationships may be used to predict phenomena in natural or designed systems.

Systems and System Models Models can be used to represent systems and their interactions—such as inputs, processes and outputs—and energy and matter flows within systems.

Disciplinary Core Ideas

PS2.B. • Gravitational forces are always attractive. There is a gravitational force between any two masses, but it is very small except when one or both of the objects have large mass—e.g., Earth and the sun. • Forces that act at a distance (electric, magnetic, and gravitational) can be explained by fields that extend through space and can be mapped by their effect on a test object (a charged object, or a ball, respectively).

1. Gravity on Earth

At the last second of a basketball game, a player shoots the ball. It arcs high in the air and comes down—*SWISH*—through the hoop. When the player shoots a ball, she does not know if the shot will be good, but she does know that the ball will follow a smooth arc. How can the player be so certain that the ball will follow a smooth arc?

The arced path that the basketball follows is an effect of gravitational forces. **Gravitational forces** are always attractive, noncontact forces between objects that have mass. When a force is **attractive,** it pulls objects together. Noncontact forces act even when the objects are not touching. For the basketball, the gravitational forces are the force of Earth on the ball, and the force of the ball on Earth. These forces cause the basketball to fall toward the center of Earth in an arced path.

Gravity causes objects to fall toward the center of Earth. Gravity and falling objects demonstrate a cause-and-effect relationship. A cause-and-effect relationship is a relationship in which one event makes another event happen. Basketball and other sports would be very different if gravity did not have a cause-and-effect relationship with falling objects.

The strength of the gravitational force on an object near Earth's surface depends on the object's mass. If the masses of the objects do not change, the gravitational forces do not change. Recall that forces can cause changes in motion. Because the gravitational force on a given object usually does not change, an object will move in predictable ways if the gravitational force is the only force on the object.

The gravitational force on a basketball always has the same strength and direction. So, the basketball will move in a smooth arc and will not suddenly change speed or direction. The effects caused by gravity are so common that, as long as the player shoots the ball the same way every time, they will make the basket.

Gravity and falling objects have a cause-and-effect relationship. Earth's gravitational force causes objects, such as basketballs, to fall toward the center of Earth.

Gravity

Although you have seen objects fall, you probably have not timed how long it takes an object to fall. You might be surprised to learn that if there was no air, all objects fall at the same rate, regardless of their mass. How does gravity cause this surprising effect?

Gravitational forces, like all forces, can cause objects to accelerate. Recall that acceleration is a change in an object's speed or direction. The greater the mass of the object is, the greater the gravitational force is. Suppose you have a 10 kg watermelon and a 20 kg pumpkin. The gravitational force on the pumpkin is two times greater than the gravitational force on the watermelon. In fact, the force on the pumpkin is 196 N and the force on the watermelon is 98 N. You might think that the more massive pumpkin would have a greater acceleration than the watermelon, but that is not the case.

According to Newton's second law of motion, an object's acceleration is equal to the force on the object divided by its mass. The gravitational force on the pumpkin is two times greater than the force on the watermelon, but the mass of the pumpkin is also two times greater than the mass of the watermelon. If you put the gravitational forces and the masses into the equation for the second law of motion, you will find:

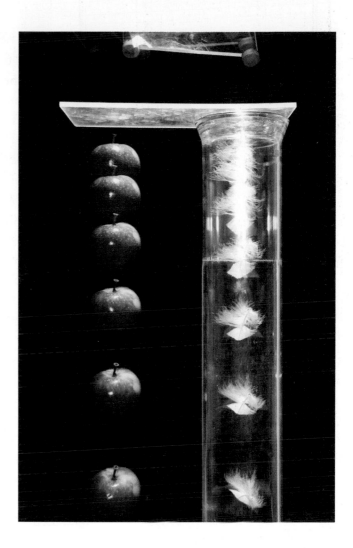

If gravitational forces are the only forces acting on falling objects, the objects will have the same acceleration. When a feather is dropped inside a vacuum tube (a tube with no air inside it), it falls at the same rate as an apple.

$$a = \frac{196 \text{ N}}{20 \text{ kg}} = \frac{98 \text{ N}}{10 \text{ kg}} = 9.8 \text{ m/s}^2$$

The difference in gravitational force is balanced by the difference in mass. So, the two fruits accelerate at the same rate. If you did this calculation for any object near Earth's surface, you would find gravity always causes an acceleration of 9.8 m/s^2.

The idea that all falling objects have the same acceleration might seem wrong. You know that if you dropped a feather and an apple at the same time from the same height, the apple would reach the ground first. The fact that they have different accelerations is evidence that gravity is not the only force acting on them. Air resistance pushes upward on both objects. It is caused by particles of air colliding with the objects as they fall. The feather is flat, wide, and light, so it is slowed down more by the air particles it collides with. Therefore, the force of air resistance reduces its downward acceleration more than the apple's. As a result the acceleration of the feather is lower and it falls more slowly. However, if you dropped the feather inside an airless tube, you would see the feather fall with the same rate of change in velocity as the apple: 9.8 m/s^2.

2. Gravity in Space

You learned that gravitational forces cause objects to fall to Earth. So, why don't the gravitational forces between Earth and the moon make the moon fall and come crashing to Earth?

The moon *is* falling to Earth; it just never lands. The moon moves in an orbit around Earth, and that motion is falling in a special way. An **orbit** is the path that an object in space follows around another object due to gravitational forces between the objects. A thought experiment, illustrated by Figure 4.2A, can help you understand how moving in an orbit is falling without landing.

In this thought experiment, a ball is put in orbit by throwing it. If you throw the ball lightly, it will travel slowly and move only a short distance before landing. It lands as a result of the cause-and-effect relationship between gravity and falling objects. If you throw the ball harder, it moves forward faster and will travel farther before landing. The ball travels farther before landing partly because of its increased forward speed and partly because Earth's surface ever so slightly curves away from the ball. As Earth's surface curves away from the ball, the ball has to fall farther before landing.

Now think about throwing the ball so hard that it flies all the way around Earth. The ball is falling the whole time, but Earth's surface is curving away from the ball at the same rate as the ball falls. The ball keeps moving forward while continually "falling around" Earth. When an object "falls around" Earth in this way, the object is said to be in an orbit. Moving in an orbit is another effect caused by gravity.

This thought experiment explains how spacecraft are put in orbit around Earth. Rockets push the spacecraft up and then push it horizontally to "throw" the spacecraft around Earth. If the spacecraft travels with the right speed, it falls into orbit around the planet.

Figure 4.2A

A thought experiment can explain how an object is put in an orbit. As a ball is thrown harder and harder, it travels farther and father before landing because Earth's surface curves away from the ball. If the ball is thrown fast enough, it never lands because it falls at the same rate as Earth's surface curves away.

The Orbit of Objects

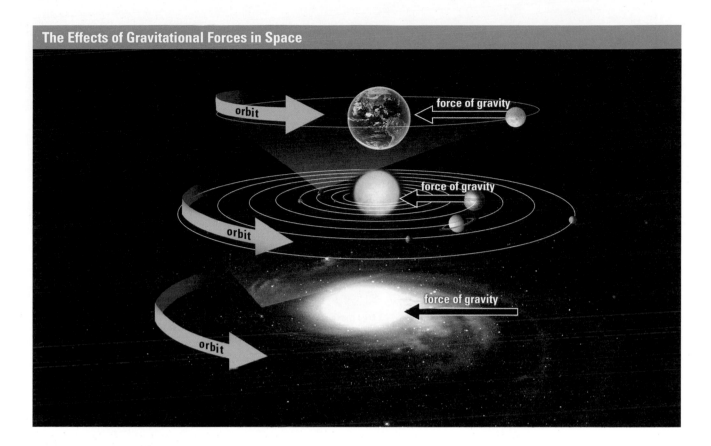

The system of a spacecraft orbiting Earth is a model for how all orbits work. The gravitational force pulls on the spacecraft perpendicularly to the direction that the spacecraft is traveling. The perpendicular force causes the spacecraft to accelerate. In this case, it accelerates by changing direction, and it turns and circles Earth.

The moon "falls around" Earth similarly to the way a spacecraft does. The moon constantly moves forward while gravitational forces constantly pull it toward Earth. As a result, the moon is always turning and falling toward Earth, but it is moving forward fast enough that it never reaches Earth.

The moon is just one of countless objects in space that is in orbit around another object because of gravity. In our solar system, gravitational forces cause planets to fall into orbit around the sun. In our Milky Way galaxy, the sun and the other stars are in orbit around a large cluster of stars and a black hole in the galaxy's center.

The gravitational forces that hold objects in orbit cause the objects to have similar motions, group together, and form similar shapes. As shown in Figure 4.2B, the solar system has a disk shape because the planets orbit in almost the same plane. The Milky Way and most other galaxies in space are also disk shaped.

Gravitational forces form the structures in space because stars and planets have such large masses. These large masses of stars and planets mean that gravitational forces are still strong enough to pull objects together even across large distances.

Figure 4.2B

Gravitational forces hold objects in space together in similarly shaped groups. The orbit of the moon around Earth is a disk shape, and the orbits of the planets around the sun form a disk shape. The sun and the other stars in the Milky Way also have orbits that are disk-shaped.

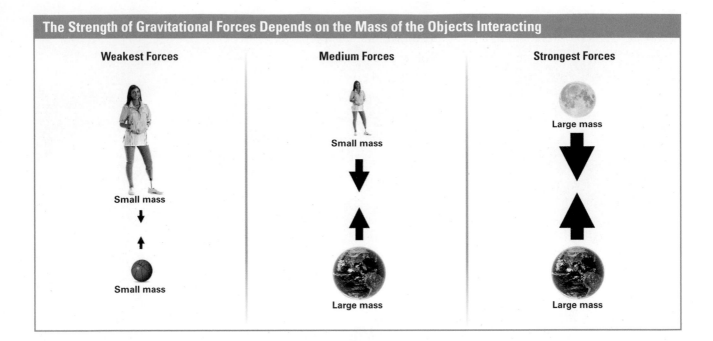

The Strength of Gravitational Forces Depends on the Mass of the Objects Interacting

Weakest Forces

Small mass

Small mass

Medium Forces

Small mass

Large mass

Strongest Forces

Large mass

Large mass

Fig. 4.3A

Two objects with small masses (left) have weak gravitational forces between them. If one of the objects has a very large mass (center), the gravitational forces between the objects are strong enough for us to observe their effects. If both objects have very large masses (right), the gravitational forces between them are even stronger.

Isaac Newton recognized that gravitational forces attract objects toward the center of Earth and hold the moon in orbit around Earth.

3. The Strengths of Gravitational Forces

According to legend, Sir Isaac Newton came up with the idea of gravity as a universal force after he was hit on the head by a falling apple. It sounds like a silly story, but even Newton himself told stories about how a falling apple caused him to study gravity. Of course, he never claimed to have been hit on the head by the apple. What about the falling apple did Newton find so interesting?

People have always known that when objects fall, they fall down. But when Newton saw the apple fall he wondered why it fell downward instead of another direction, like upward or sideways. He concluded that a force had to be pulling the apple down and that the force was related to Earth. He then wondered how far this pulling acted. Could it reach as far as the moon?

To answer his question, Newton gathered evidence of the effects of gravity. A lot of the evidence he found was observations of objects in space. He looked at patterns such as the moon's orbit around Earth, the orbits of the planets around the sun, and the orbits of moons around Jupiter and Saturn. Using math, Newton developed a model of gravity that explained the various orbits of these objects in space. He was then able to use his model to explain the acceleration of objects falling near Earth's surface.

Realizing that the force that made objects fall on Earth also kept the moon in orbit was one of Newton's greatest ideas. This force is now known as the gravitational force. Newton's ideas about the gravitational force are also closely related to his three laws of motion.

Newton did more than identify gravitational forces and their effects. He also found the factors that affect the strength of the gravitational force between any two objects.

When you think of gravitational forces pulling objects to Earth you may only think of forces pulling the objects down. But recall Newton's third law of motion. It states that when an object exerts a force on a second object, the second object exerts an equal and opposite force on the first object. So when Earth exerts a downward force on an object, the object exerts an equal, upward force on Earth! Why doesn't this force make Earth move upward? The answer has to do with Newton's second law of motion. The acceleration of Earth is equal to the force on Earth divided by its mass. The mass of Earth is huge, so its acceleration is so tiny that you do not observe it.

The gravitational force between two objects depends on two factors: the masses of the objects and the distance between them. The strength of the gravitational forces between two objects is greater when one or both objects has a large mass. Figure 4.3A models this idea. Gravitational forces between you and a basketball are very small. The force does pull the basketball ever so slightly toward you, but the force is so weak that you do not feel it. But the forces between you and Earth are strong enough to observe. And when two objects have very large masses, such as the moon and Earth, the gravitational forces are much stronger.

The strength of the gravitational force between two objects is stronger when the objects are near, and it's weaker when the objects are farther apart. If you are in a spacecraft that is taking off, you will move farther and farther away from Earth. Figure 4.3B shows that as the distance between you and Earth increases, the gravitational force pulling you and Earth together weakens. For example, the gravitational force on the astronaut at the beginning of the lesson is weaker when he is on a spacewalk than when he is standing on Earth.

Figure 4.3B

Gravitational forces are strongest when two objects are close together. The farther apart the two objects are, the weaker the forces are between them. If the two objects are far enough apart, the forces between them are so weak that you can no longer observe their effects.

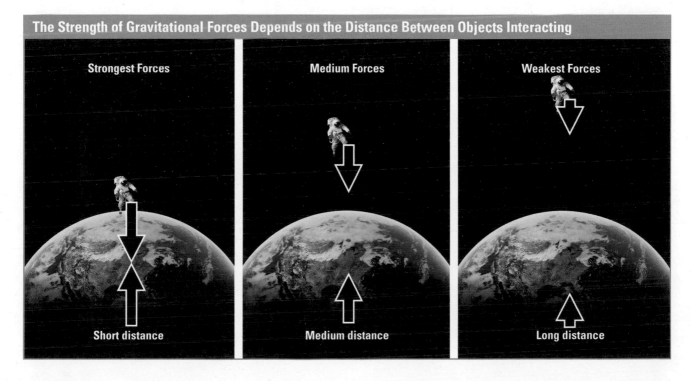

The Strength of Gravitational Forces Depends on the Distance Between Objects Interacting

Strongest Forces

Short distance

Medium Forces

Medium distance

Weakest Forces

Long distance

Modeling Gravitational Forces

The strength of gravitational forces between two objects depends on their mass and the distance between them. The greater the masses of the objects, the greater the gravitational forces between them. However, the greater the distance between objects, the weaker the gravitational forces between them. In this thought experiment, a satellite moves from the moon to Earth with longer arrows representing more force than shorter arrows.

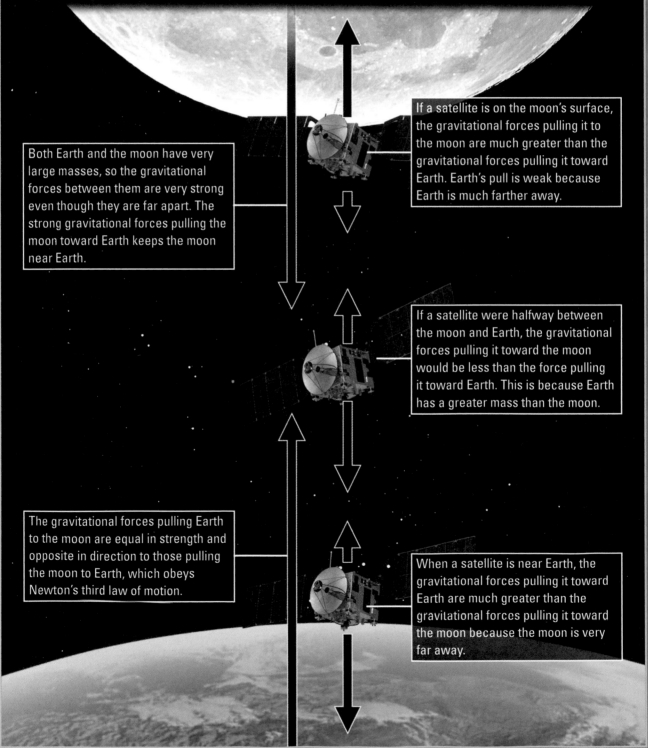

Both Earth and the moon have very large masses, so the gravitational forces between them are very strong even though they are far apart. The strong gravitational forces pulling the moon toward Earth keeps the moon near Earth.

If a satellite is on the moon's surface, the gravitational forces pulling it to the moon are much greater than the gravitational forces pulling it toward Earth. Earth's pull is weak because Earth is much farther away.

If a satellite were halfway between the moon and Earth, the gravitational forces pulling it toward the moon would be less than the force pulling it toward Earth. This is because Earth has a greater mass than the moon.

The gravitational forces pulling Earth to the moon are equal in strength and opposite in direction to those pulling the moon to Earth, which obeys Newton's third law of motion.

When a satellite is near Earth, the gravitational forces pulling it toward Earth are much greater than the gravitational forces pulling it toward the moon because the moon is very far away.

4. Gravitational Fields

Newton's model of gravity is sometimes summarized as "what goes up, must come down." For people on Earth, "down" is toward the center of Earth. If you drop anything, it falls toward the center of Earth. However, if an astronaut drops anything on the moon, it falls toward the moon's center. What would happen to an object dropped between Earth and the moon? Which "down" direction would it fall?

Gravitational fields are maps of force fields that can be used to predict which way gravitational forces will pull objects. A model called a **force field** will describe what the force on an object would be if the object were placed in any location in space. Force fields are used to predict the strength and direction of all noncontact forces.

The gravitational field around Earth is represented by arrows pointing toward Earth. An object placed in the force field will be pulled toward Earth in the same direction as the gravitational field arrows. In Figure 4.4, the gravitational field is represented by light gray arrows, while the gravitational forces are represented by black arrows. Remember, the gravitational *field* arrows are not *forces*—they are part of the model you can use to predict what the gravitational forces on an object will be. The spacing of the arrows shows how strong the forces will be. The forces will be stronger where the arrows are closer together, and weaker where the arrows are farther apart.

The strength of a gravitational field decreases with distance. Earth's gravitational field is strong near Earth's surface. The field is weaker 10 km above Earth's surface. An object placed between Earth and the moon is in both Earth's and the moon's gravitational fields. It is in a tug-of-war as it is being pulled toward Earth and the moon. The object's position will determine the winner of the tug-of-war. At a certain distance from the moon, the moon's gravitational field is stronger than Earth's. At that spot, the object is pulled toward the moon in the direction dominated by the moon's gravitational field.

Figure 4.4

A gravitational force field is like a topographical map that describes what the gravitational forces on an object would be at any point in space. The gravitational force fields of Earth and the moon show the direction that an object would be pulled when placed in the fields near them.

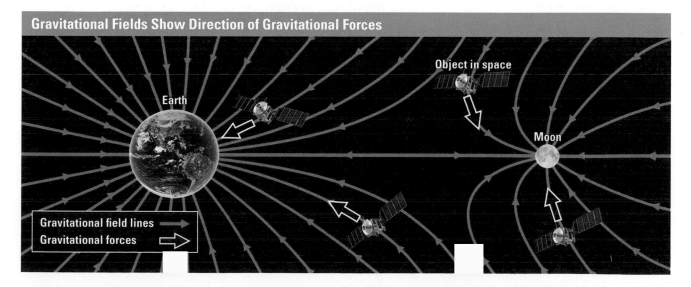

Gravitational Fields Show Direction of Gravitational Forces

Object in space

Earth

Moon

Gravitational field lines
Gravitational forces

Changes in Gravity Affect Weight and Mass

Earth	Moon	Mars
Mass 5.4 kg	Mass 5.4 kg	Mass 5.4 kg
Weight 53.4 N (12 lbs)	Weight: 8.9 N (2 lbs)	Weight 20.1 N (4.5 lbs)

Figure 4.5

Mass and weight have similar but related meanings. Mass is a measure of the amount of matter in an object, while weight is a measure of the gravitational force on an object. An object's mass stays the same wherever it is, but its weight can change depending on the strength of the gravitational force on it.

5. Mass and Weight

The astronauts who traveled to the moon were on an amazing weight loss plan. In just three days, they lost 83 percent of their weight! Of course, when they returned to Earth a few days later, they gained back all that weight. How did they do it?

The trick to the astronauts' weight loss had to do with the difference between mass and weight. In everyday language, mass and weight are often used to mean the same thing. In science, however, mass and weight have different but related meanings.

Weight is the amount of gravitational force on an object. It is measured in newtons (N), just like other forces. An object's weight depends on its mass. **Mass** is the amount of matter in an object. Mass is measured in kilograms (kg). The greater the mass of an object, the greater the gravitational force on that object and the more the object weighs.

However, an object's weight can change *without changing mass* if the gravitational force on it changes. As you can see in Figure 4.5, this is true for more than just humans. The bowling ball weighs less on the moon than it does on Earth, and more on Mars than it does on the moon. However, its mass never changes. All the astronauts had to do to lose weight was to travel to a place that had weaker gravitational forces pulling on them. The moon has less mass than Earth, so gravitational forces between an astronaut and the moon are weaker. The astronaut weighs less on the moon even though his body has the same mass as it did on Earth.

6. Weight in Orbit

In videos of astronauts on the moon, they seem to jump with little effort because of their lower weight. But in videos of astronauts on the International Space Station, they float around. People mistakenly think that space station astronauts float because they are weightless.

For an object to be weightless, it has to be so far from any large object that no gravitational forces pull on the object. The astronauts in the space station are still close enough to Earth to have gravitational forces pulling them down toward Earth. In fact, gravitational forces pulling on them are about 90 percent as strong as they are on Earth's surface. So why do the astronauts float? They float because they are moving in an orbit around Earth with the space station!

Gravity causes the space station to orbit Earth. As the space station "falls around" Earth, everything inside it, including the astronauts, fall with it. The astronauts fall because, as predicted by Newton's first law of motion, the gravitational forces on them cause their bodies to accelerate toward Earth. However, the astronauts do not land on the floor of the station because gravity causes the station to fall down at the same rate. In other words, a lack of gravity does not make the astronauts weightless. Instead, the presence of gravity causes them to *appear* weightless by making them fall with the falling space station. Think about dropping two balls. The balls will fall at the same rate. Now picture one of the balls is inside the other ball. Both balls would still fall at the same rate. Similarly, the astronauts inside the space station fall at the same rate as the space station itself. So, the appearance of weightlessness is yet another effect caused by gravity.

Gravity causes astronauts in orbit to appear weightless. They appear weightless because the astronauts and their spacecraft "fall" at the same rate due to the gravitational forces on them.

LESSON SUMMARY

Gravity

Gravity on Earth Gravitational forces cause objects to fall to Earth at the same rate.

Gravity in Space Gravitational forces hold objects in orbit in space.

The Strengths of Gravitational Forces Newton developed a model of gravity that describes the relationship between gravitational force, mass, and distance.

Gravitational Fields Gravitational fields can be used to predict which way gravitational forces will pull objects.

Mass and Weight Mass and weight are related measures of matter, but only weight depends on gravity.

Weight in Orbit Gravity makes astronauts in orbit appear weightless.

Sci-Fi: Putting the Science into Fiction

When the science fiction movie *Star Wars: The Force Awakens* came out in December 2015, nearly 28.8 million people in the United States went to see it the first weekend. Sci-fi thrillers became popularized in the 1800s. How did this out-of-this world combination of science and fiction begin, and what makes it so popular?

Science fiction stories are wildly popular, perhaps because they combine the real world with the imaginary. This image of a spacecraft in a city could be from a science fiction movie or book.

Part of the appeal of science fiction stories is that they contain situations and settings that are unlike anything anyone has ever experienced. Some science fiction stories are set on imaginary planets with people traveling faster than light in spacecraft to other planets. Other stories might include cloned dinosaurs that attack and eat their human caretakers. Humans have not figured out how to travel faster than light and have never grown a dinosaur from prehistoric DNA. But they are thrilled at the thought of these imaginary scenarios.

French author Jules Verne is sometimes called the father of science fiction. His book *From the Earth to the Moon*, written in 1865, included real scientific facts to describe sending a spacecraft to the moon.

From the Earth to the Moon

Science fiction is different from other fantasy stories because science fiction features ways that science or technology affect characters or society. For example, Cinderella is an imaginary story that contains magic and is a fairy tale; it is not science fiction. Mary Shelley's sci-fi book *Frankenstein* is also imaginary, but it includes descriptions of how Dr. Frankenstein uses science to build a monster and bring it to life. Written in 1818, *Frankenstein* is considered to be one of the earliest examples of science fiction.

The person often credited for developing and popularizing science fiction was French author Jules Verne. Verne was a stock broker who dreamed of writing novels. Although he didn't have a traditional background in science, he spent a lot of time reading and researching science at the library. He knew he wanted to incorporate science in the novels he planned to write.

One of Verne's most famous books is *From the Earth to the Moon*. In it, a large cannon is built to send people in a spacecraft to the moon. The book was written in 1865—well before any space travel had been done. As Verne worked on this book and its sequel, *Trip Around the Moon*, he spoke to scientists and mathematicians to be as accurate as possible. For example, Verne included a close prediction of the escape velocity for Earth in his book. A planet's escape velocity is the velocity at which an object must travel to break free of the planet's gravitational forces. Verne also closely described what weightlessness in space would be like. Although Verne's books were fantasies, they were grounded in science, which made the events in them seem possible.

This illustration from Verne's *From the Earth to the Moon* shows three people climbing into the spacecraft. All Apollo missions to the moon had three astronauts. This is just one of the similarities between Verne's story and reality.

True Story—Later

Verne's books about traveling to the moon were written about 100 years before Apollo 10 became the first crewed mission to orbit the moon. Yet, many of the details that Verne included matched details of the real Apollo missions.

In Verne's book, three people traveled in the spacecraft, which was launched from Tampa, Florida. Once in space, the travelers used rockets to slow their craft, and people on Earth were able to watch their journey using telescopes. Upon returning to Earth, the spacecraft "landed" by splashing down in the Pacific Ocean.

Each Apollo crew consisted of three astronauts. The missions were all launched from Merritt Island, Florida, which is about 215 km away from Tampa. While in space, the Apollo astronauts used retro-rockets to steer and slow the space modules. Most people did not use telescopes to watch the Apollo missions, but NASA scientists could see the command module for part of its journey with their high-powered telescopes. And finally, every Apollo mission ended with a splashdown in the ocean, just as Verne had written.

Of course, not everything that Verne wrote came true. For example, the Apollo missions were launched with rockets, not giant cannons. But despite the differences, the many similarities make it seem as if Verne could predict the future!

Like the spacecraft in Verne's book, the Apollo missions were launched from Florida. But unlike the travelers in Verne's books, the Apollo astronauts, such as this astronaut on Apollo 9, sometimes left their spacecraft to do spacewalks.

Science Fiction to Science Fact

Verne's uncanny ability to see into the future was not limited to the Apollo missions. He wrote more than 60 books, plays, and short stories, and in those works, he sometimes described technology that would be invented years later. For example, in one book, Verne described how the character Captain Nemo took a trip through the ocean in an electric submarine named the *Nautilus*. Scientists have been using electric submarines to explore the deep ocean since the mid-1960s. Verne also described skywriting and news broadcasts as a way of getting information to a lot of people at once.

Verne was not the only science fiction storyteller to imagine objects that would later come to be. Science fiction writers wrote about credit cards, earbuds, and tanks before any of these things were invented. Science fiction TV shows and movies showed driverless cars, tablet computers, and video calls. All these technologies were futuristic when they first appeared, but today they are commonplace.

So, when you watch a science fiction movie, perhaps some of the amazing things you see might actually come true! Maybe someday humans will find a way to travel faster than light and go zipping across the galaxy to visit other planets. Maybe scientists will clone a prehistoric animal. But, hopefully, they will start with an animal that won't consider people its lunch! ◆

Jules Verne and other science fiction writers wrote about imaginary things that later became real. In an essay, Verne predicted that advertisements would be written in the sky for many people to see at once. Today, skywriting is used for advertising and for fun.

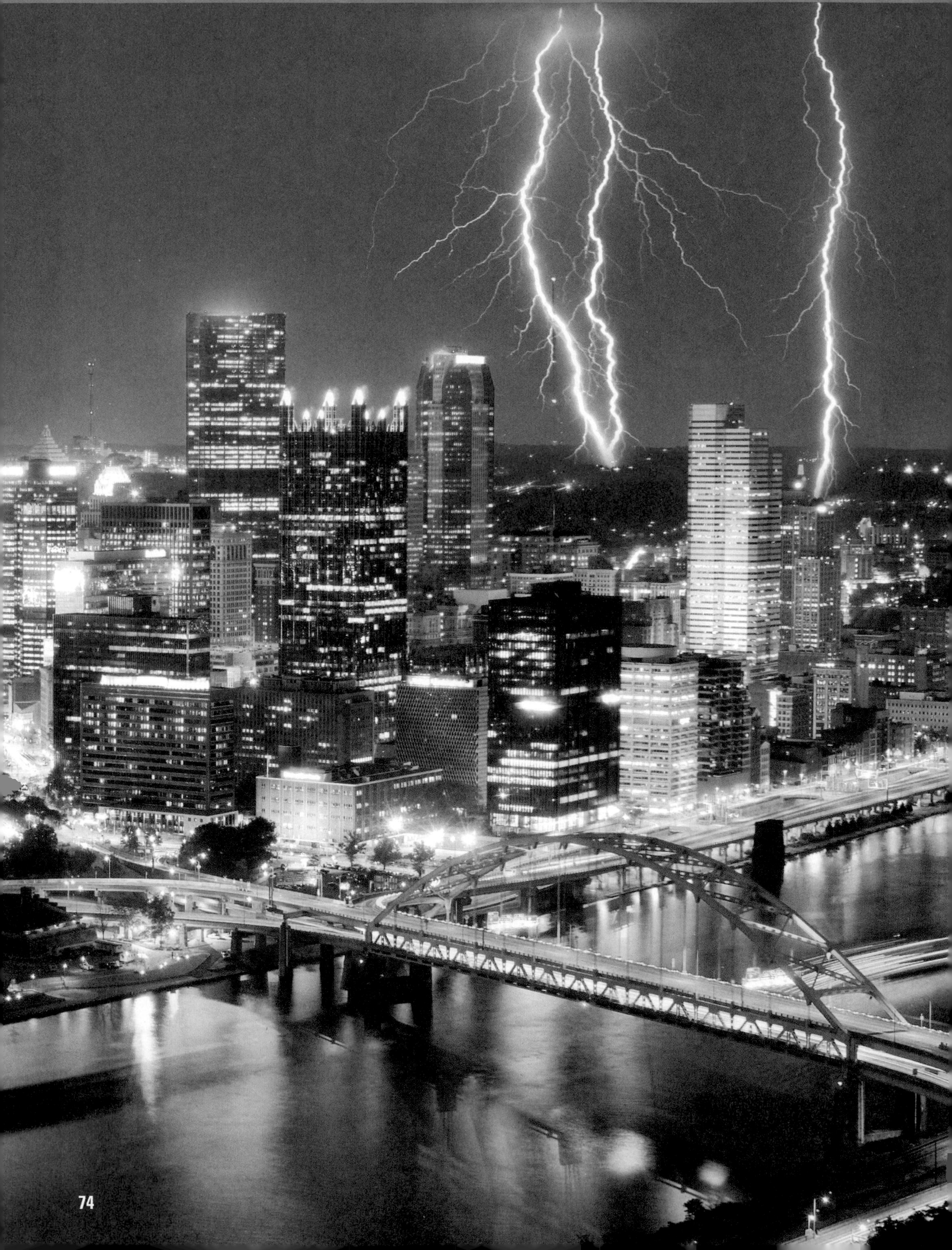

Electricity

What is electricity?

Introduction

Look at the bolts of lightning in the image. Each bolt is a stream of electrically charged particles flying through the air. In everyday terms, it is electricity. Is it possible that this lightning is the same stuff that powers your cell phone?

You have learned about how forces cause motion and how the effects of forces on an object can be predicted using Newton's laws of motion. You have also learned about gravitational force, a noncontact force that makes objects fall and holds the planets in orbit around the sun.

In this lesson, you will explore several cause-and-effect relationships involving a second noncontact force—electric force. You will discover what electric force is, and how it does all these things. First you will learn how the electric force affects charged particles. Next you will see how the strength and direction of the electric force can be described by an electric field, similarly to how a gravitational force was described by a gravitational field. Then you will learn how these charged particles create electric currents and power every electronic device. Finally, you will discover how engineers use robots to test and improve smartphone touch screens.

Vocabulary

electric charge a property of matter that causes electrical phenomena

electric forces attractive or repulsive noncontact forces between charged particles

repulsive when referring to forces, pushing apart

electric field a force field surrounding an electrically charged object

electric current a flow of particles with electric charge

resistance opposition to the flow of electric charge

prototype a working model of a design solution that can be used for testing and refining the design

Next Generation Science Standards

Performance Expectations
MS-PS2-3. Ask questions about data to determine the factors that affect the strength of electric and magnetic forces.
MS-PS2-5. Conduct an investigation and evaluate the experimental design to provide evidence that fields exist between objects exerting forces on each other even though the objects are not in contact.
MS-ETS1-4. Develop a model to generate data for iterative testing and modification of a proposed object, tool, or process such that an optimal design can be achieved.

Science and Engineering Practices
Asking Questions and Defining Problems Ask questions that can be investigated within the scope of the classroom, outdoor environment, and museums and other public facilities with available resources and, when appropriate, frame a hypothesis based on observations and scientific principles.

Planning and Carrying Out Investigations Conduct an investigation and evaluate the experimental design to produce data to serve as the basis for evidence that can meet the goals of the investigation.

Developing and Using Models Develop a model to generate data to test ideas about designed systems, including those representing inputs and outputs.

Crosscutting Concepts
Cause and Effect Cause and effect relationships may be used to predict phenomena in natural or designed systems.

Disciplinary Core Ideas
PS2.B. • Electric and magnetic (electromagnetic) forces can be attractive or repulsive, and their sizes depend on the magnitudes of the charges, currents, or magnetic strengths involved and on the distances between the interacting objects. • Forces that act at a distance (electric, magnetic, and gravitational) can be explained by fields that extend through space and can be mapped by their effect on a test object (a charged object, or a ball, respectively).
ETS1.B. • A solution needs to be tested, and then modified on the basis of the test results, in order to improve it. • Models of all kinds are important for testing solutions.
ETS1.C. The iterative process of testing the most promising solutions and modifying what is proposed on the basis of the test results leads to greater refinement and ultimately to an optimal solution.

Balloons will stick to a wall after you rub them on your hair.

1. Electric Charge and Forces

You and your friends are decorating the school gym for a dance. As you blow up balloons, you decide to do a magic trick. You rub a balloon on your hair and then place the balloon on the wall where it sticks. How could you explain this trick?

The explanation for the sticking balloon starts with charged particles. All matter is made of particles that are too small to see. Some of these particles have electric charge. **Electric charge** is a property of matter that causes electrical phenomena. Particles with electric charge interact with other particles with electric charge.

Two kinds of electric charge exist. These kinds of charges are called *positive* and *negative*, names chosen to show that the charges have opposite effects.

As demonstrated in Figure 5.1A, objects may have either equal or unequal numbers of positively charged particles and negatively charged particles. Objects that have equal numbers of positively charged particles and negatively charged particles are called *neutral* because they have no overall charge. Most objects you regularly encounter are neutral.

Most of the time, your hair and a balloon have equal numbers of positively charged and negatively charged particles and are neutral. However, when you rub a balloon on your hair, negatively charged particles from your hair are transferred to the balloon. Your hair now has more positively charged particles than negatively charged particles, and has an overall positive charge. The balloon, on the other hand, has more negatively charged particles and has an overall negative charge.

Figure 5.1A

All objects contain positively charged particles and negatively charged particles. If an object has equal numbers of positively and negatively charged particles, the object is neutral. If an object has unequal numbers of positively and negatively charged particles, the object has an overall charge.

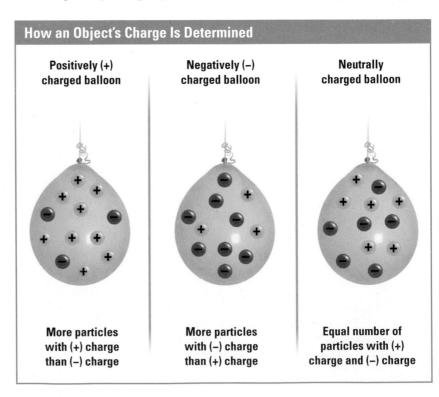

How an Object's Charge Is Determined

Positively (+) charged balloon	Negatively (−) charged balloon	Neutrally charged balloon
More particles with (+) charge than (−) charge	More particles with (−) charge than (+) charge	Equal number of particles with (+) charge and (−) charge

Charged objects can interact through electric forces. **Electric forces** are attractive or repulsive noncontact forces between charged particles. Recall that an attractive force pulls objects together. On the other hand, a **repulsive** force pushes objects apart. Whether an electric force is attractive or repulsive depends on the charges of the objects. You can investigate this in an experiment similar to the one shown in Figure 5.1B. It shows two balloons hanging side by side on strings to explore the cause-and-effect relationships involved. Neutral objects, such as the first pair of balloons, do not experience electric forces.

The electric forces between two objects are repulsive when they have the same kind of charge. In Figure 5.1B, pairs of balloons with the same kind of charge are pushed apart. In another example, when your friend pulls a wool sweater over his head, negatively charged particles from the sweater transfer to each hair on his head. As a result, each strand of hair has more negatively charged particles and therefore, is negatively charged. Because all strands of hair have the same charge, the electric force between them is repulsive. The strands of hair push each other away.

On the other hand, when two objects have opposite charges, the electric forces between them are attractive. Figure 5.1B shows how pairs of balloons will behave. Now recall the balloons for the school dance. Rubbing a balloon on your hair will give the balloon a negative charge. When you hold the balloon close to the wall, the negatively charged balloon pushes the negatively charged particles in the wall away, giving the area near the balloon a positive charge. The balloon and the area of wall near the balloon have opposite charges, so the electric force between them is attractive. As a result, the balloon and the wall pull together and the balloon sticks to the wall.

Figure 5.1B

The electric force is an attractive or repulsive force between charged objects. The electric force pushes objects apart if they have the same charge, but pulls objects together if they have opposite charges. No electric force exists between neutral objects.

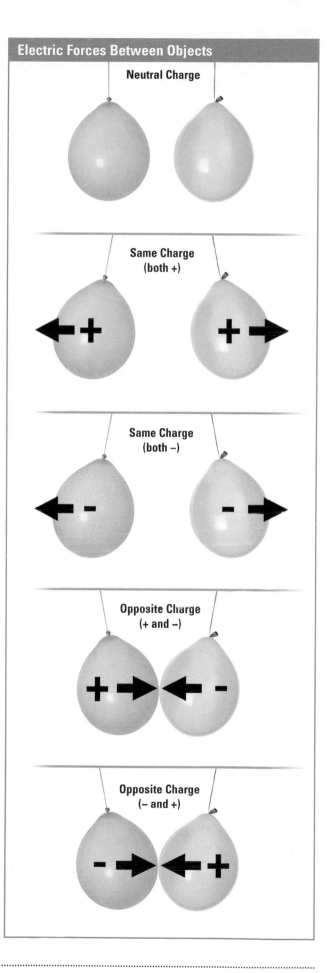

Electric Forces Between Objects

Neutral Charge

Same Charge (both +)

Same Charge (both –)

Opposite Charge (+ and –)

Opposite Charge (– and +)

2. The Strengths of Electric Forces

Suppose that you have a positively charged balloon hanging between two negatively charged balloons. The positively charged balloon is attracted to both negatively charged balloons, so how can you predict which way it will move?

To answer this, you need to know the strengths of the electric forces between the balloons. Like gravitational forces, electric forces can vary in strength. The strengths of electric forces depend partly on the amount of charge on the interacting objects. The more charge an object has, the stronger the electric force it exerts. You can use this cause-and-effect relationship to make your prediction. Look at Figure 5.2. A positively charged balloon will be attracted by a stronger force to a balloon that has a more negative charge than it would to a balloon that has a less negative charge. The positively charged balloon will be repelled with a stronger force from a balloon with a greater positive charge.

The strength of the electric force also depends on the distance between interacting objects. This dependence is similar to the way that the gravitational force depends on distance. As Figure 5.2 shows, the closer together charged objects are, the stronger the electric force between them. When you want to stick a balloon to the wall using an electric force, you have to hold the balloon close to the wall. The electric force is only strong enough to attract the balloon to the wall when they are close together.

Figure 5.2

The strength of the electric force depends on the amount of charge on the objects and on the distance between the objects. The electric force increases when the charges on the objects increase, and the force decreases when the distance between the objects increases.

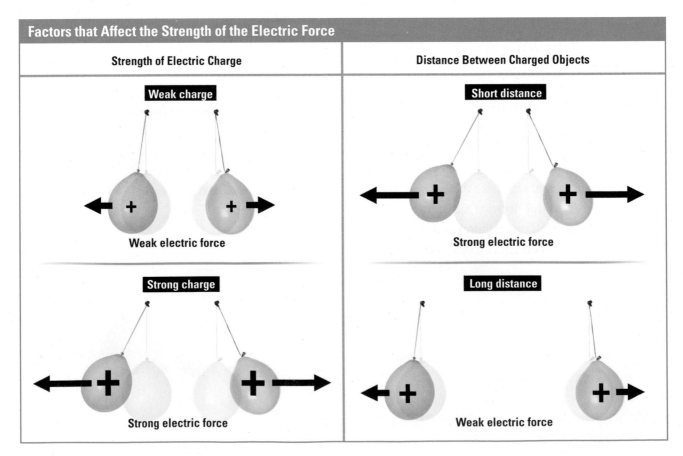

Factors that Affect the Strength of the Electric Force

Strength of Electric Charge

Distance Between Charged Objects

Weak charge

Weak electric force

Strong charge

Strong electric force

Short distance

Strong electric force

Long distance

Weak electric force

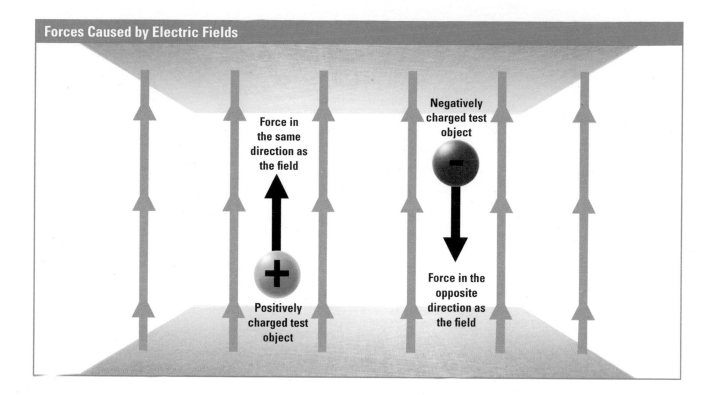

Forces Caused by Electric Fields

Force in the same direction as the field

Negatively charged test object

Positively charged test object

Force in the opposite direction as the field

3. Electric Fields

Think about walking into a school's cafeteria and getting a whiff of the day's meal. It smells good, and you head toward the counter. As you move closer, the yummy scent becomes stronger. It's pizza! You walk faster because you cannot wait to get your lunch. How can the delicious scent of pizza help you understand electric forces?

The scent of a pizza surrounds the pizza, and the scent is stronger the closer you are to the pizza. Just as a pizza can be detected by the scent that surrounds it, a charged object can be detected by something that surrounds it. An **electric field** is a force field surrounding an electrically charged object. It can be used to predict the electric force exerted on a positively charged test object.

What is a *test object*? When discussing electric fields, a test object is an imaginary object with exactly 1 C of charge (the units of electric charge are coulombs, abbreviated C). So, the strength of the field tells you how strong the force would be if you put a particle with 1 C of charge in it. A particle with 2 C of charge would experience twice as much force. Similarly, a particle with 0.5 C of charge would experience half as much force.

Electric fields that surround charged objects are similar to gravitational fields that surround objects that have mass. Recall that gravitational fields predict which way gravitational forces will pull an object. Look at Figure 5.3A. Electric fields also predict the force on an object—specifically a positively charged test object. However, because electric forces can be attractive or repulsive, electric fields predict which way electric forces will pull *or* push an object.

Figure 5.3A

In diagrams, electric fields are represented by arrows. A positively charged test object moves in the same direction as the field. A negatively charged test object will move in the opposite direction of the field.

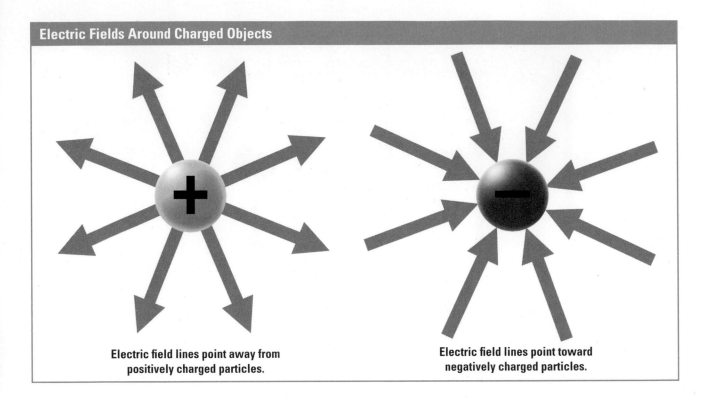

Electric field lines point away from positively charged particles.

Electric field lines point toward negatively charged particles.

Figure 5.3B
All charged objects create an electric field. The arrows point toward negatively charged objects and point away from positively charged objects. The amount of space between arrows shows the strength of the electric force on a test object.

All charged objects create electric fields, and the electric fields exist whether or not a test object is present. Similarly, all objects that have mass are surrounded by gravitational fields whether or not another mass is close enough to experience it.

Remember that in a diagram showing a gravitational field, the field was represented by arrows. An electric field is also represented by arrows in diagrams. In a gravitational field diagram, the arrows always pointed toward the object that created the field. That's because other objects would always be pulled toward the object in the diagram. But in an electric field diagram, the arrow can point toward *or* away from the object that created the field. The arrows point toward the object if it is negatively charged. The arrows point toward the object because a positively charged test object will be pulled toward a negatively charged object. On the other hand, the arrows point away from an object if it is positively charged because a positively charged test object will be pushed away from another positively charged object.

Another similarity between gravitational fields and electric fields is that the amount of space between arrows in an electric field diagram shows how strong the field is. Arrows that are close together indicate that the field is strong. Arrows that are far apart indicate that the field is weak. The electric field diagrams in Figure 5.3B show that the arrows are close together near charged objects and grow farther apart as the distance from the charged object increases. As the distance from the charged object increases, the strength of the electric field decreases. This confirms that the electric force of an object decreases with distance as well.

Causes and Effects: Electric Charge, Forces, and Fields

Objects can be positively charged, negatively charged, or neutral. Rubbing certain neutral objects can cause them to gain charges by gaining or losing charged particles. An effect of charging an object is that it creates an electric field. The electric field describes the force caused by the charged object on positively charged objects. How can you determine whether an object has a positive or negative charge?

Building Up Charge on an Object

A person rubs a balloon on their hair.
The balloon becomes negatively charged.

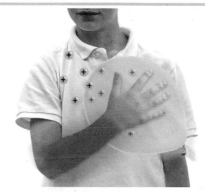

A person rubs a balloon on a polyester shirt.
The balloon becomes positively charged.

Finding the Forces and Electric Field with a Positively Charged Test Object

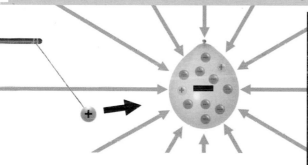

A positively charged test object is held near the negatively charged balloon. Since the charge on the test object and balloon are opposite, they are attracted to each other.

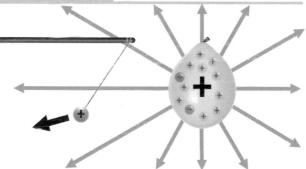

A positively charged test object is held near the positively charged balloon. Since the charge on the test object and balloon are the same, they repel each other.

Finding the Forces and Electric Field with a Negatively Charged Test Object

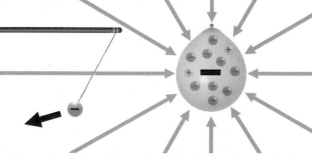

A negatively charged test object is held near the negatively charged balloon. Since the charge on the test object and balloon are the same, they repel each other.

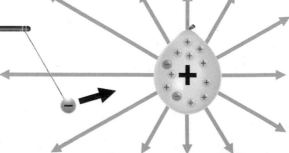

A negatively charged test object is held near the positively charged balloon. Since the charge on the test object and balloon are opposite, they attract each other.

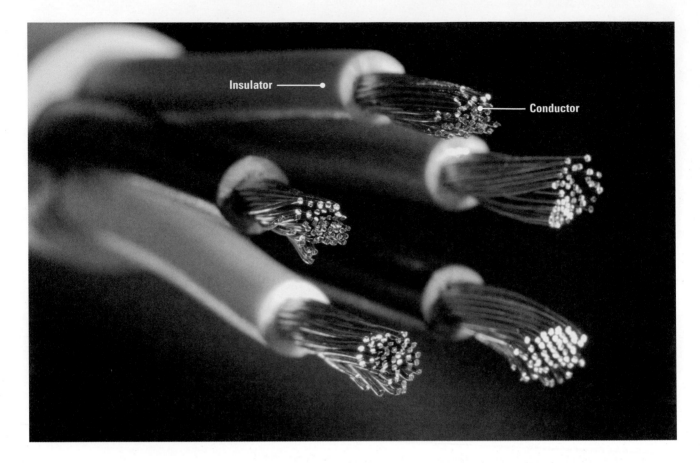

Insulator ——————•

Conductor

Electric current travels through conductors but cannot travel through insulators. Wires contain metal conductors that carry electric current, and are also covered in insulating plastic that keeps current from leaving the wire.

Semiconductors are materials that sometimes act as conductors and sometimes act as insulators. Computer chips and other electronic parts are made from semiconductors.

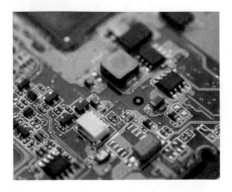

4. Electric Current

When you rub a balloon on your hair, the negatively charged particles that moved to the balloon stay near the surface of the balloon. They do not move around in the rubber that makes up the balloon. However, electric charges do move through some materials. Why can charges move through some materials and not others?

When electric charges move, they form an electric current. An **electric current** is a flow of particles with electric charge. Electric current can travel through some materials better than others. How well an electric current travels depends on a property called resistance. **Resistance** is the opposition to the flow of electric charge.

Some materials, called *insulators*, have resistances that are so high that almost no electric current can travel through them at all. Rubber, plastic, wood, and some cloths are all insulators. Insulators can sometimes be charged, but charged particles do not flow through them.

Other materials, called *conductors*, have low resistances, and electric current travels easily through them. Most metals, such as copper, iron, and gold are conductors. Power cords for electric devices contain metal wires so that electric current can travel from a power source to the device.

Computer chips and other parts of electronic devices are made of semiconductors. Semiconductors are materials that act as a conductor under certain circumstances, and as an insulator under other circumstances.

How does an electric current cause a battery-powered heater to warm up? A battery-powered heater works by taking advantage of resistance. If you look inside a battery-powered heater, you will likely see coils of wire. The coils are made of a metal conductor with a relatively high resistance. Electric charges have a hard time traveling through the coils because of the high resistance. This resistance causes the coil to heat up. The temperature of the coil rises and gives off heat that you can feel.

Although electric current can travel through conductors, conductors do not always have currents in them. Currents only travel through conductors such as copper wire when there is an electric charge, including when the conductor is in an electric circuit. Figure 5.4 shows an example of an electric circuit. An electric circuit usually contains a current source, such as a battery or an electrical outlet, electric devices, and wires that connect the source and the device. Notice that wires and the other parts of the circuit form a complete loop that does not have any breaks in it. Like the circuit shown, all electric circuits form closed loops.

A battery can be used as a current source. When a loop of wire connects the negative end of the battery to the positive end, charged particles flow as a current from the negative end to the positive end. If an electric device, such as a heater, is placed within the loop of wire, the current travels through the device and powers it.

After the current goes through an electric device, it follows the wire to the positive end of the battery. If any of the wires were disconnected, the circuit would be broken, the electric current would not flow, and the electric device would not work.

Figure 5.4

A battery-powered heater takes advantage of resistance to produce heat. The coil inside the heater is made of a conductor that has a relatively high resistance. When electric charges flow through the coil, the temperature of the coil rises.

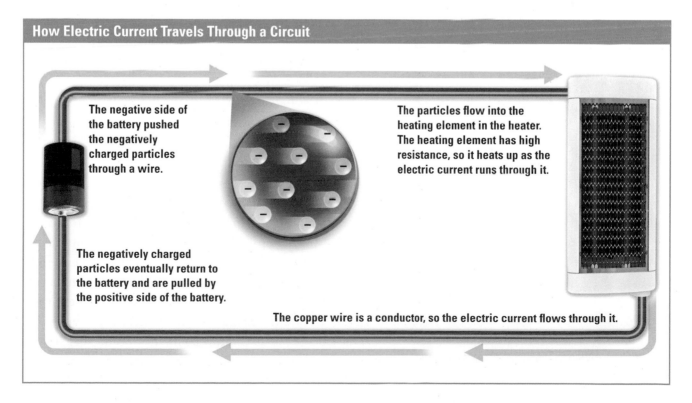

How Electric Current Travels Through a Circuit

The negative side of the battery pushed the negatively charged particles through a wire.

The particles flow into the heating element in the heater. The heating element has high resistance, so it heats up as the electric current runs through it.

The negatively charged particles eventually return to the battery and are pulled by the positive side of the battery.

The copper wire is a conductor, so the electric current flows through it.

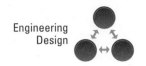

5. Testing Touch Screens

Think about sending a text message on a smartphone. To write your message correctly, you have to type on a tiny keyboard on the screen. How do touch screens work, and how do phone engineers make sure that the screens work well enough to type accurately?

How Capacitive Touch Screens Work Touch screens on phones and tablet computers work by changing electric currents in the screens. A touch screen has two sets of tiny parallel wires inside it. The first set of wires carries currents. The second set of wires is perpendicular to the first set of wires and measures the currents in the first set.

Your skin is a conductor, so when you touch the screen, a small part of the current from the screen goes into your finger. As a result, the amount of current in the first set of wires changes. The second set of wires detects the change and sends a message to the phone's computer. The computer then calculates where the change in current happened. All of this happens within a fraction of a second.

Touch Screen Accuracy The accuracy of a phone's touch screen depends on how well the phone's computer can pinpoint where the screen was touched. One way that accuracy is tested is by tracing straight lines on the screen. The sensor points on a touch screen are arranged in a grid, as demonstrated in Figure 5.5. So when a horizontal line is traced on the screen, the sensors triggered should be in a single row. Older touch screens were not very accurate, and sensors in more than one row would be triggered. If someone tried to draw a straight line on an inaccurate screen, the line would appear bumpy or wavy. Another problem users experienced was that many of these screens could only process touch in one location. The addition of a second pressure point, another finger on the screen for example, would cause inaccurate messages to be sent to the phone's computer.

The inaccurate touch screens of older phones frustrated users because they led to typos in texts and losses in games. Phone engineers had to find ways to improve the touch screens. They improved the screens by using prototypes. A **prototype** is a working model of a design that can be tested as part of the design process. On each prototype, engineers changed one thing, such as the spacing between the wires, and tested how the change affects the screens performance. If the change was an improvement, they would keep it in the next prototype. In this way, engineers worked up to designing a much more accurate touch screen.

Figure 5.5

Touch screen sensors are arranged in a grid. You can test the accuracy of a touch screen by tracing straight lines on the screen when using a drawing app. If your screen is accurate, you will see a straight line. If the screen is inaccurate, you may see bumpy or wavy lines.

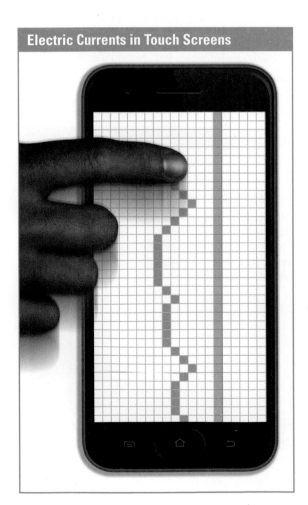

Electric Currents in Touch Screens

Robotic Testing of Touch Screens Engineers cannot rely on people to test their prototype models. Humans do not have perfect control. When people trace a line with their fingers, they may not be able to move their fingers in a perfectly straight line. If a person tries to test a touch screen by drawing lines, he or she may introduce error in the test. So, some engineers use robots specially designed to test their touch screen prototypes.

A robotic touch screen tester can be programmed to trace perfectly straight lines and to test specific points on the screens of prototypes. An engineer designing a touch screen might use an iterative process to make improvements on the design. In an iterative process, the engineer will make a small change to a design, build another prototype model, and then test the model again. A robot can repeat the exact same test for many prototype models to compare their performances. Phone manufacturers use robotic testing to identify areas where the touch screen is inaccurate, make design changes as needed in prototypes, and then test again to check that the changes result in improvements.

The touch screen of a smartphone is just one part of the phone that relies on electric fields and electric charge. The circuit boards of the computer inside the phone are made of conductors, insulators, and semiconductors that control signals sent using electric charges. Then, of course, electric current from the battery is needed to make the phone work at all!

Electricity

Electric Charge and Forces Particles in matter have an electric charge, which leads to objects being positively or negatively charged and allows them to interact through electric forces. Electric forces are attractive between objects that have opposite charges and repulsive between objects that have the same charge.

The Strengths of Electric Forces The strengths of the electric forces between objects depends on the amount of charge on the objects and the distance between them.

Electric Fields Electric fields surround every charged object and describe the electric forces exerted on a positively charged test object.

Electric Current Electric current is a flow of electric charges that powers electric devices.

Testing Touch Screens Engineers can use prototypes and an iterative process to improve touch screens on phones and tablet computers.

Lightning Strikes!

During the summer of 2014, wildfires tore through northern Washington state, burning down forests and destroying property. The four separate fires, which became the largest fire in the state's history, burned a little over 1,000 square kilometers of land and hundreds of buildings including homes. What caused these devastating fires?

Although many wildfires and forest fires are caused by careless people who drop cigarettes or do not put out campfires, the 2014 fires in Washington were started by lightning. The damage caused by these lightning bolts was an extreme example of lightning's destructive power.

On smaller scales, lightning can affect people and property in many ways. Remember that lightning can cause a fire when it hits a tree. Lightning can also damage trees without sparking a flame. Sometimes lightning will strip some or all the bark off a tree that it hits. Because bark protects a tree, a tree can become vulnerable to disease and insect damage after lightning hits it. Lightning can even split a tree apart!

Of course, lightning can hit buildings and other human-made objects, too. As when lightning hits trees, it can cause buildings to catch fire. It can also cause structural damage and power outages. The current from the lightning can even travel through a building's electrical system or plumbing system and destroy property inside the building.

Lightning can be very destructive. The bricks of this building were blown off when lightning hit the building. Despite the damage to this building, it is still safer to be inside rather than outside when lightning strikes.

Where Lightning Strikes

The frequency of lightning depends on location and weather. Believe it or not, scientists estimate that worldwide a total of about 1.4 billion lightning flashes happen every year. Scientists have used satellites to map where lightning strikes all over the world. They found that some areas have more lightning than others. For example, Florida has a lot of lightning while parts of California have hardly any. However, the amount of lightning in Florida is insignificant compared to what happens in one region of Venezuela.

Venezuela is a country in South America, and the area around Lake Maracaibo in the northern part of the country could be called the lightning capital of the world. The region has thunderstorms an average of 260 days each year. The storms can last for hours and can produce thousands of lightning bolts each hour!

Scientists are taking advantage of the high lightning activity at Lake Maracaibo to develop a lightning prediction system. The system does not predict exactly where lightning will happen. Instead, it is designed to predict how much lightning activity an area will have three months in the future. Scientists hope that information from their system will improve lightning safety in rural areas and around the power grids that provide electricity to buildings and homes.

Some areas of the world experience more lightning than others. The area where the Catatumbo River empties into Lake Maracaibo in Venezuela, shown here, has more lightning bolts each year than any other place on Earth.

In a Flash

Scientists are not sure why Lake Maracaibo has so much lightning. But, they may get clues by knowing how lightning generally forms and that a bolt of lightning is a giant electrical spark.

Lightning is a result of the separation of positive and negative charges in a storm cloud. A storm cloud contains rising and falling columns of air called *updrafts* and *downdrafts*. Updrafts carry water droplets from the bottom to the top of the cloud, while downdrafts carry ice and hail from the top to the bottom. The water droplets collide with the ice and hail, and negatively charged particles are pulled off the droplets. As a result, the bottom of the cloud is negatively charged and the top of the cloud is positively charged.

As you have learned, opposite charges attract. The negatively charged bottom of the cloud causes positive charges in the ground to collect beneath the cloud. As a stream of negative charges travels downward and nears the ground, a stream of positive charges reaches up from the ground. When the negative and positive charges meet, a type of lightning called *cloud-to-ground lightning* forms.

Another kind of lightning is called *intra-cloud lightning*. Sometimes lightning stays within a cloud. Streams of negatively charged particles from the bottom of the cloud meet streams of positively charged particles from the top of the cloud, and you will see flashes inside the cloud, which is intra-cloud lightning.

Thunder is caused by lightning. The instant that lightning flashes, it quickly heats the air around it to temperatures almost as high as 30,000°C. That's five times hotter than the surface of the sun! The heating of the air causes it to expand rapidly, which creates a shockwave. The shockwave travels away from the lightning bolt, and when the wave reaches your ear, you hear thunder. If you are close to where the lightning happened, the thunder will sound like a loud, sharp crash. If the lightning is farther away, the shockwave spreads out before it reaches you, and the thunder is a low rumble.

A bolt of lightning is a giant electric spark. Air movement in clouds creates charge separation, and lightning forms when streams of positive and negative charges meet.

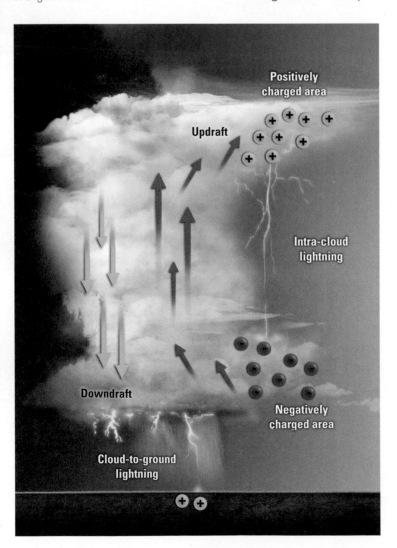

Positively charged area

Updraft

Intra-cloud lightning

Downdraft

Negatively charged area

Cloud-to-ground lightning

Stay Safe

Although a lightning bolt comes and goes in less than a second, lightning is very dangerous. Each year, around 300 people are hit by lightning in the United States, and about 30 of those people are killed. People who survive being hit by lightning often suffer from long-term medical problems. So, whenever you see lightning or hear thunder, you need to take precautions to stay safe.

The best action to take when you hear thunder or see lightning is to go inside an enclosed building that has plumbing and electrical wiring. The metal that makes up plumbing and electrical systems will conduct the electric current from lightning, which keeps the current from entering your body. That said, you should avoid using plumbing fixtures and electric devices during storms because, when you touch them, electric current can travel from them to your body.

As you head to a place of shelter, don't believe the saying "Lightning never strikes the same place twice." Lightning can and will hit the same object or place more than once. Standing under a tree that has just been hit by lightning is no safer than standing under a tree that has not been hit. Both are equally dangerous.

Lightning can be beautiful to watch. But remember that one powerful electric spark can rip bricks off a building, demolish a forest, or kill a person. Respect it, and watch it safely. ◆

Being struck by lightning is a very real danger for people who are outside during a storm. Whenever you see lightning or hear thunder, you should try to get inside an enclosed building. This tent is not a safe place.

Magnetism and Electromagnetism

What are magnets?

Introduction

The photo shows Hoover Dam. Water flows down more than 220 m from Lake Mead above the dam into the Colorado River. Every year, this downward flowing water produces electricity for thousands of homes in Arizona, California, and Nevada. How is flowing water used to produce electricity? How is this similar to wind turbines and power plants that burn fossil fuels?

In the previous two lessons, you learned about two forces that act at a distance—gravitational forces and electric forces. In this lesson, you will first learn about magnetic forces and how they cause several familiar effects on magnets and other objects. Next, you will explore magnetic fields. Understanding magnetic field diagrams will allow you to predict how the magnetic force will affect objects in the field.

You will also learn about electromagnetic forces, an effect caused by the interaction between magnetic and electric fields. You will then explore how electromagnetic forces make electric motors and electric generators work. Finally, you will learn about one way that engineers optimize wind turbines to be more efficient.

Vocabulary

magnetic forces attractive or repulsive forces between magnets or attractive forces between a magnet and certain materials

magnetic poles the regions where the magnetic forces exerted by a magnet are the strongest

magnetic field a force field created by a magnet

electromagnet a magnet made with a current-carrying wire whose strength can be varied and turned on and off

permanent magnet a magnet that is always surrounded by a magnetic field

electric motor a device that uses electric currents to produce motion using permanent magnets and electromagnets

electric generator a device that uses permanent magnets and electromagnets to produce electric current; an electric generator is an electric motor running backward

Next Generation Science Standards

Performance Expectations

MS-PS2-3. Ask questions about data to determine the factors that affect the strength of electric and magnetic forces.

MS-PS2-5. Conduct an investigation and evaluate the experimental design to provide evidence that fields exist between objects exerting forces on each other even though the objects are not in contact.

MS-ETS1-4. Develop a model to generate data for iterative testing and modification of a proposed object, tool, or process such that an optimal design can be achieved.

Science and Engineering Practices

Asking Questions and Defining Problems Ask questions that can be investigated within the scope of the classroom, outdoor environment, and museums and other public facilities with available resources and, when appropriate, frame a hypothesis based on observations and scientific principles.

Planning and Carrying Out Investigations Conduct an investigation and evaluate the experimental design to produce data to serve as the basis for evidence that can meet the goals of the investigation.

Developing and Using Models Develop a model to generate data to test ideas about designed systems, including those representing inputs and outputs.

Crosscutting Concepts

Cause and Effect Cause and effect relationships may be used to predict phenomena in natural or designed systems.

Systems and System Models Models can be used to represent systems and their interactions—such as inputs, processes and outputs—and energy and matter flows within systems.

Disciplinary Core Ideas

PS2.B. • Electric and magnetic (electromagnetic) forces can be attractive or repulsive, and their sizes depend on the magnitudes of the charges, currents, or magnetic strengths involved and on the distances between the interacting objects. • Forces that act at a distance (electric, magnetic, and gravitational) can be explained by fields that extend through space and can be mapped by their effect on a test object (a charged object, or a ball, respectively).

ETS1.B. • A solution needs to be tested, and then modified on the basis of the test results, in order to improve it. • Models of all kinds are important for testing solutions.

ETS1.C. The iterative process of testing the most promising solutions and modifying what is proposed on the basis of the test results leads to greater refinement and ultimately to an optimal solution.

Magnetic forces are attractive between magnets and objects that contain iron, nickel, cobalt, and certain mixtures of metals. Thumbtacks that contain iron are attracted to magnets.

Figure 6.1A

Magnetic forces are noncontact forces that can be attractive or repulsive between magnets. Magnetic forces are repulsive between similar poles of two magnets but are attractive between opposite poles of magnets.

1. Magnetic Forces

You know refrigerator magnets can hold papers to a refrigerator door, but those magnets are weak compared to magnets used in industry and science. For example, junkyard magnets lift cars and can be 200 times stronger than refrigerator magnets. How do magnets pull things together?

Magnets keep things together using magnetic forces. **Magnetic forces** are attractive or repulsive forces between magnets or attractive forces between a magnet and certain materials. Common materials that are pulled by magnetic forces may include iron, nickel, cobalt, and certain mixtures of metals. Objects that contain any of these materials are attracted to magnets. For example, some paperclips contain iron, so they are attracted to magnets.

Magnetic forces are noncontact forces, which means that they can act at a distance. If you hold a magnet near a paperclip, the paperclip will be pulled toward the magnet. The magnet is able to attract the paperclip without touching it because the magnetic forces acted at a distance and pulled the clip to the magnet.

Recall that you have already learned about two other noncontact forces: electrical forces and gravitational forces. Magnetic forces are similar to electrical forces because both forces can be either attractive or repulsive. Gravitational forces are only attractive.

You can predict whether magnetic forces between two magnets will be attractive or repulsive based on how the magnets are positioned, as seen in Figure 6.1A. Every magnet has two **magnetic poles,** which are the regions where magnetic forces exerted by the magnet are the strongest. A magnet's poles are called its north pole and south pole and are usually on opposite ends (or opposite sides) of the magnet.

Magnetic Forces Are Repulsive or Attractive

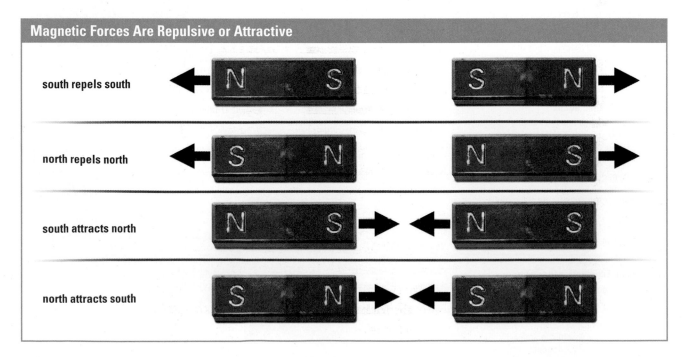

The magnetic forces between opposite poles of two magnets are attractive. That means that magnetic forces pull the north pole of one magnet and the south pole of another magnet together. Some everyday objects contain magnets that take advantage of these attractive forces. What examples can you find around your home?

The magnetic forces between similar poles of two magnets are repulsive. In other words, magnetic forces push the north poles of magnets apart or push the south poles of magnets apart. You can feel repulsive magnetic forces when you try to push similar poles of two magnets together. In fact, as you push the poles closer together, you will feel that the forces pushing them apart are stronger. If you aren't holding the magnets tightly, the repulsive force can be so strong that the magnets may flip so that the opposite poles are next to each other.

The strengths of magnetic forces depend on the distance between a magnet and the object it acts on. Look at Figure 6.1B. When similar poles of two magnets are close together, the forces of repulsion are strongest. As the distance between the magnets increases, the forces of repulsion decrease. Similarly, an increase in distance affects magnetic forces between opposite poles. As the distance between the magnets increases, the forces of attraction decrease. A magnet will not stick to a refrigerator door until the magnet is held close to the door. If it is too far away, magnetic forces will not be strong enough to pull it to the door.

The strengths of magnetic forces also depend on the materials involved. For example, a particular magnet may only be able to hold two sheets of paper to a refrigerator door because the magnetic materials exert weak forces. However, a different magnet may be able to hold ten or more sheets of paper up because its materials exert stronger forces.

Figure 6.1B

The strengths of magnetic forces depend on the distance between a magnet and the object it acts on. The repulsive force between the north poles of these two magnets decreases as the magnets are moved farther apart.

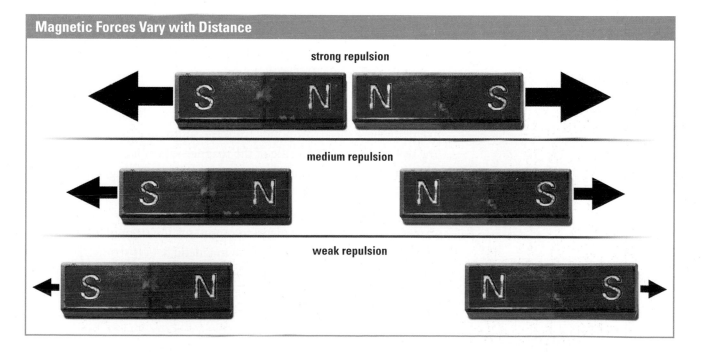

Magnetic Forces Vary with Distance

strong repulsion

medium repulsion

weak repulsion

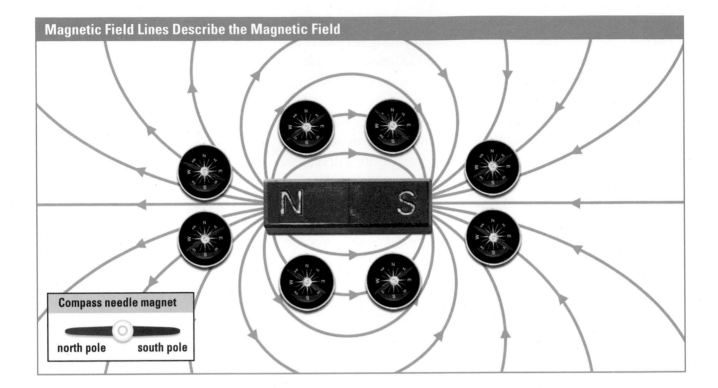

Compass needle magnet

north pole   south pole

Figure 6.2A

A magnetic field is a force field created by a magnet. The field can be detected by compass needles. Regions where lines are close together in the diagram indicate places where the magnetic field is strongest.

2. Magnetic Fields

On a hike with your friends, you reach a fork in the trail, and don't know which way to go. One friend pulls out a map and a compass. She holds the compass flat, waits for it to point north, aligns north on the map with the compass, and tells you which way to go. Why does the compass always point north?

A compass needle is a magnet, and like all magnets, it can be attracted or repelled by magnetic forces. The needle points north because magnetic forces cause it to turn until it points north. How magnetic forces will move a compass needle can be described by a magnetic field. A **magnetic field** is a force field created by a magnet.

Recall that diagrams of gravitational and electrical fields used arrows to represent force fields. Similarly, magnetic field diagrams use arrows to represent a magnetic field, as shown in Figure 6.2A. The arrows in a magnetic field diagram form loops. Part of each loop is inside the magnet, where the arrow points from the south pole to the north pole. The rest of the loop is outside of the magnet, where it circles from the north pole back to the south pole. The loops in a magnetic field diagram never cross.

Like gravitational and electrical field diagrams, the spacing of the arrows in a magnetic field diagram represents the strength of the field. Arrows are close together where the magnetic field is strong. The magnetic field is strongest inside the magnet and at the poles, so the magnetic field arrows are closest together at those places. Arrows are far apart where the magnetic field is weak. The magnetic field arrows are farther apart away from its poles.

The arrows in a magnetic field diagram show how magnetic forces on a magnet will act. A magnet placed at a particular spot in a magnetic field will spin to align with the field arrow at that spot. Using Figure 6.2A, you can do a thought experiment to predict how a compass needle would behave in a magnetic field. A compass needle has a north pole (often painted red) and a south pole. When the compass is in a magnetic field, magnetic forces cause it to spin until it aligns with the magnetic field arrows. Remember that the north pole of a magnet—such as the painted end of a compass needle—is attracted to the south poles of other magnets. So, a compass needle spins to align with the magnetic field, such that the painted end points to the south pole of the magnet.

If a compass needle aligns with magnetic field arrows, what magnetic field is a compass in when you are on a hike? The magnetic field that the compass and you are in is Earth's magnetic field.

Earth's magnetic field is similar to the magnetic field around a bar magnet. Recall that a compass needle points toward the south pole of a magnet. So, when a compass needle is in Earth's magnetic field, it points toward Earth's magnetic south pole. However, Earth's *magnetic* south pole is near Earth's *geographic* North Pole as seen in Figure 6.2B. So, when you use a compass to tell direction, it points to the north. That also means that Earth's *magnetic* north pole is near Earth's *geographic* South Pole. Thanks to Earth's magnetic field, a compass can always help you find Earth's geographic north.

Figure 6.2B

Earth has a magnetic field that is similar to a bar magnet's magnetic field. Compasses always point north because Earth's magnetic south pole is near Earth's geographic North Pole.

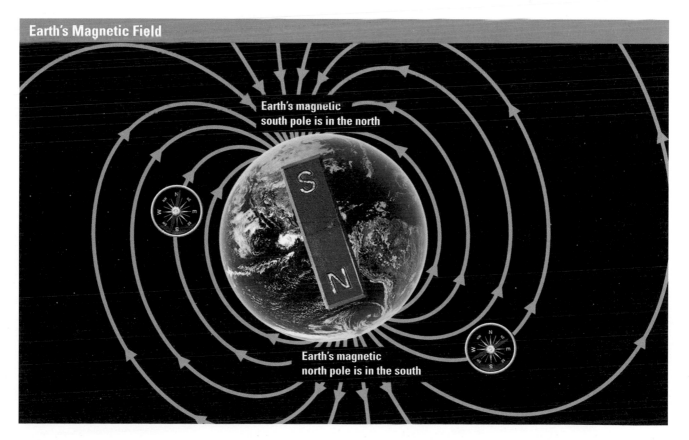

Earth's Magnetic Field

Earth's magnetic
south pole is in the north

Earth's magnetic
north pole is in the south

3. Electromagnetic Forces

If you are using a compass to find north, be sure that no one holds an electronic device near the compass. Electronic devices can change the direction compasses point to. Why does this happen?

Electronic devices interfere with compasses because the devices cause magnetic fields. However, these magnetic fields are not caused by magnets. Instead, the magnetic fields are caused by moving particles with electric charge. Charged particles move as electric currents in the devices' circuits as you learned in the previous lesson.

Can you predict how a magnetic field created by a current will affect compasses? On the left in Figure 6.3A, the wire in the center of the compasses does not carry a current. Because no magnetic field surrounds the wire, there is no effect on the compasses. All the needles point north to align with Earth's magnetic field. However, when the wire carries a current, there is an effect on the compass as seen on the right in Figure 6.3A. The compass needles align with the stronger magnetic field caused by the current. The needles form a circle, lining up with the magnetic field around the wire.

The compass needles are turned by magnetic forces caused by the electric current. The magnetic forces caused by an electric current are one kind of *electromagnetic forces*. Another kind of electromagnetic force is the force on electric charges caused by a changing magnetic field. How can a magnetic field change? You can change the magnetic field around charges in a wire in two ways. You can either move a magnet near the wire or you can move the wire near a magnet. Either way, the electromagnetic forces on the charges in the wire cause the charges to move and form a current.

Figure 6.3A

Moving electric charges can cause a magnetic field. The compass needles in the image on the left all point north because of Earth's magnetic field. But when the wire carries a current, the current causes a magnetic field around the wire, and the compass needles turn to align with the field.

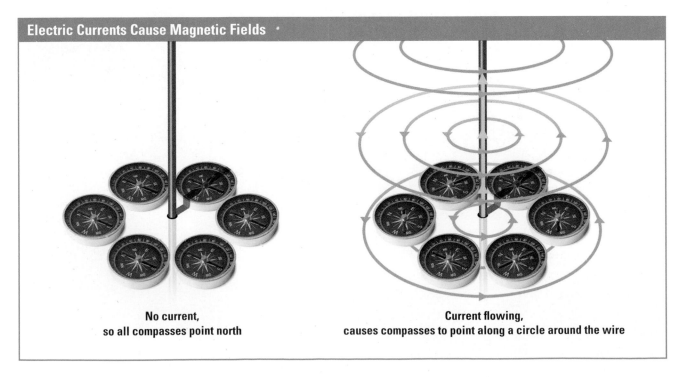

Electric Currents Cause Magnetic Fields

No current,
so all compasses point north

Current flowing,
causes compasses to point along a circle around the wire

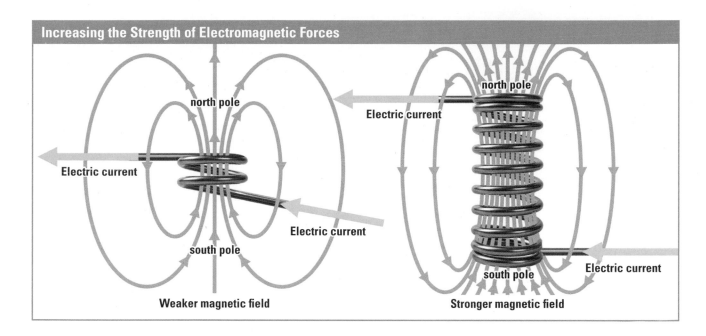

Increasing the Strength of Electromagnetic Forces

north pole

Electric current

Electric current

Electric current

south pole

Weaker magnetic field

north pole

Electric current

south pole

Electric current

Stronger magnetic field

The electromagnetic forces from a current-carrying wire are strong enough to move the compass needles. The forces can be made stronger by forming loops to make a coil out of the wire, as seen in Figure 6.3B. The more loops formed in the coil, the stronger the magnetic forces exerted by the coil. The forces can be made even stronger by wrapping the current-carrying wire around a piece of iron.

A magnet made with a current-carrying wire whose strength can be varied and turned on and off is called an **electromagnet**. Electromagnets are different from refrigerator magnets and the other magnets you use in everyday life. Refrigerator magnets and other everyday magnets are permanent magnets. A **permanent magnet** is a magnet that is always surrounded by its magnetic field.

Electromagnets differ from permanent magnets in several ways. First, electromagnets can be turned on and off. Second, the strength of an electromagnet's force can be changed by changing the amount of current in the wire or by changing the number of loops in the coil. Third, an electromagnet's poles can be changed. The direction the current travels determines which end of the electromagnet is the north pole and which is the south pole. If the current's direction is switched by switching the wires on a battery or by rewiring the circuit, the poles of the electromagnet switch places.

The properties of electromagnets make them useful in industry. For example, an electromagnet can be used to move metal objects in junkyards. A current-carrying wire is wrapped around an iron core, increasing the the magnetic forces of the electromagnet. The electromagnet is turned on, and a magnetic force lifts the objects. A crane moves the electromagnet and the objects to a different location. Once the electromagnet is turned off, the objects are no longer attracted to the electromagnet and will fall to a new place.

Figure 6.3B
The electromagnetic forces exerted by a current-carrying wire can be strengthened by forming loops to make a coil. Increasing the number of loops in the coil increases the wire's electromagnetic forces.

The electromagnet in the photo can be turned on and off by turning the current on and off. This property of electromagnets makes them useful for moving metal objects.

Permanent Magnets and Electromagnets

Permanent magnets and electromagnets have some similar properties and some different properties. What are some effects caused by these properties?

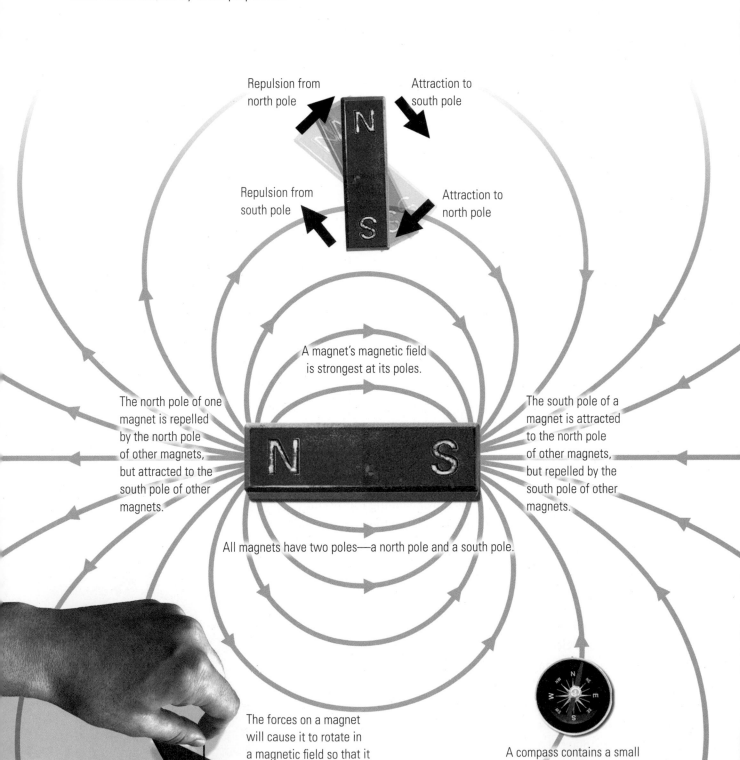

Repulsion from north pole

Attraction to south pole

Repulsion from south pole

Attraction to north pole

A magnet's magnetic field is strongest at its poles.

The north pole of one magnet is repelled by the north pole of other magnets, but attracted to the south pole of other magnets.

The south pole of a magnet is attracted to the north pole of other magnets, but repelled by the south pole of other magnets.

All magnets have two poles—a north pole and a south pole.

The forces on a magnet will cause it to rotate in a magnetic field so that it lines up with the field.

A compass contains a small permanent magnet, which aligns to any magnetic field it is placed in.

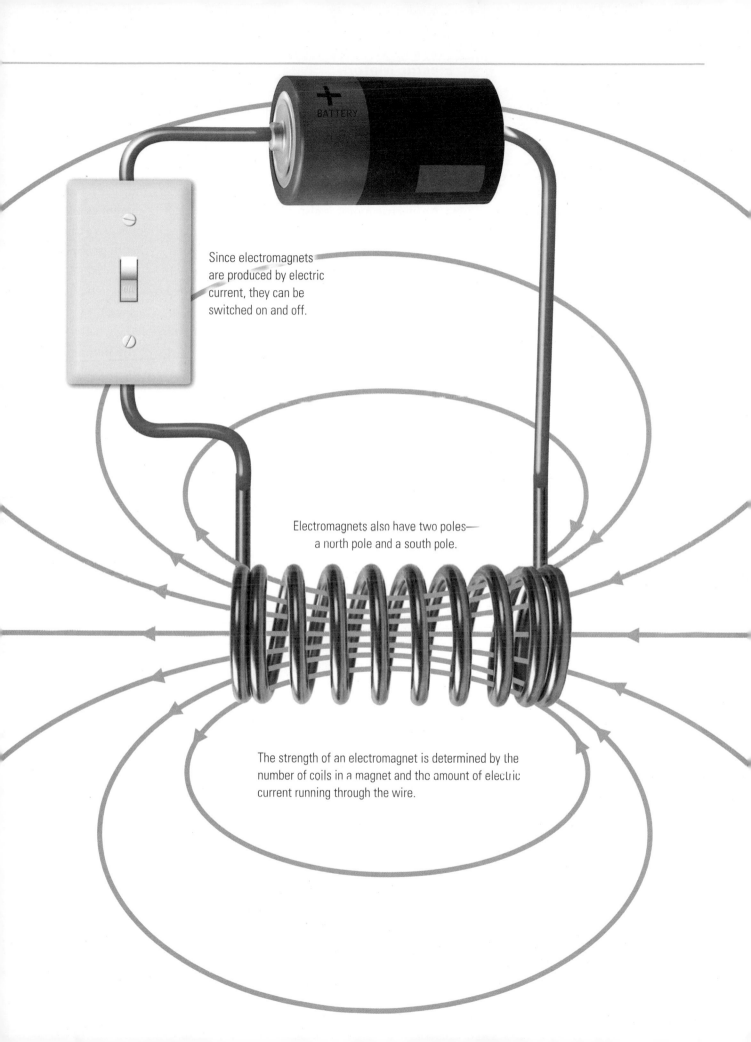

Since electromagnets are produced by electric current, they can be switched on and off.

Electromagnets also have two poles— a north pole and a south pole.

The strength of an electromagnet is determined by the number of coils in a magnet and the amount of electric current running through the wire.

An electric motor is a device that uses electromagnetic forces to produce motion.

Figure 6.4A

When a wire with current flowing through it is placed between the poles of a permanent magnet, the electromagnetic forces between the wire and the magnet cause the wire to move. The direction that the wire moves depends on the direction of the current in the wire.

4. Electric Motors

Think about electric devices that have moving parts. Electric toothbrush heads and fan blades spin, while wheels on remote controlled cars turn. How do electromagnetic forces make all these devices work?

Electric devices that have moving parts contain electric motors that move those parts. An **electric motor** is a device that uses electric currents to produce motion using permanent magnets and electromagnets. An electric motor is also a system that has electric current as an input and motion as an output. Electric motors have loops of wire that are pushed by magnetic forces. Motors are designed so that these loops of wire continually spin when a current is in the wire.

Recall that a current-carrying wire is surrounded by a magnetic field. As a result, permanent magnets exert forces on wires with current running through them. Look at the system involving a battery, a loop of wire, and a U-shaped magnet in Figure 6.4A. If you put the current-carrying wire between the poles of a permanent magnet, the magnetic forces between the wire and the magnet will act on the wire and make it move. The wire is pushed upward when the current runs forward between the poles of the magnet, and it is pushed downward when the current is reversed.

However, when both sides of the loop of wire are between the poles of the U-shaped magnet, the current travels forward in one side of the loop and backward in the other side. So, one side of the loop is pushed up while the other side of the loop is pushed down.

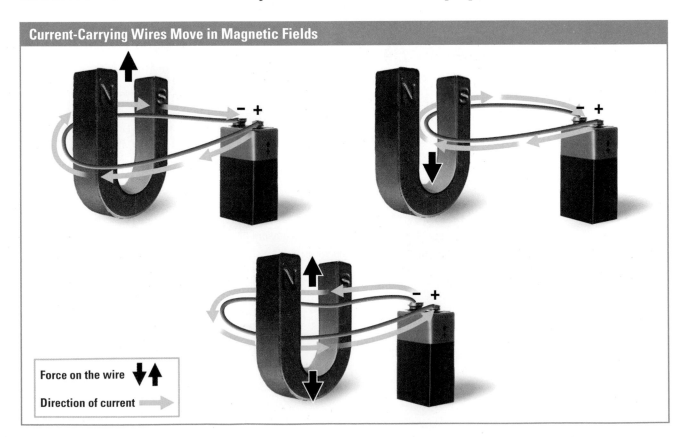

Current-Carrying Wires Move in Magnetic Fields

Force on the wire ⬇⬆

Direction of current ➡

Figure 6.4B shows the parts and design of a simple electric motor. You can see that a loop of wire is placed between the poles of a permanent magnet. The ends of the wire are attached to a part called a *commutator*, which changes the direction of the current in the wire every half a turn. The yellow arrows on the wire show the direction of the current in the wire. In the first image, the purple side of the wire is pushed up and the green side is pushed down, which causes the wire loop to rotate. As the loop rotates, the commutator rotates as well, and it changes the direction of the current in the wire. When the current is reversed, the purple side of the wire is pushed down and the green side is pushed up as seen in the second image. As a result, the wire loop keeps rotating. Changing the direction of the current makes the wire keep turning.

In an electric device, the loop of wire is attached to a rod that rotates with the wire. The rotating rod is then attached to the moving parts of the electric device. For example, a rotating rod can be the axle of the wheels on a remote controlled car. The motor turns the axle, the axle turns the wheels, and the car moves.

Motors can rotate at different speeds. The factors that cause the speed of a motor to change are the strength of the permanent magnet, the number of loops in the wire, and the strength of the current that runs through the wire. How would you predict the speed of the motor would change if the magnet were stronger or if more loops were added to the wire? The effect of increasing the strength of the permanent magnet is that the motor will rotate more quickly. Increasing the number of loops in the wire will have a similar effect. Motors in small devices such as remote controlled cars have relatively weak magnets and only a few loops of wire. Motors found in large machines have stronger magnets and many loops of wire.

Figure 6.4B

In a motor, a loop of wire rotates between the poles of a permanent magnet. A commutator attached to the wire changes the direction of the current in the wire, which keeps the loop rotating.

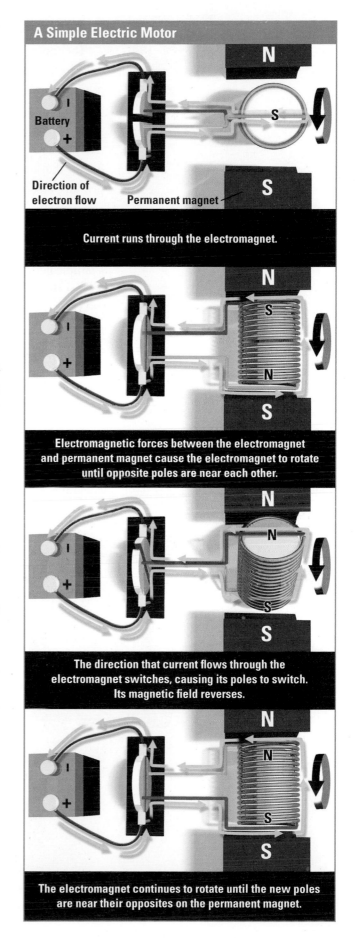

A Simple Electric Motor

Battery

Direction of electron flow   Permanent magnet

Current runs through the electromagnet.

Electromagnetic forces between the electromagnet and permanent magnet cause the electromagnet to rotate until opposite poles are near each other.

The direction that current flows through the electromagnet switches, causing its poles to switch. Its magnetic field reverses.

The electromagnet continues to rotate until the new poles are near their opposites on the permanent magnet.

5. Electric Generators

The motor of an electric toothbrush or a remote controlled car uses an electric current from a battery. But electric devices and appliances in your home, such as lamps and refrigerators, use electric current from outlets. Where does this current come from?

The electric current used in homes and other buildings comes from electric generators in power plants. An **electric generator** is a device that uses moving permanent magnets and electromagnets to produce electric current. Like an electric motor, an electric generator is a system. In an electric generator system, the input is motion and the output is electric current. Note that the inputs and outputs of a motor system and a generator system are reversed. In fact, a simple motor and a simple generator have the same design, but run in opposite directions so that they have opposite outputs.

An electromagnetic force can be caused by a changing magnetic field. This electromagnetic force can make electric charges move through a conductor and form a current. Such a current will form in a wire either when a magnet is moved near the wire or when the wire is moved near a magnet. Electric generators work by moving a coil of wire between the poles of a magnet.

Figure 6.5 models the parts and design of a simple electric generator system. Like in an electric motor, a loop of wire is placed between the poles of a magnet. The loop of wire is turned, and an electric current forms in the wire. The current can then be used to power an electric device.

Figure 6.5

This is a model of an electric generator system. The generator uses electromagnetic forces to produce an electric current. When a wire loop is turned between the poles of a permanent magnet, electromagnetic forces cause electric charges in the wire to move. The moving charges form an electric current that can power a device such as a light bulb.

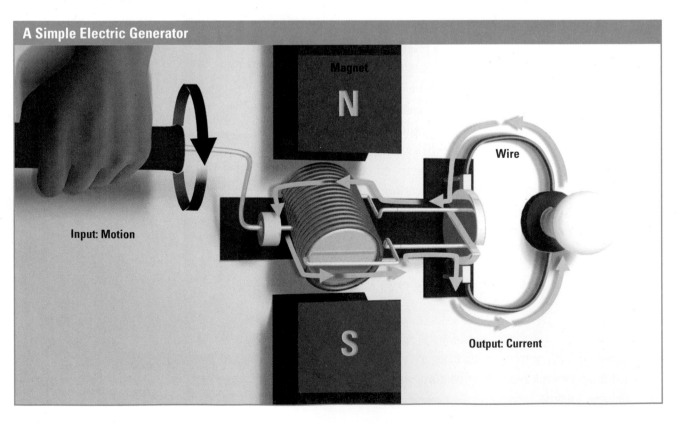

A Simple Electric Generator

Magnet

N

Wire

Input: Motion

S

Output: Current

The electric generators in power plants have the same basic parts as a simple generator. However, the loops of wire and the magnets are bigger because power plants have to produce a lot of current.

You could use a hand-cranked generator to produce enough current to charge a cellphone, but you would have a hard time producing enough current to run a refrigerator. So, the electric generators in a power plant have to be much larger to produce enough current for everyone who uses their electricity. Power plant generators, such as those found in Hoover Dam, have many large loops of wire rotating between very strong magnets.

How the loops of wire are turned in a power plant generator varies from plant to plant. Different power plants use various energy sources to turn turbines attached to the loops. A *turbine* is a device that has blades like a fan. Liquids or gases flowing through the turbine push on its blades and make the turbine turn. Because the turbines are attached to the loops of wire, the loops also turn.

Many factors affect which energy source is used in a power plant. Hydroelectric plants use falling or flowing water to turn turbines. Geography is important when building a hydroelectric plant. Such a plant can only be built next to a source of moving water. Wind power plants, or wind farms, use windmills to turn turbines. Wind turns the windmill blades, which then turn the turbine in a generator. Wind farms usually have several windmills and generators all producing electric current at the same time. Wind farms are best built in flat, open areas with fairly constant winds.

The environment is also a factor in choosing an energy source. Fossil fuel plants burn coal or natural gas, which boils water to produce steam. This steam then blows on turbine blades to make the turbine turn. Fossil fuel plants burn nonrenewable resources and cause air pollution. Nuclear power plants also boil water to produce steam to turn turbines. However, they also use fuel and waste material that can be very dangerous to living things if they leaked out of the plants.

Wind farms use giant windmills to turn the wire coils in their generators. As each windmill turns, it turns coils in a generator to produce an electric current.

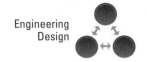

Engineering Design

6. Optimizing Wind Turbine Designs

Wind is a renewable energy resource, and generating electric current from wind energy is nonpolluting. As a result, people have constructed wind farms in regions of strong wind. However, wind farms are not as efficient at producing electric current as some other types of power plants. So, engineers are constantly trying to improve the designs of the wind turbines that collect wind energy. How could a pickup truck be used to test their designs?

The efficiency of a wind farm is a measure of how well the windmills use the motion of the wind to generate useable electric current. Many variables affect the efficiency of a wind farm. For example, the shape and length of the windmill blades can determine how well the blades catch the wind. Wind speed and turbulence in the air can affect how fast the windmills will turn. Turbulence is any irregular movement of gases or liquids. Wind generally blows horizontally in straight lines. Turbulence happens when wind swirls or blows upward or downward.

Suppose that a small engineering company has an idea of how to improve wind turbines. Wind turbines are very large and expensive to build. Building a new wind turbine just to test a new design is not very practical. The engineers might start testing their design with a computer model. Using a computer model, engineers can change variables and see how the changes affect the efficiency of the turbine. A computer model is just one kind of model that engineers might use when planning and designing a solution.

Engineers use different types of models to study and improve their designs. The models can be physical models like this model wind turbine riding in the back of a pickup truck. But often, the models are computer-modeling systems, which can be programmed to test many different variables.

After testing their turbine design with a computer model, and narrowing down the features of the design, the engineers build a prototype based on the computer model. A prototype is a working, physical model of a design solution. The engineers may start by making a small-scale model of their experimental design. Then, the engineers would do an investigation to evaluate the prototype.

To evaluate the prototype, the engineers might load the prototype into the bed of a pickup truck with the blades facing forward. Then, the engineers would drive the truck at various speeds to simulate wind blowing on the blades. As they drive their mini turbine around, they could gather data to use as evidence to decide if the prototype meets the goals of their design. The data gathered would be measurements of electric current produced by the windmill as they drove the truck.

The engineers would then analyze the current measurements from the prototype. Did it perform as well as expected? Did something unexpected happen when the turbine was turning at a high speed? They could then use the computer model again to make tweaks to their design to address any issues that arose during prototype testing.

Engineers may go through several rounds of modeling and testing before settling on a final design. A full-size turbine is not built until the design that best fits the criteria and constraints is found. Thanks to the engineering process, wind farms are more efficient than they once were. As wind farm and wind turbine designs improve, more and more people will be able to use wind energy as their source of electricity.

LESSON SUMMARY

Magnetism and Electromagnetism

Magnetic Forces Magnetic forces can repel or attract magnets and certain other materials. The strength of magnetic forces depends on the distance an object is from a magnet and the type of magnet.

Magnetic Fields Magnets and Earth are surrounded by magnetic fields, which can predict magnetic forces on other magnets.

Electromagnetic Forces An electromagnetic force is a magnetic force caused by an electric current or an electrical force caused by a changing magnetic field.

Electric Motors An electric motor is a system that uses electric current to produce motion.

Electric Generators An electric generator is a system that uses motion to produce an electric current.

Optimizing Wind Turbine Design Engineers may use computer modeling and prototypes to evaluate the efficiency of turbine designs and make modifications to improve them.

Louder! The Electric Guitar

The guitar is a simple instrument that may date back to the 16th century. It has serenaded kings in ancient castles and rocked crowds of fans at half-time shows at the Super Bowl. How has the guitar changed through the years?

The earliest guitars were probably made around 500 years ago. Today, musicians such as Esperanza Spalding play guitars that have many similarities to the first guitars.

Historians are not certain when the first guitar was made, but they know that instruments similar to the modern-day guitar were being played in Spain during the 1500s. Like the guitar, these early instruments were hollow, made of wood, and were played by plucking the strings that stretched from one end of the instrument to the other.

Since their invention, guitars have undergone changes in structure. These changes include the way strings are attached, the materials used to build the instrument, and the shape and structure of the instrument's body. Some of these changes affected the way the guitar was played, and some changes affected the guitar's tone, or overall sound.

Today, some hollow, wooden guitars are called *acoustic guitars*. When a string of an acoustic guitar is plucked, it vibrates and produces a sound. The vibrations of the string make the guitar's body and the air inside the body vibrate, too. The vibrating body and air amplifies the guitar's sound, which means that it makes the sound louder. Modern-day rock and jazz stars such as Jack Johnson and Esperanza Spalding can play the acoustic guitar, but many people who play guitars in large concerts often choose to play electric guitars.

Plug It In

Engineers started working on designing an electric guitar in the 1920s. Around this time, musicians were playing concerts in larger bands and in larger concert spaces. They were also playing in dance halls where people talked and laughed while the music played. Guitar players needed a way to make their instruments louder so that they could be heard over the noise of a crowd. Some instrument designers tried to make guitars louder by making them bigger, but eventually, the idea of using electricity for amplification won out. The first commercially successful electric guitar hit the stages in 1931.

Musicians who played electric guitars soon learned that they could do things with these guitars that could not be done with acoustic guitars. For example, guitar players started using feedback in their music. Feedback happens when an electrically amplified sound from a speaker is picked up by a microphone or other device that amplifies sound. The amplified sound is amplified again, and a distorted and often high-pitched sound is produced. Feedback can be annoying and unwanted, but musicians sometimes purposely use it. The Beatles are credited with recording what is perhaps the first intentional feedback in a song. The song "I Feel Fine" starts with a droning note that is actually feedback noise from an electric guitar. The use of feedback and other electric guitar techniques were only possible with the electric amplification and manipulation of the sound.

Electric guitars were developed in the 1920s as a way to make a guitar sound louder. Eventually, musicians learned to make sound effects unique to the electric guitar.

It's Electrifying!

Electric guitars can make louder sounds than acoustic guitars because they use electric amplifiers. An electric amplifier is a box-shaped device attached to an electric guitar by a cord. Amplifiers contain speakers that can produce loud sounds by creating large vibrations in the air. How does the vibration of the strings on an electric guitar get turned into the vibrations made by the amplifier? It happens with the help of electromagnetism!

Electric guitars have parts called *pickups* near the ends of the strings. Each string has at least one pickup underneath it. You can see the small round silvery pickups in the photo. Pickups are small magnets wrapped in wire coils. The strings are very close to the pickups but do not touch them.

Recall that every magnet is surrounded by a magnetic field. When a metal string vibrates above a pickup, it changes the magnetic field. As you learned, a changing magnetic field causes electromagnetic forces. The electromagnetic forces create a current in the wire wrapped around the magnet. The current travels through cables to an amplifier, where the current is translated into sound by vibrating the speakers in the amplifier. The sound can be made louder simply by turning up the amplifier. Doing this causes the speakers to produce larger vibrations, which is what is needed to make a louder sound.

The pickups on electric guitars work by using electromagnetism. A vibrating string causes changes in the pickup's magnetic field, which creates a current in the pickup's wire coil. The current travels to the amplifier which produces the sound you hear.

An Electric Orchestra

Electric guitars are just one example of how electronic technology has changed music. One of the most important technological advances in music is the ability to record it. Before recordings could be made, the only way that you could enjoy music was to hear someone sing or play an instrument in person. Recordings allowed people to listen to music in their own homes using record players, CD players, smartphones, and other devices.

Today, music studios use various electronic devices to produce the best recordings possible. The studios have microphones to pick up singers' voices and instrument sounds. Artists wear headphones which allow them to hear the music very clearly so that they stay synchronized and in tune. Studio sound engineers have mixers that allow them to increase and decrease the sounds picked up by the microphones. The mixers balance the sounds so that they blend well together. Thanks to these technologies, listening to modern recordings sound like, or better than, hearing the performance live.

The popularity and power of electric guitars have given rise to other electric instruments. Some electric instruments have computers that are programmed to produce particular sounds. An electric keyboard can be made to sound like a piano, an organ, a brass band, or even a human voice.

Other electric instruments are similar to the electric guitar in that they are amplified versions of their acoustic counterparts. Electric violins and electric cellos are examples. These electric stringed instruments are played just like acoustic stringed instruments, but instead of producing loud sounds by vibrating the body of the instruments, they use pickups and an amplifier.

Electrifying stringed instruments allow them to compete in volume with electric guitars. As a result, some rock bands now include people playing electric stringed instruments such as violins or cellos. Thanks to electromagnetism, music is always changing! ◆

The electric guitar is just one example of electronic technology used in rock concerts. Microphones and sound mixers, like the one shown here, are other pieces of technology that help produce the great music that you hear.

UNIT 3

Kinetic and Potential Energy

OVERVIEW

As this ball rolls down the surface of a path, it will make contact with other objects. It is part of a Rube Goldberg machine, a system that uses a complex combination of kinetic and potential energy to complete a simple task. In this unit, you will observe different kinds of energy and how that energy is stored, transferred and transformed within a system. You will analyze the different parts of a Rube Goldberg machine and determine their functions as the machine completes a simple task.

Phenomenon-Based Storyline
One small action in a Rube Goldberg machine causes a chain reaction of effects. How can you use the ideas of kinetic and potential energy to figure out how the machine works?

Investigations Model potential and kinetic energy conversions with a 3-D bar graph. Then, construct an argument about the energy conversions in hands-on experiments.

Investigations Observe and graph relationships between kinetic energy, mass, and speed by constructing pendulums.

Investigations Model gravitational potential energy, and other types of potential energy, by using a skateboarding simulation.

Engineering Challenge Design musical instruments based on principles of energy conversion, transfer, and transformation.

Performance Assessment Analyze parts of a Rube Goldberg machine in a video to understand the transfers and transformations of energy involved in chain reactions.

UNIT 3

Performance Expectations

MS-PS3-1. Construct and interpret graphical displays of data to describe the relationships of kinetic energy to the mass of an object and to the speed of an object.

MS-PS3-2. Develop a model to describe that when the arrangement of objects interacting at a distance changes, different amounts of potential energy are stored in the system.

MS-PS3-5. Construct, use, and present arguments to support the claim that when the kinetic energy of an object changes, energy is transferred to or from the object.

MS-ETS1-2. Evaluate competing design solutions using a systematic process to determine how well they meet the criteria and constraints of the problem.

MS-ETS1-4. Develop a model to generate data for iterative testing and modification of a proposed object, tool, or process such that an optimal design can be achieved.

Science and Engineering Practices

Developing and Using Models
• Develop a model to describe unobservable mechanisms. • Develop a model to generate data to test ideas about designed systems, including those representing inputs and outputs.

Engaging in Argument from Evidence
• Construct, use, and present oral and written arguments supported by empirical evidence and scientific reasoning to support or refute an explanation or a model for a phenomenon.
• Evaluate competing design solutions based on jointly developed and agreed-upon design criteria.

Analyzing and Interpreting Data
Construct and interpret graphical displays of data to identify linear and nonlinear relationships.

Connections to Nature of Science: Scientific Knowledge is Based on Empirical Evidence
Science knowledge is based upon logical and conceptual connections between evidence and explanations.

Crosscutting Concepts

Systems and System Models
Models can be used to represent systems and their interactions—such as inputs, processes, and outputs—and energy and matter flows within systems.

Energy and Matter
• Energy may take different forms (e.g., energy in fields, thermal energy, energy of motion).
• The transfer of energy can be tracked as energy flows through a designed or natural system.

Scale, Proportion, and Quantity
Proportional relationships (e.g., speed as the ratio of distance traveled to time taken) among different types of quantities provide information about the magnitude of properties and processes.

Disciplinary Core Ideas

PS3.A: Definitions of Energy
• A system of objects may also contain stored (potential) energy, depending on their relative positions. • Motion energy is properly called kinetic energy; it is proportional to the mass of the moving object and grows with the square of its speed.

PS3.B: Conservation of Energy and Energy Transfer
When the motion energy of an object changes, there is inevitably some other change in energy at the same time.

PS3.C: Relationship Between Energy and Forces
When two objects interact, each one exerts a force on the other that can cause energy to be transferred to or from the object.

ETS1.B: Developing Possible Solutions
• A solution needs to be tested, and then modified on the basis of the test results, in order to improve it. • There are systematic processes for evaluating solutions with respect to how well they meet the criteria and constraints of a problem. • Models of all kinds are important for testing solutions.

ETS1.C: Optimizing the Design Solution
The iterative process of testing the most promising solutions and modifying what is proposed on the basis of the test results leads to greater refinement and ultimately to an optimal solution.

Connect Your Learning

At the top of a slide you give yourself a push. Down you go! Two forms of energy, potential and kinetic, can help to explain and predict changes in motion in all kinds of objects. This includes the movement of things as large as an airplane landing and as small as your body as you glide down a slide. Knowing how these types of energy can be converted from one to the other can help you to explain many phenomena related to motion.

Kinetic and Potential Energy

Downhill skiers can reach speeds faster than a moving car! How can skiers use their kinetic energy to control and maintain their high speed?

This remote-controlled car moves quickly over the ground, kicking sand into the air. How can tracing the transformation of potential energy into kinetic energy, and vice versa, help you explain how this system works?

Two arms of a bridge lift into the air as it opens to let ships through underneath. What type of potential energy do you share with a massive structure?

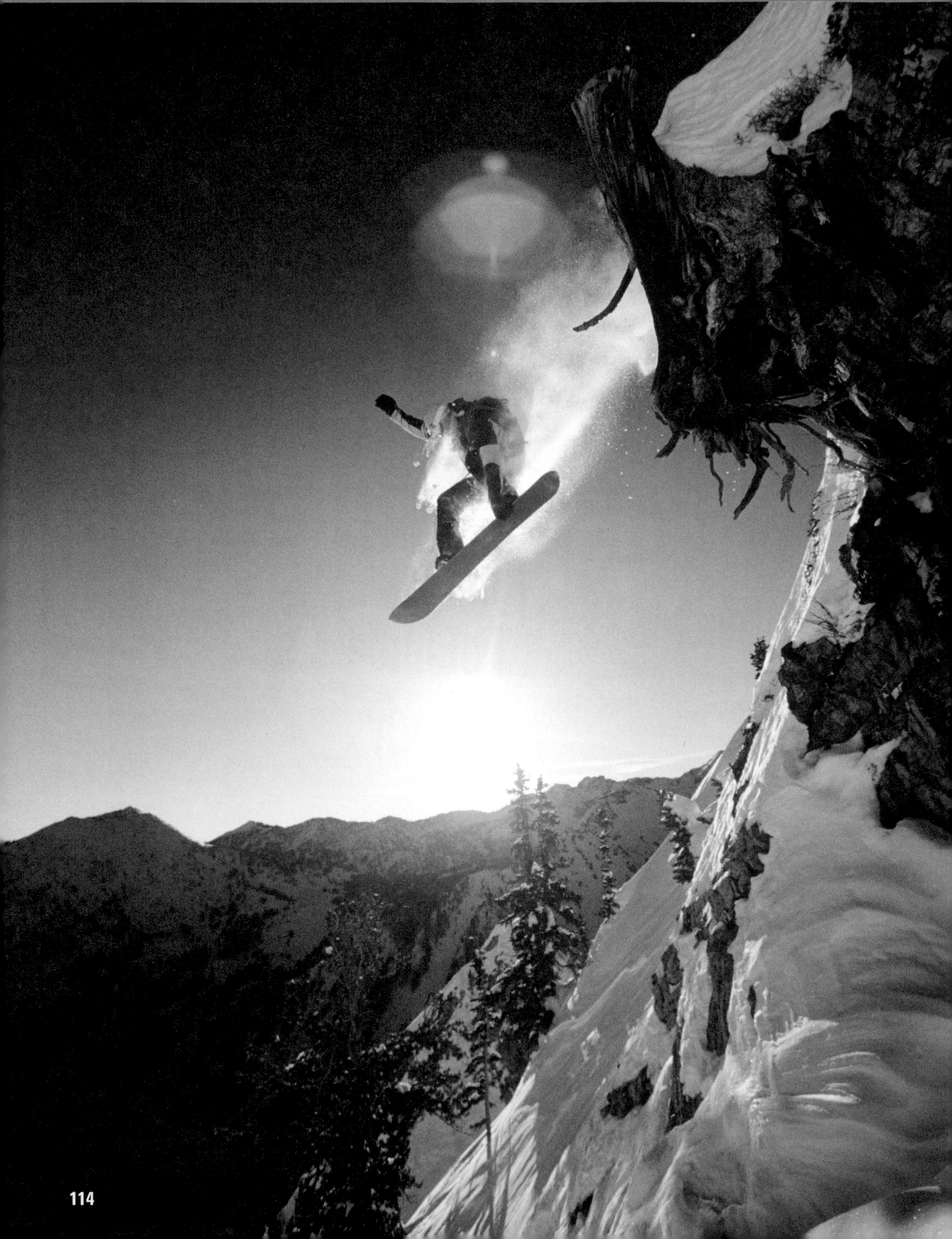

Forms of Energy

What is energy?

Introduction

A snowboarder rides a ski lift up a tall mountain. At the top, he admires the view before heading down the steep slope. He picks up speed as he moves downhill, and turns to control his speed. During each turn, snow sprays outward from the board. He reaches an over-hang and jumps, flying through the air while falling three, four, five meters before landing perfectly on the ground below.

You could use what you learned about forces to explain what happens with the snowboarder. For example, you know that the snowboarder moves down the hill and falls down through the air after his jump because gravitational forces pull him down toward Earth's center. How can energy add to your explanation of the snowboarder's motion? Can energy, like forces, be used to predict motion?

In this lesson, you will develop and use models to learn how energy and changes in energy can also be used to explain and predict motion. You will begin by learning what energy is and why it is important. You will then read about the two basic forms of energy: potential energy and kinetic energy. Next, you will find out how energy can be converted from one form into another. Finally, you will learn what it means to say, "energy is conserved."

Vocabulary

energy the ability to cause motion or change

potential energy the energy stored in a system due to the positions of objects in the system that are interacting at a distance

kinetic energy the energy an object has due to its motion

law of conservation of energy a scientific law that states that the total energy of an isolated system always remains the same

Next Generation Science Standards

Performance Expectations

MS-PS3-2. Develop a model to describe that when the arrangement of objects interacting at a distance changes, different amounts of potential energy are stored in the system.

MS-PS3-5. Construct, use, and present arguments to support the claim that when the kinetic energy of an object changes, energy is transferred to or from the object.

Science and Engineering Practices

Developing and Using Models Develop a model to describe unobservable mechanisms.

Engaging in Argument from Evidence Construct, use, and present oral and written arguments supported by empirical evidence and scientific reasoning to support or refute an explanation or a model for a phenomenon.

Scientific Knowledge is Based on Empirical Evidence

Crosscutting Concepts

Systems and System Models Models can be used to represent systems and their interactions—such as inputs, processes, and outputs—and energy and matter flows within systems.

Energy and Matter • Energy may take different forms (e.g. energy in fields, thermal energy, energy of motion). • The transfer of energy can be tracked as energy flows through a designed or natural system.

Disciplinary Core Ideas

PS3.A. A system of objects may also contain stored (potential) energy, depending on their relative positions.

PS3.B. When the motion energy of an object changes, there is inevitably some other change in energy at the same time.

PS3.C. When two objects interact, each one exerts a force on the other that can cause energy to be transferred to or from the object.

1. Energy

It's Monday morning, and your alarm has just woken you up. You stumble out of bed and into the kitchen, yawning. "Eat your breakfast," your dad says. "It will give you energy." What is energy and how can your breakfast give it to you?

Energy is the ability to cause motion or change. Everything around you has energy. For example, a rolling bowling ball has energy and can knock over bowling pins. A hot frying pan has energy and can change a raw egg into a cooked egg. Food, including your breakfast, has stored energy. When you digest food, the energy is released and your body uses this energy to do things like breathe and move around. Energy is not made of matter, but all matter has energy.

Energy is a concept that scientists use to construct explanations about motion and change. It can be used to predict how much change can occur in a particular system, given evidence such as measurements of the motion and positions of the system's components. For example, scientists studying the phenomena shown in the photos may ask questions like why do healthy ecosystems have more prey than predators? How fast will the wind blow in a hurricane? How much electricity can solar panels produce? How bright will fireworks be?

Scientists track the energy in each part of the system, and use it to predict the motion and change that can occur in other parts of the system. For example, they could add up all the energy available from eating prey in an ecosystem, and use that to determine how many predators could survive using that amount of energy.

Energy is the ability to cause motion or change. Understanding changes and transfers of energy are important in all fields of science. How is energy important in each of these photos?

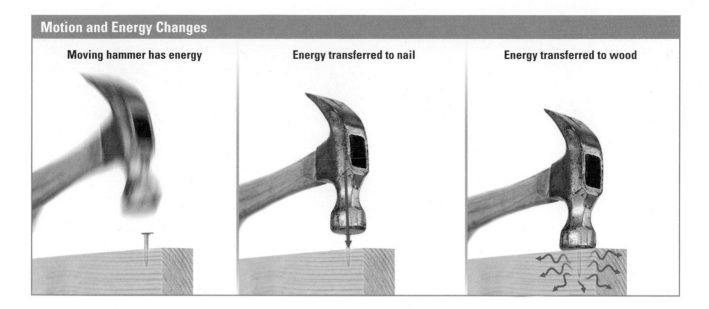

Moving hammer has energy

Energy transferred to nail

Energy transferred to wood

Scientists can use the concept of energy to explain complex interactions such as those that happen in ecosystems and hurricanes. But energy can also explain simpler events, such as the one shown in Figure 7.1. Look closely at the image of the hammer hitting a nail. What is happening? You might describe the scenario using forces. You exert a force on the hammer to make it move. Then, the hammer exerts a force on the nail to make it move. Finally, the nail exerts a force on the wood to change its shape.

However, you can also describe this scenario using energy. When you swing the hammer, your hand and the hammer have energy because they are moving. When the hammer hits the nail, some of the energy is transferred to the nail, and the nail moves down. As the nail moves, it transfers some energy to the wood as it pushes the wood out of its way.

Although you can use either energy or forces to explain what happens when objects interact, the two concepts are actually related. When one object exerts a force on a second object, and the second object moves in the direction of the force, the force adds energy to the second object. Think about paddling a canoe. The paddle pushes the canoe forward, so the force of the paddle on the water adds energy to the canoe.

However, if an object exerts a force on a second object, and the second object moves in the opposite direction as the force acts, the force subtracts energy. Water pushes back on a canoe when it moves forward. The force of the water on the canoe is in the opposite direction as the canoe is moving, so the force subtracts energy from the canoe. The canoe gains energy from the force of the paddle but loses energy from the force of the water. Note that when a force acts on an object over some distance, the object either gains or loses energy. You can describe this as forces causing changes in energy.

Figure 7.1
Energy changes can explain why motion happens. A person transfers energy to a hammer to make it move. When the hammer hits the nail, it transfers energy to the nail, which drives the nail into the wood.

The force of the water moves in the opposite direction of the canoe, so the canoe loses energy over a distance.

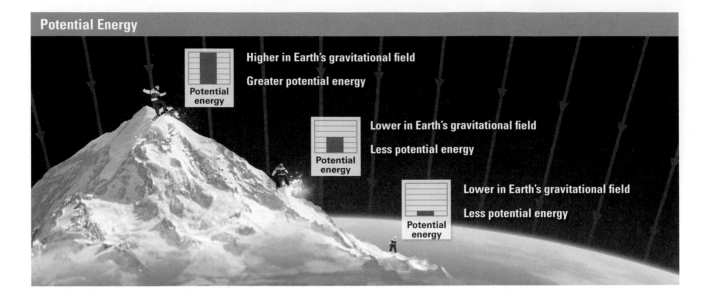

Potential Energy

Higher in Earth's gravitational field

Greater potential energy

Potential energy

Lower in Earth's gravitational field

Less potential energy

Potential energy

Lower in Earth's gravitational field

Less potential energy

Potential energy

Figure 7.2A

Potential energy is energy stored in a system due to the position of objects in the system. For objects positions near Earth, the higher they are, the larger their gravitational potential energy is. A snowboarder at the top of a hill has potential energy because she is positioned high above the defined zero energy point within Earth's gravitational field.

2. The Two Forms of Energy

A snowboarder stands at the top of a hill and looks down. She sees a second snowboarder gliding on a flat area at the bottom of the hill. Which snowboarder has energy?

Both snowboarders have energy; they just have different forms of energy. Energy exists in two forms. The form of energy stored in a system due to the positions of objects interacting at a distance is **potential energy**. The second form of energy is **kinetic energy,** which is the energy an object has due to its motion.

Potential Energy Potential energy exists when objects within the system are interacting in a force field. The positions of the objects determine how much potential energy there is. For example, look at the snowboarder at the top of the hill in Figure 7.2A. She is located high in Earth's gravitational field. As a result of her position relative to Earth, there is potential energy. Now, observe her when she is halfway down the hill. At this location, she is lower in Earth's gravitational field. As a result, there is less potential energy. As she descends the hill and approaches the bottom, her potential energy decreases.

How can you determine how much potential energy there is in a given system? Recall how reference points determine the speed and direction in which an object is moving. Similarly, reference points determine how much potential energy there is. The position of the objects is relative to a reference point that is defined as having zero potential energy. Once the snowboarder reaches the bottom of the hill, she cannot move farther down. So, you might define the bottom of the hill as the point that has zero potential energy. But what if you designated the middle of the hill as the point with zero potential energy? Then, at the bottom of the hill, the snowboarder would have negative potential energy!

All moving objects have kinetic energy. This remote-controlled car has kinetic energy as it moves across the sand. The sand that the car kicks up also has kinetic energy as it flies through the air.

Kinetic Energy Of course, a snowboarder is not going to stay at the top of a hill. She will eventually go down the hill on her board, as seen in Figure 7.2B. When she moves, she has kinetic energy. All moving objects and particles have kinetic energy because they have the ability to move another object or particle and cause it to move or change. The snowboarder gliding along at the bottom of the hill also has kinetic energy because he is moving.

Both Forms of Energy A system may have only potential energy, only kinetic energy, or both. The system with the snowboarder standing still at the top of the hill has only potential energy. She is not moving, so she does not have kinetic energy. The system with the snowboarder gliding at the bottom of the hill has only kinetic energy because we defined the bottom of the hill as the reference point for the potential energy. A system with a snowboarder going down a hill has both potential energy and kinetic energy. The system has potential energy because the snowboarder is in Earth's gravitational field and she is above the point in the system defined as having zero potential energy. The system also has kinetic energy because the snowboarder is moving.

Figure 7.2B
Kinetic energy is the energy an object has that is due to its motion. This snowboarder has kinetic energy because she is moving.

Kinetic Energy

Not moving — Kinetic Energy

Moving slowly — Kinetic Energy

Moving fast — Kinetic Energy

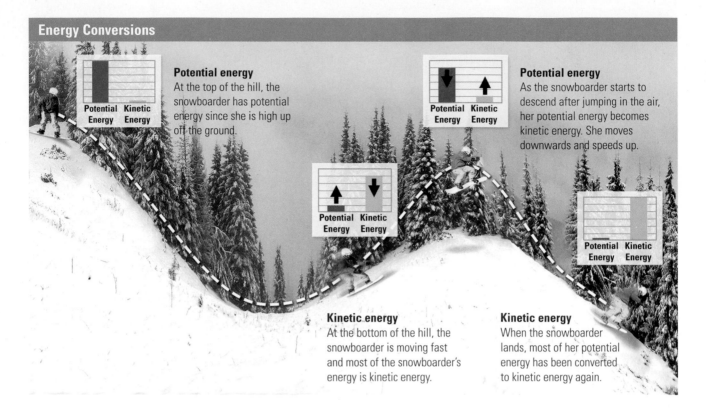

Energy Conversions

Potential energy
At the top of the hill, the snowboarder has potential energy since she is high up off the ground.

Potential Energy / Kinetic Energy

Potential energy
As the snowboarder starts to descend after jumping in the air, her potential energy becomes kinetic energy. She moves downwards and speeds up.

Potential Energy / Kinetic Energy

Potential Energy / Kinetic Energy

Potential Energy / Kinetic Energy

Kinetic energy
At the bottom of the hill, the snowboarder is moving fast and most of the snowboarder's energy is kinetic energy.

Kinetic energy
When the snowboarder lands, most of her potential energy has been converted to kinetic energy again.

Figure 7.3

Changes in energy in a system from one form to another can be described using the model of a snowboarder going downhill. When a snowboarder goes down a hill and makes a jump, potential energy is converted into kinetic energy, back into potential energy, and then into kinetic energy again.

3. Tracing Energy Transformation in a System

Recall that a snowboarder experiences different amounts of potential energy and different amounts of kinetic energy at different points along the hill. As she travels down the hill, the amount of potential energy and kinetic energy she has changes. How can you track these energy changes?

Scientists use models to describe energy changes within a system to make predictions about how much energy an object has at a given time. A system is made of components, inputs, processes, and outputs. The components interact in processes that cause changes in the form of energy; inputs and outputs are energy that enter and leave the system.

What are the components of the system shown in Figure 7.3? The snowboarder has energy, so it is the component. To get to the top of the hill, the snowboarder rides a chairlift to the top of the hill. This input results in the system of the snowboarder and Earth having potential energy.

The snowboarder starts going downhill, losing potential energy and gaining kinetic energy. This process converts the potential energy gained from the input into kinetic energy.

As the snowboarder continues moving, she undergoes other processes that change the energy's form. Kinetic energy is changed into potential energy at one moment as the snowboarder jumps up into the air. Then, the potential energy is converted to kinetic energy again as she descends and lands. As she slides to the bottom of the hill, the kinetic energy is used to overcome friction with the snow. This output results in energy leaving the components of the system—the snowboarder.

Potential and Kinetic Energy During a Roller Coaster Ride

A roller coaster is a good system to use to study energy conversions. The components of this system are the roller coaster car, the track, and Earth. Earth is an important component to this system because the potential energy of the system is due to the position of the car within Earth's gravitational field. The bar graphs and the diagram shown are models of the system. The graphs show how much potential energy and kinetic energy the system has at different points in the ride.

1 **Energy Input** A motor inputs energy into the system by pulling the roller coaster car up the hill. As the car gets higher, it gains potential energy.

Potential Energy | Kinetic Energy

2 When the car reaches the top of the hill, the motor stops pulling it up. Here, all of the car's energy is potential energy.

Potential Energy | Kinetic Energy

3 When the car reaches the bottom of the hill, it is moving very fast. At this point, all of the car's energy is kinetic energy.

Potential Energy | Kinetic Energy

4 **Processes** As the car starts going around the loop, its kinetic energy is converted into potential energy, and the car slows down.

Potential Energy | Kinetic Energy

5 **Processes** As the car passes the top of the loop, it begins to speed up again as potential energy is converted back into kinetic energy.

Potential Energy | Kinetic Energy

6 **Energy Output** When the brakes are applied, the car slows down and loses kinetic energy. The energy is transferred out of the system as heat.

Potential Energy | Kinetic Energy

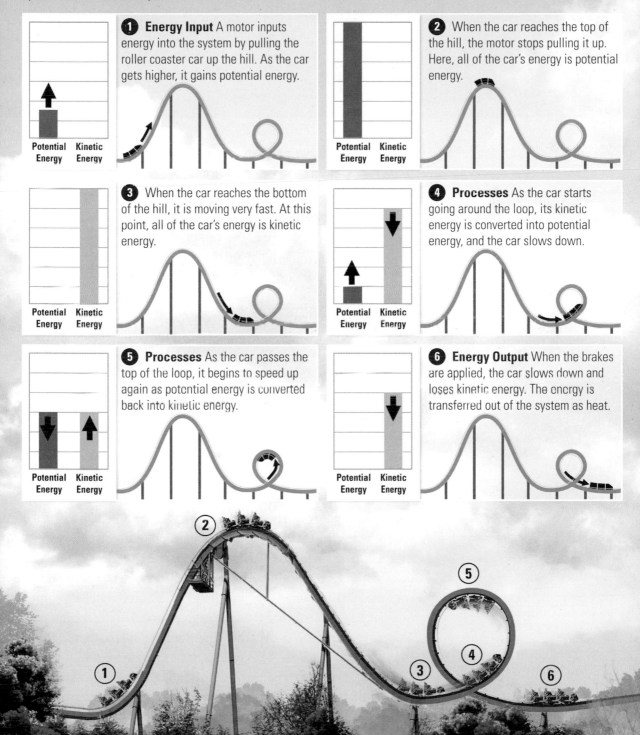

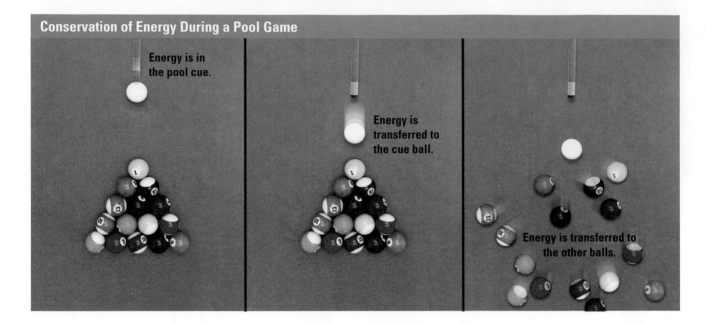

Energy is in the pool cue.

Energy is transferred to the cue ball.

Energy is transferred to the other balls.

Figure 7.4

Conservation of energy is a scientific law stating that energy cannot be created or destroyed. In the system of pool balls, the amount of energy input by the player is equal to the energy of the rolling balls.

4. Conservation of Energy

A game of pool starts when a player uses a cue stick to push a cue ball into an arrangement, or "rack," of 15 colored pool balls. The cue ball hits the colored balls, which go rolling in all directions. How does the energy input compare to the kinetic energy of the rolling balls?

Observe Figure 7.4. What are the components of the system? All the objects that have energy are components of the system: the cue stick, the cue ball, and the pool balls. But what are the processes, inputs, and outputs of the system?

Believe it or not, the total energy of all the rolling balls does not change. The break of a rack of pool balls demonstrates a scientific law about energy. The **law of conservation of energy** is a scientific law that states the total energy of an isolated system always remains the same. An isolated system is a system that does not have any energy inputs or outputs. This law means that that energy cannot be created or destroyed. It does not mean that a given form of energy always remains the same. The energy of an object can be converted. The law also does not mean that a single object always has the same amount of energy. An object's energy can be transferred to another object in the isolated system when the two objects exert forces on each other.

The kinetic energy of a rolling cue ball can be transferred to a pool ball when they collide. Some or all of the kinetic energy may be transferred. Then when that pool ball hits another pool ball, some or all of the first ball's energy may be transferred to the second ball. During the start of a pool game, kinetic energy is transferred from ball to ball, which sends the balls rolling in various directions. If you could add up all the kinetic energy of all the balls at any moment in time, you would find that the total amount always remains the same and is equal to the starting energy of the cue ball.

After a rack of pool balls is hit by a cue ball, the balls roll around for a while, bouncing off each other and the sides of the pool table. Eventually, the balls all come to a stop, and once they all stop moving, the system no longer has kinetic energy. Where does the energy go? Does this mean that energy is not conserved? No, energy is always conserved, but some energy seems to be lost. This is energy that is output from the system.

Energy can be lost in several ways. The sound made by the balls hitting each other is one way that energy is lost. Some of the kinetic energy is converted to the kinetic energy of vibrating air particles to create sound waves. As a result, the balls slow down. However, the most common process in losing energy is through friction. Friction happens when objects rub against each other, such as when pool balls roll on a pool table. The force of friction causes the molecules of the table to move faster. When the particles move faster, the temperature of the objects increases. Since the particles are moving faster, their kinetic energy has increased. How? Kinetic energy from the moving objects (such as the rolling pool balls) is transferred to the particles. Because kinetic energy is transferred away from the moving objects, the objects slow down.

Although the energy of the cue ball is converted into kinetic energy—a result of vibrating particles in sound waves and vibrating particles of objects whose temperature increased—energy is still conserved. The sum of the particles' energy plus all the other energy in a system will always be the same.

LESSON SUMMARY

Forms of Energy

Energy Energy is the ability to cause motion or change. Energy is a concept that scientists use to explain phenomena, such as why a rolling bowling ball knocks over pins.

The Two Forms of Energy Energy exists in two forms. Potential energy is stored in a system due to the positions of objects in the system, and kinetic energy is the energy an object has due to its motion. A system can have only potential energy, only kinetic energy, or both forms of energy.

Tracing Energy Transformation in a System The flow of energy and energy changes can be traced in systems. The amount of energy a component of the system has can be defined by its potential and kinetic energy. Inputs add energy to components, and outputs remove energy from components. The energy a component of the system has can change between potential and kinetic energy in processes.

Conservation of Energy The total energy in an isolated system always remains the same.

Castles and Catapults

A medieval castle is under attack, and the castle residents have been trapped inside for two weeks while their enemies surround the castle walls. The residents shoot arrows and pour boiling water on the invaders to keep them from climbing the walls. Suddenly the invaders send a dead cow flying over the wall, knocking over residents and smelling very bad. What is going on, and how did the cow get over the tall wall?

During a siege, attackers surround a castle or town to trap people inside and to cut off supplies. In this engraving of the Siege of Chartres, which took place in France in 1568, identify the attackers and the weapons they are using.

The attack on the castle is called a *siege*, which means enemy forces surround a town or building to trap people inside and to cut off supplies. The goal of a siege is to force the people inside to surrender by making them run out of food, water, and ammunition. Because medieval castles had thick, tall walls, invading armies used specialized weapons in their attacks.

One of those specialized weapons was a catapult, which is used to throw objects such as huge stones and dead animals over castle walls. Dead animals were thrown in hopes that they would spread disease and weaken the castle defenders over time.

A trebuchet is a kind of catapult that throws heavy objects by converting potential gravitational energy into kinetic energy. A trebuchet consists of an arm on a frame, a counterweight (the triangular shaped object on the right), and a sling (the rope on the left is part of the sling). When preparing this catapult, the payload (which is not present in the photo) would be loaded into the part of the sling that is not visible.

Potential for Victory

Obviously, throwing a large stone or a dead cow is a difficult feat requiring a lot of energy to send heavy objects hurtling over a castle wall. This energy comes from potential energy stored in the catapult. Different kinds of catapults store potential energy in various ways. One kind of catapult, called a *trebuchet*, stores potential energy due to Earth's gravitational field.

The photo shows a trebuchet, which is made of a swinging arm attached to a frame. A heavy counterweight hangs from the short end of the arm, and a sling is attached to the long end of the arm.

To use a trebuchet, the long end of the arm is pulled down, which raises the counterweight. When the counterweight is raised above Earth's surface, it has a lot of potential energy. Once raised, the arm is held up by a rope, and the payload (the object to be thrown) is then loaded into the sling. To fire the trebuchet, the rope is cut or released, allowing Earth's gravity to pull the counterweight downward.

As gravity pulls the counterweight down, the counterweight's potential energy is converted into kinetic energy. The counterweight end of the arm swings down, the sling end swings up, and the payload is flung upward. All these moving parts have kinetic energy. When the sling end of the arm nears the top of its swing, the arm, the sling, and the payload are moving very fast. The payload is released from the sling and flies off. This output energy originated from the energy the soldiers put into the system at the beginning by pulling the sling down and raising the counterweight.

Make a Tabletop Trebuchet

You can make your own mini trebuchet. You will need craft sticks (at least 6), a 30 cm x 30 cm piece of corrugated cardboard, string, a AA battery (or something with a similar size and weight), a paperclip, a pencil, a straw large enough for the pencil to fit inside it, a marshmallow, scissors, glue, and tape. Use the images as a guide as you build your trebuchet.

Start by making the frame of your trebuchet. Cut or break one craft stick in half. It will help if you use a ruler to measure the half way point of the craft stick. Use one half stick and two whole sticks to form an A shape, but cross the whole sticks so that a small V forms on the top of the A. Glue the pieces together. Make another A shape using two more whole sticks and the other half stick. Make sure your A shapes are as close to the same size as possible.

Next, you have to make the two A frames stand upright on the cardboard. The frames will stand facing each other about 10–15 cm apart. Take one A frame, hold it up on the cardboard, and gently push its "feet" into the cardboard to make indentations in the cardboard. Use the scissors to carefully make slits in the cardboard at each indentation. Repeat this process with the other A frame. Place the feet of the two A frames into the slits that you made. Use tape or glue to make sure the frames are stable and upright. If you have extra craft sticks, you can use them to help stabilize the frames. To do this, break a craft stick into four pieces and secure the broken craft sticks to each foot of your A frame, as shown in the photo below.

A working, mini trebuchet can be constructed using common materials. Study these images if you need help while building your trebuchet.

To construct the trebuchet arm, use a piece of string to hang the battery (the counterweight) from one end of a craft stick. Use tape to secure the string to the battery and the stick. Unbend one end of the paperclip and form that end into a very slight hook. Use tape or glue to attach the paperclip to the other end of the craft stick. Next, cut a 3-cm long piece of straw and position the straw perpendicular to the craft stick and a little more than ¼ of the way from the end with the counterweight. Attach the straw to the craft stick using tape. Slide the pencil through the straw, and place it in the Vs of the two A frames. Secure the pencil to the frames with tape.

The marshmallow is the payload for your trebuchet. Attach a small loop of string to the marshmallow using glue or tape. The loop of string is a substitute for the sling on a real trebuchet. For this mini trebuchet, the sling will travel with the payload when it is fired. It is advised that whatever you choose to use for your payload, it should have a smaller mass than your counterweight.

Your trebuchet is now ready for use. Set up your trebuchet in an open area away from other people. Never fire your trebuchet at another person. Pull the hook end of the trebuchet arm downward, hold it in place, and loop the marshmallow's string onto the hook. Let go of the arm and watch the payload go!

Test your trebuchet a few times, and then make adjustments to improve its performance each time. You can adjust the position of the straw, the curve of the paperclip hook, and alter the length of the strings. You can also use different objects as the counterweight and payload. You could even change the payload to a small toy cow! ◆

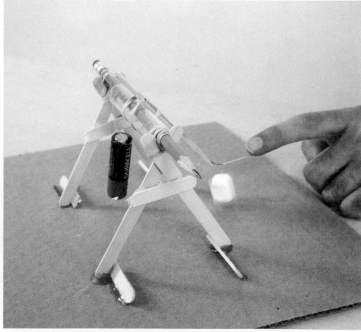

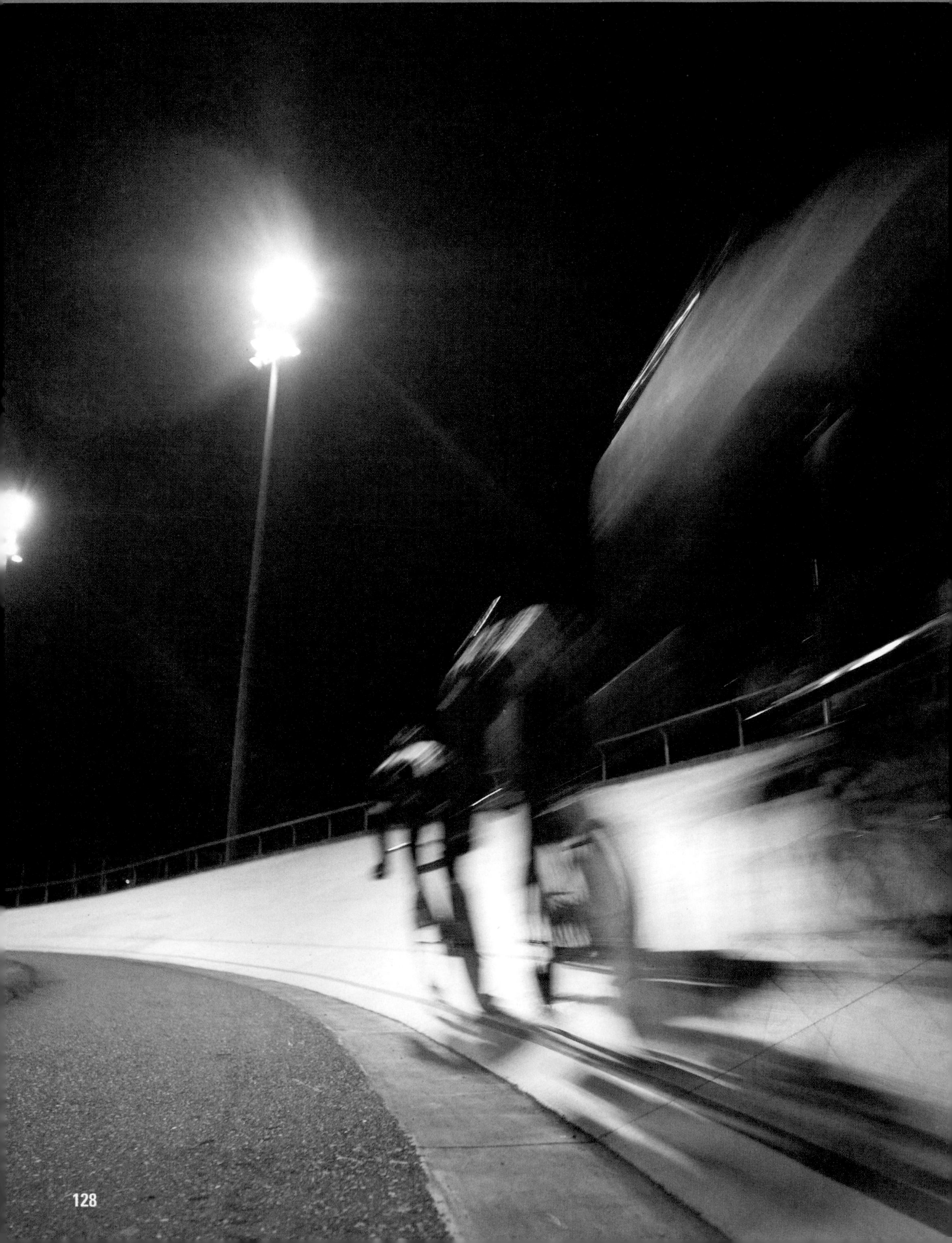

Measuring Kinetic Energy

How much kinetic energy do moving objects have?

Introduction

Track cycling is a sport in which people ride bicycles on a banked track like the one shown in the photo. The cyclists you see are in a sprint race, which is a short race on the track. During this race, the cyclists may hit speeds of nearly 65 km/h!

How much energy is needed to make a bike move that fast? How much energy do cyclists have to use to get through the race? Does the amount of kinetic energy that a cyclist has determine who wins the race? What determines how much kinetic energy a cyclist, or any moving object, has?

In this lesson you will learn how the kinetic energy of an object depends on two factors: the object's mass and the object's speed. You will find out that the proportional relationship between kinetic energy and mass is different from the proportional relationship between kinetic energy and speed. You will then see how the two relationships are combined into one equation to calculate kinetic energy. Finally, you will read about how engineers reduce the mass of racing bicycles so that the cyclists will move at faster speeds.

Vocabulary

proportional relationship the relationship between two variables when the ratio between the variables is constant; a graph of a proportional relationship is a straight line through the origin

linear relationship a relationship between two variables when a graph of one variable versus the other is a straight line; it can be represented by the equation $y = mx + b$

slope the steepness of a line on a graph, calculated by dividing the change in the y-value by the change in the x-value for any two points on the line

nonlinear relationship a relationship between two variables when a graph of one variable versus the other is not a straight line

constant describes a value that does not change

Next Generation Science Standards

Performance Expectations

MS-PS3-1. Construct and interpret graphical displays of data to describe the relationships of kinetic energy to the mass of an object and to the speed of an object.

MS-ETS1-4. Develop a model to generate data for iterative testing and modification of a proposed object, tool, or process such that an optimal design can be achieved.

Science and Engineering Practices

Analyzing and Interpreting Data Construct and interpret graphical displays of data to identify linear and nonlinear relationships.

Developing and Using Models Develop a model to generate data to test ideas about designed systems, including those representing inputs and outputs.

Crosscutting Concepts

Scale, Proportion, and Quantity Proportional relationships (e.g. speed as the ratio of distance traveled to time taken) among different types of quantities provide information about the magnitude of properties and processes.

Disciplinary Core Ideas

PS3.A. Motion energy is properly called kinetic energy; it is proportional to the mass of the moving object and grows with the square of its speed.

ETS1.B. • A solution needs to be tested, and then modified on the basis of the test results, in order to improve it. • Models of all kinds are important for testing solutions.

ETS1.C. The iterative process of testing the most promising solutions and modifying what is proposed on the basis of the test results leads to greater refinement and ultimately to an optimal solution.

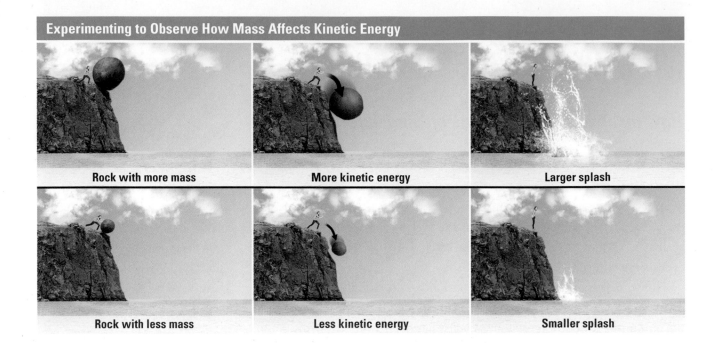

Experimenting to Observe How Mass Affects Kinetic Energy

Rock with more mass | More kinetic energy | Larger splash

Rock with less mass | Less kinetic energy | Smaller splash

Figure 8.1A

The kinetic energy of an object is related to the mass of an object. If a large rock and a small rock are pushed off a cliff into a lake under the same conditions, the large rock will have more kinetic energy at the bottom of the cliff than the small rock. As a result, the large rock makes a larger splash when it hits the lake.

1. Kinetic Energy and Mass

A cyclist riding around a track has energy. A rocket taking off also has energy, as does a dog trotting along a sidewalk and a tiny speck of dust floating through the air. Every moving object has energy, but the amount of energy each object has can vary. What factors affect the amount of energy that an object has?

Recall that energy is the ability to cause motion or change and that kinetic energy is the energy an object has due to its motion. The amount of kinetic energy an object has depends on only two factors: mass and speed. As you learned when studying matter, mass is the amount of matter in an object. A rocket is big and has a large mass, while a speck of dust has a very small mass.

You can do a thought experiment to see the connection between kinetic energy and mass. Imagine that you are at the top of the cliff shown in Figure 8.1A, which has a lake at its base. You have two rocks: one that has a large mass and one that has a small mass. If you push the rocks, they will fall off the cliff and splash into the lake. Recall that the acceleration due to gravity is the same for all objects falling near Earth's surface. As a result, the two rocks hit the lake with the same speed. When the rocks hit the lake the rock with the larger mass makes a huge splash, and the rock with the smaller mass makes a small splash. Which rock had more kinetic energy when it hit the lake?

The large rock caused more water to move, which means that it had more kinetic energy when it hit the lake. The thought experiment shows that the kinetic energy of an object increases as the mass of the object increases. However, the thought experiment does not tell you exactly how mass and kinetic energy are related.

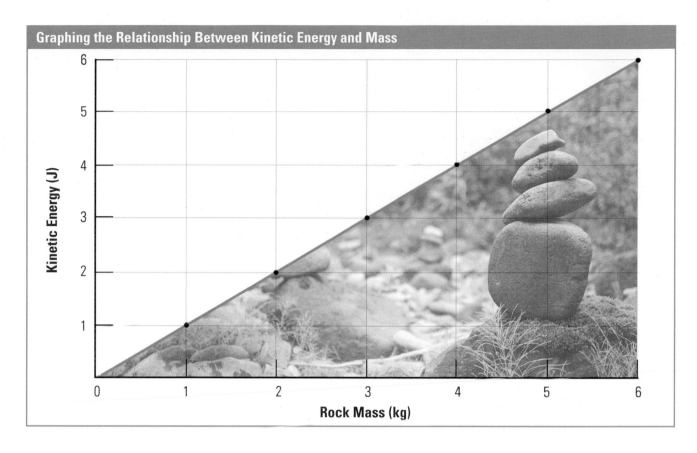

Graphing the Relationship Between Kinetic Energy and Mass

Kinetic Energy (J) / Rock Mass (kg)

Figure 8.1B

A graph of mass versus kinetic energy shows the relationship between the two. This graph shows the results of an experiment measuring the kinetic energies of bags of rocks all traveling at 2 m/s. The graph shows that kinetic energy and mass have both proportional and linear relationships.

If all other factors, including speed, stay the same, a graph of mass versus kinetic energy shows the relationship between the two. To make such a graph, you plot mass on the *x*-axis and kinetic energy on the *y*-axis, as shown in Figure 8.1B. If you compare the kinetic energies of a 1 kg rock and a 2 kg rock, you see that kinetic energy doubles. If you compare the kinetic energies of a 1 kg rock and a 3 kg rock, you see the kinetic energy triples. This relationship is true for all parts of the graph. Mass and kinetic energy have a **proportional relationship,** which means that the ratio between the two quantities or variables is always the same. If you double one value, the other value also doubles. However, a proportional relationship cannot tell us what happens to one variable if we add a value to the other variable. Also notice that the line in Figure 8.1B is straight. A straight line on a graph shows that the variables on the graph have a **linear relationship**. Mass and kinetic energy have both proportional and linear relationships.

The relationship between mass and kinetic energy is always linear for objects traveling at the same speed. If you graph kinetic energy versus mass for objects traveling at 1 m/s, the graph will be a straight line. If you graph the kinetic energies of the same objects traveling at 2 m/s, the graph will still be a straight line, but it will be steeper. The steepness of a line on a graph is called its **slope**. Slope is calculated by dividing the change in the *y*-value by the change in the *x*-value for any two points on the line. The graph of objects traveling at 2 m/s has a larger slope than the graph of objects traveling at 1 m/s.

Kinetic Energy of a Person Riding a Bike

Riding slowly
Less kinetic energy

Riding fast
More kinetic energy

Figure 8.2A

The kinetic energy of an object depends on the speed of an object. A cyclist traveling at a slow speed has less kinetic energy than a cyclist traveling at a fast speed. The cyclist that has more kinetic energy has a harder time stopping quickly than a cyclist that has less kinetic energy.

2. Kinetic Energy and Speed

Some track cycling races begin with a standing start, which means that the bicycles are not moving when the race starts. So a cyclist moves slowly at first and accelerates to reach the high speed she needs to win the race. Does the cyclist have more kinetic energy at the beginning of the race or at the end of the race?

You might correctly guess that the cyclist has more kinetic energy at the end of the race, but why is that true? You learned that an object's kinetic energy depends on its mass. A cyclist does not change mass during a race. So how does the cyclist's kinetic energy change? The kinetic energy changes because it also depends on something other than mass. That something is the speed of the object. Recall the rocks being thrown off a cliff. If you threw two rocks of the same size off cliffs of different heights, the rock thrown off a higher cliff would make a bigger splash. This is because its final speed is larger. Figure 8.2A shows how the kinetic energy of a cyclist depends on speed.

Just as water splashed by a rock can be used as a measure of the kinetic energy of the rock, water splashed by a bicycle going through a puddle can be used as a measure of the kinetic energy of the bicycle. If you ride a bike at a slow speed through a puddle, the kinetic energy of the bike will produce gentle ripples in the water. However, if you ride at a fast speed through the same puddle, the kinetic energy of the bike will spray water outward in big waves. Therefore, you know that you and the bike have more kinetic energy when you are moving at a fast speed.

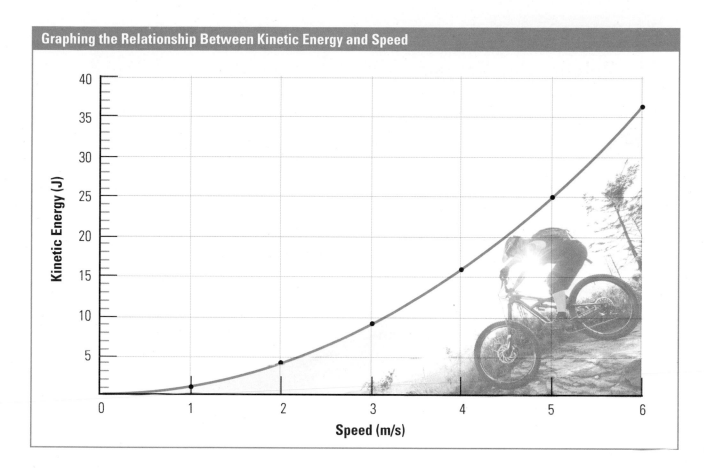

Graphing the Relationship Between Kinetic Energy and Speed

In general, the kinetic energy of an object increases as the speed of the object increases. Exactly how kinetic energy depends on speed can be seen in a graph of kinetic energy versus speed. To make the graph, you plot speed on the *x*-axis and kinetic energy on the *y*-axis, as shown in Figure 8.2B. In this graph, the line connecting the plot points is curved, not straight as was the line in a graph of kinetic energy versus mass. When a graph of two variables produces a line that is not straight, the variables have a **nonlinear relationship**.

The nonlinear relationship between kinetic energy and speed does not mean that the two variables are not related mathematically. Look at the graph. If the speed of the cyclist doubles, the kinetic energy increases four times. If the speed triples, the kinetic energy increases nine times. So, kinetic energy *is not* proportional to *speed* because they do not change at the same rate. However, kinetic energy *is* proportional to *speed squared*.

Figure 8.2B shows the kinetic energy and speed of one cyclist riding the same bicycle. The mass of a cyclist and bicycle does not change. Any value that does not change is said to be **constant**. If a smaller cyclist with less mass rode the same bicycle, the mass of the cyclist and the bicycle would be smaller but still constant. A graph of kinetic energy versus speed for the smaller cyclist would produce a different line than the graph of the larger cyclist, but both lines will curve in the same way.

Figure 8.2B

A graph of speed versus kinetic energy shows the mathematical relationship between the two variables. As an object's speed increases, its kinetic energy increases as the square of the object's speed. Kinetic energy and speed have a nonlinear relationship and kinetic energy is proportional to the square of the speed.

The Relationship Between Kinetic Energy, Mass, and Speed

The kinetic energy of an object changes when its mass, its speed, or both changes. You can predict these changes by graphing the relationship between kinetic energy and mass or kinetic energy and speed. Kinetic energy and mass have a proportional relationship and a linear relationship. Kinetic energy and speed squared have a proportional relationship and a nonlinear relationship.

Ball	Mass	Speed	Kinetic Energy
Plastic Ball	35 g	10 m/s	1.75 J
Tennis Ball	60 g	10 m/s	3.00 J
Baseball	150 g	10 m/s	7.50 J
Basketball	625 g	10 m/s	31.25 J

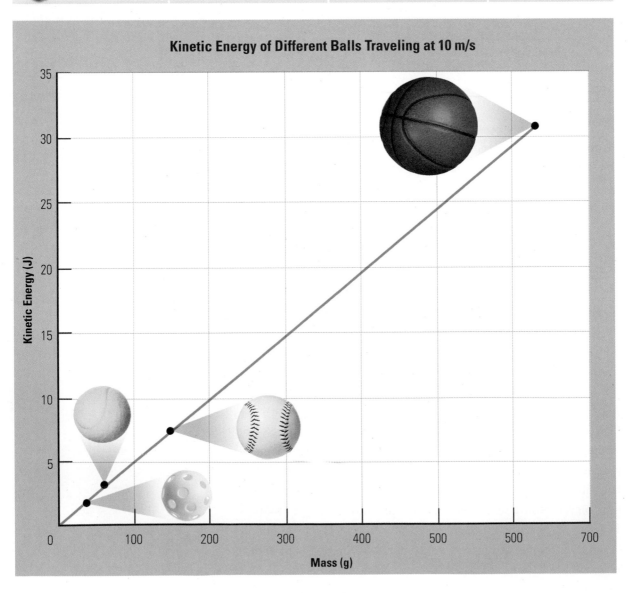

Kinetic Energy of Different Balls Traveling at 10 m/s

Ball		Mass	Speed	Kinetic Energy
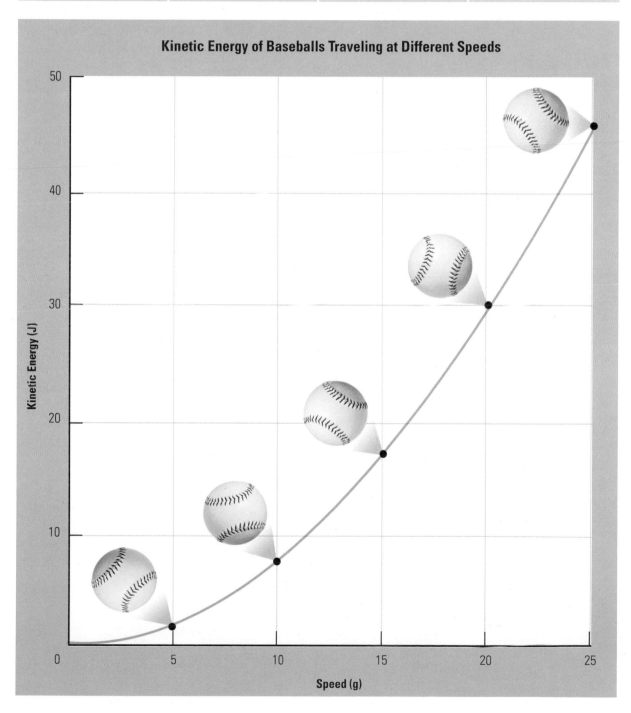	Baseball	150 g	5 m/s	1.875 J
	Baseball	150 g	10 m/s	7.500 J
	Baseball	150 g	15 m/s	16.875 J
	Baseball	150 g	20 m/s	30.000 J
	Baseball	150 g	25 m/s	45.875 J

Kinetic Energy of Baseballs Traveling at Different Speeds

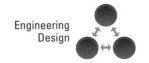
Engineering
Design

3. Optimizing a Racing Bike's Design

Suppose that you could get any bicycle that you wanted. What features, or criteria, would you choose? You might consider different colors, different tires, or different numbers of gears. But if you were a track-racing cyclist, you would focus on two criteria: mass and frame strength. How do engineers optimize racing bicycles?

Defining the Problem A cyclist transfers kinetic energy to a bicycle to get it to move. Recall that kinetic energy is proportional to mass. Bicycles of different masses need different amounts of kinetic energy to accelerate to a certain speed. To reach a speed of 10 m/s, twice as much energy has to be transferred to a 14 kg bicycle than to a 7 kg bicycle. So, cyclists want bicycles with low masses because they require less energy to accelerate to high speeds. However, a bicycle also must have a strong frame because a cyclist exerts strong forces on it to quickly transfer kinetic energy to it. If the frame is not strong, it may bend or crack under the forces on it. Thus, two criteria for a track-racing bicycle are that it must be lightweight and have a strong frame.

A racing bicycle needs to be lightweight so that it is easy to accelerate to a high speed, but it also has to be strong enough to stand up to the forces exerted on it. Engineers test different materials to find a balance between mass and strength. A machine that mimics a person pedaling can be used to test the strength of the bicycle.

Testing Solutions Engineers try to improve bicycles by changing the bicycle shape and by using different materials to build it. Some materials they might use include aluminum, titanium, and carbon fiber. Engineers build model bicycles similar to the one shown in the photo and compare their masses and strengths. Comparing the masses of the model bicycles is easy. The engineers simply use a scale to find the masses of the different models.

To compare the strength of the model bicycles, engineers use a process involving a machine to "ride" the bicycle. The machine pushes on the pedals of a bicycle similarly to how a person would push on the pedals. Furthermore, the force exerted by the machine can be controlled. Engineers can use the machine to test the bike the same way every time. This allows them to gather data to compare the effectiveness of different designs.

Optimizing the Design How can engineers use the pedaling machine to optimize a bicycle design? They may start with an existing bicycle model, test it with the machine, make a change to the model, and test it again. Then they compare the results of the tests to find which model could withstand the forces better. But the design process does not stop with one change. Engineers will take the model that performed better on the first test and make a different change to the model. This third model is tested and compared with the model that performed better on the previous test. Engineers continue the process until they are satisfied that they have made a good bicycle.

The engineers can then use the results of the mass and strength tests to find the bicycle design that they want to manufacture. For example, they might look at the masses of all the designs to find which design had the smallest mass. They may also look at the strength tests to find the design that could withstand the strongest forces. A very lightweight design may be weak, and a very strong design may be heavy. The engineers may decide to balance the two and select a design that is neither the lightest nor the strongest, but is still light and strong enough to be a great racing bicycle.

LESSON SUMMARY

Measuring Kinetic Energy

Kinetic Energy and Mass Kinetic energy and mass have a proportional relationship and a linear relationship. So, kinetic energy increases as the mass increases. These two variables will increase at the same rate because of their linear relationship.

Kinetic Energy and Speed Kinetic energy has a nonlinear relationship with speed and a proportional relationship with speed squared. So, kinetic energy increases as speed increases. However, it does not increase at the same rate as speed does.

Optimizing a Racing Bike's Design Engineers build and test various bicycle models to find a design that is both lightweight and strong. Models allow them to make changes to develop the best design.

Science and Sports

Faster. Higher. Stronger. Those words are the Olympic motto. Every two years, athletes from around the world gather to see who can best live up to that motto. Most competitors train for years in preparation for the Olympic Games. Traditionally, athletes work with coaches to improve their performance. But today, many athletes are also turning to scientists for help. How is science involved in Olympic sports?

Athletes train for years to prepare for the Olympic Games. Most of them work with coaches to improve their performance, but some are now also working with biomechanical scientists.

One of the newest ways that science has become involved in sports is through a branch of science called *biomechanics,* which is a combination of physics and biology and is the study of the effect of forces on the motion of living things. When biomechanical scientists work with athletes, they use ideas from physics to help the athletes move in ways that will improve their performance.

High-Tech Training

To help an athlete improve, biomechanical scientists have to collect data about how the athlete moves. But collecting motion data is not easy. In every sport, people move in complex ways, and in many sports, people move very fast. Therefore, scientists rely on electronic technologies to gather and analyze data.

One of the main ways scientists gather data is by using high-speed cameras. These cameras take thousands (or millions!) of photos each second. When these photos are played at a slower speed, scientists can view an athlete in slow motion and can analyze each tiny movement she makes.

Scientists also use lasers to gather data. For example, a runner's speed and acceleration can be measured using a tool that shines a special laser on the runner's back. Scientists then share the data and video of the runner with the runner's coach so that the coach can figure out things like when and why the runner slows down during a race.

Sometimes motion sensors are placed directly on athletes. Javelin throwers have to move their bodies in a specific way to get the most power in their throws. Scientists put sensors on an athlete's hips and shoulders to see if he is turning his body and moving his arms in the best way possible.

Athletes like this javelin thrower move their bodies in complex ways. Scientists use electronic technologies to analyze their movements and look for ways to improve.

Skiing Speed Demons

Since the word *faster* is part of the Olympic motto, you might have wondered what is the fastest sport in the Olympic Games. The Olympic sport that has the fastest moving people is downhill skiing during the Winter Olympics. Some skiers have reached speeds of more than 160 km/h!

In downhill skiing, skiers try to complete a marked course in the shortest time possible. The course does not take the skiers straight down a slope. Instead, the competitive skiers are required to pass through "gates," which are pairs of flags along the course. The gates are positioned so that skiers have to turn several times as they race downhill.

How can downhill skiers reach such fast speeds? Downhill skiers are able to go so fast because their potential energy at the top of the hill is converted into kinetic energy. To keep their high speed, skiers must work to reduce the amount of energy transferred to the environment as they go downhill. Energy can be transferred to the environment because of air resistance and friction.

Skiers reduce air resistance in different ways. One way they reduce air resistance is by wearing smooth jumpsuits and helmets, which allow air to move around their bodies more easily. They also try to keep their bodies in a tucked and crouched position as much as possible. This position reduces their surface area and thus reduces air resistance.

Skiers also do different things to control friction. They coat the bottoms of their skis with wax to make the skis as smooth as possible. The smooth surface reduces the friction between the skis and the snow. However, skiers need friction to make the turns on the course. They tilt their skis so that the skis' edges dig into the snow to provide friction to make the turn. Getting enough friction to turn without losing too much energy is a balancing act that the skiers must learn to perform well.

The fastest moving athletes in the Olympics are the downhill skiers. Skiers move so fast because a lot of potential energy is converted into kinetic energy as they travel downhill.

The fastest moving object in the Olympics is found in the sport of badminton. This player is performing a smash, which is a move that can send a shuttlecock flying at speeds of more than 300 km/h.

Surprisingly Swift Shuttlecock

Downhill skiing may have the fastest moving people in the Olympics, but the fastest moving object in the Olympics is the shuttlecock. A shuttlecock is the funny-looking object that is hit back and forth in the sport of badminton. A shuttlecock is made of feathers attached to a round piece of cork. Players hit it with relatively light-weight rackets. Although the equipment seems dainty, the shuttlecock can reach speeds more than 300 km/h (186 mi/h)!

A shuttlecock moves at high speeds after a player performs a move called a smash. To do a smash, a player leans back, puts his weight on his right foot (if he's right-handed), then pushes off with his right foot. The power from his leg muscles transfers energy up through his body. He puts his right arm and the racket behind him then twists his body as he swings the racket in a wide arc over his head. He hits the shuttlecock near the top of the racket's swing.

The player has a lot of kinetic energy as he twists his body and swings his arm, and the energy is transferred to the shuttlecock when it is hit. Because the shuttlecock has a small mass, its large amount of kinetic energy means that it travels at a very fast speed.

The smash is an important part of a badminton player's game because smashed shuttlecocks are difficult for an opponent to return. But perfecting the smash is not easy. So, an Olympic hopeful may want to get help from a biomechanical scientist during training to make sure he's doing it right! ◆

The object that is hit back-and-forth in badminton is a shuttlecock. It is made of feathers or plastic feathers and cork and is very lightweight.

Potential Energy in Systems

How is energy stored?

Introduction

Suppose you and two of your friends are the people in the photo. The three of you are at the pool getting ready for an exciting cannonball competition to see who can make the biggest splash. Another friend who is standing next to the pool will serve as the judge to determine whose splash is the tallest and widest. When she yells, "JUMP!" you and your friends all leap off your platform and grab your knees.

If you want to win this competition, which platform should you start from to make the biggest splash? The size of your splash depends on your potential energy before your jump. How can you predict which position will give you the most potential energy?

You have learned about potential and kinetic energy, and how to use models to trace the energy within a system. In this lesson, you will use models to learn that potential energy can be stored in different ways. You will also learn that how much potential energy can be stored in a system depends on a variety of factors. Then you will explore how potential energy can be used to move the roadway of a movable bridge and learn how different movable bridge designs are evaluated.

Vocabulary

gravitational potential energy potential energy stored in a system of objects interacting due to gravitational forces

electric potential energy potential energy stored in a system of objects interacting by electric forces

magnetic potential energy potential energy stored in a system of objects interacting by magnetic forces

elastic potential energy potential energy resulting from elastic forces; elastic potential energy is a combination of different types of energy

chemical potential energy potential energy stored in the chemical bonds that hold particles of matter together; chemical potential energy is a combination of different types of energy

Next Generation Science Standards

Performance Expectations

MS-PS3-2. Develop a model to describe that when the arrangement of objects interacting at a distance changes, different amounts of potential energy are stored in the system.

MS-ETS1-2. Evaluate competing design solutions using a systematic process to determine how well they meet the criteria and constraints of the problem.

Science and Engineering Practices

Developing and Using Models Develop a model to describe unobservable mechanisms.

Engaging in Argument from Evidence Evaluate competing design solutions based on jointly developed and agreed-upon design criteria.

Crosscutting Concepts

Systems and System Models Models can be used to represent systems and their interactions—such as inputs, processes, and outputs—and energy and matter flows within systems.

Disciplinary Core Ideas

PS3.A. A system of objects may also contain stored (potential) energy, depending on their relative positions.

PS3.C. When two objects interact, each one exerts a force on the other that can cause energy to be transferred to or from the object.

ETS1.B. There are systematic processes for evaluating solutions with respect to how well they meet the criteria and constraints of a problem.

1. Gravitational Potential Energy

Think about the people in the photo at the beginning of the lesson. The people may not be participating in a cannonball contest, but they are waiting to jump or dive into the water below. As they wait, each person is part of a system that has potential energy, and each system has a different amount of potential energy. What determines how much potential energy they have?

A system has potential energy if the objects in it have attractive forces between them but have been pulled apart. A system also has potential energy if objects have repulsive forces between them but have been pushed together. Forces in systems that have potential energy are often noncontact forces, such as gravitational forces, magnetic forces, and electric forces. These are all examples of potential energy, but we often give additional information by describing the force that is causing the objects to interact. Thus, *gravitational, magnetic,* and *electric* can all be used to describe the force causing the objects to interact and store potential energy.

Each person in the photo at the beginning of the lesson is part of a system that has potential energy due to gravitational forces. A system has **gravitational potential energy** when potential energy is stored in a system of objects interacting due to gravitational forces. For example, a system of a book (on a bookshelf), Earth, and the gravitational forces pulling them together has gravitational potential energy. You are not able to see the potential energy that the books have. Nor are you able to measure it directly. But, using a model of potential energy, you can infer how much it has. In the model, gravitational potential energy depends on two factors—the mass of the interacting objects, and the distance between them.

Figure 9.1A

The amount of gravitational potential energy stored in a system depends partly on the masses of the objects in the system. A system stores more gravitational potential energy when objects have larger masses. The system that includes the more massive book has more gravitational potential energy than the system that includes the less massive book.

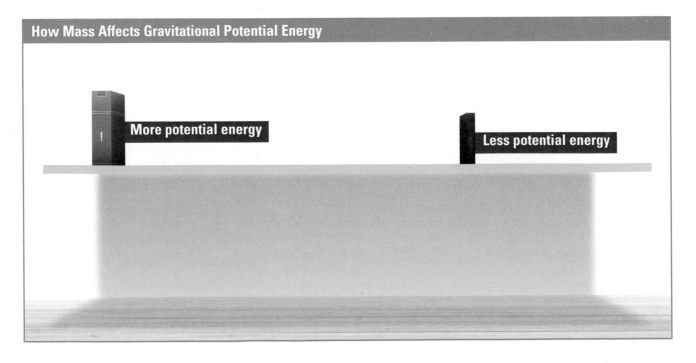

How Mass Affects Gravitational Potential Energy

More potential energy

Less potential energy

Gravitational Potential Energy and Mass Recall that the strength of the gravitational forces between objects increases as the masses of the objects increase. Similarly, the gravitational potential energy in a system increases as the masses of the objects in the system increases. Figure 9.1A is a model that can help you understand this relationship. The model shows two books on a shelf. Each book is part of a system that stores gravitational potential energy. The system that includes the book with the larger mass stores more gravitational potential energy than the system that includes the book with the smaller mass.

Gravitational Potential Energy and Distance The amount of gravitational potential energy in a system also depends on the distance between the objects in the system. Specifically, the gravitational potential energy of a system increases as the distance between the objects in the system increases.

Each book in Figure 9.1B is above the floor, so each book is part of a system that stores potential energy. The books in this model all have the same mass. So when you compare the potential energies of the various systems, you only have to consider the distances between the books and the floor. The system that includes the book on the top shelf has the most potential energy. The system that includes the book on the bottom shelf has the least potential energy.

When measuring distance in a system that has potential energy, a position in the system is selected to be the position where potential energy is zero. Look at the model in Figure 9.1B. In this model, the floor is selected to be the position where potential energy is zero for all the books. Any system that includes an object above the floor stores potential energy.

Figure 9.1B

The amount of gravitational potential energy stored in a system depends partly on the distance between the objects in the system. A system stores more gravitational potential energy when objects are separated by larger distances. The system that includes the book on the top shelf has more gravitational potential energy than a system that includes any of the books with the same mass on the lower shelves.

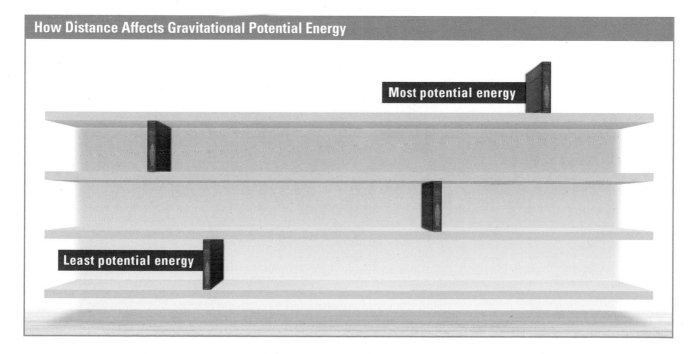

How Distance Affects Gravitational Potential Energy

Most potential energy

Least potential energy

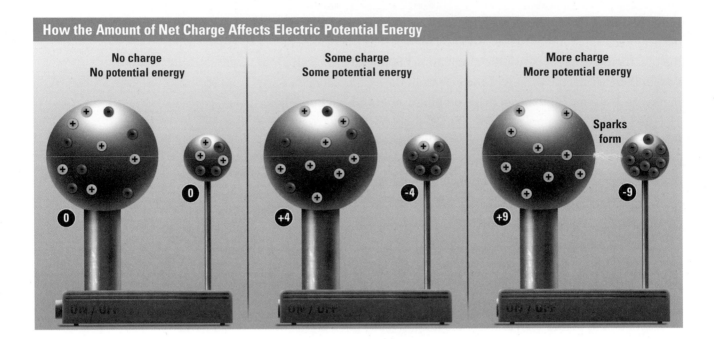

No charge
No potential energy

Some charge
Some potential energy

More charge
More potential energy

Sparks form

Figure 9.2A

The amount of electric potential energy in a system depends on the amount of net charge on the objects in the system. Van de Graaff generators that have different amounts of charge on the globe and the wand are systems that have different amounts of electric potential energy.

2. Electric Potential Energy

If you rub a balloon on your hair and then pull it away, your hair will stick out. This is because it is attracted to the balloon by electric forces. Can systems that include electric forces store potential energy similar to systems that include gravitational forces?

Yes! Electric forces are involved in storing electric potential energy. **Electric potential energy** is potential energy stored in a system of objects interacting by electric forces. A Van de Graaff generator, shown in Figure 9.2A, is a system that can store electric potential energy. The amount of electric potential energy stored in a system depends on three factors. Those factors are the amount of charge on the objects in the system, the signs of the charges on the objects in the system, and the distance between the objects in the system. Figure 9.2A shows that the greater the charges on the objects in a system, the more electric potential energy the system has.

In the first image, the generator is off, and the globe and the wand are uncharged. Because no parts of the system have a net charge, no electric forces exist. So, the system has no electric potential energy.

In the second image, the generator is turned on. The globe and the wand each have a small amount of net charge. Positive charge builds up on the globe at the top of the generator and negative charge builds up on the wand. Because the globe and the wand have opposite charge, they are attracted by a weak electric force, and the system stores a small amount of electric potential energy.

In the third image, the generator has been on for a long time. The globe and the wand each have a large amount of net charge. The globe and the wand are attracted by a strong electric force, and the system stores a large amount of electric potential energy.

Electric Potential Energy and the Signs of Charges Remember that the electric force is attractive between objects that have opposite charges and is repulsive between objects that have the same charge. Whether forces are attractive or repulsive affects potential energy. So electric potential energy depends on the signs of the charges of the objects in a system.

Look at the model systems in Figure 9.2B. In the first system, the objects have the same charge, so the electric force between them is repulsive. In the second system in Figure 9.2B, the objects have opposite charges, so the electric force between them is attractive.

Electric Potential and the Distance Between Objects The amount of electric potential energy in a system is not only determined by whether or not the electric force between objects is repulsive or attractive. To determine the amount of electric potential energy in a system, you need to consider both the charges of the objects in the system and the distance between them.

Look at the two model systems on the left of Figure 9.2B. The top system has more electric potential energy than the bottom system. The objects in both systems have the same charge, but the objects are separated by different distances. These systems illustrate that when the electrical force is repulsive between objects, a system with smaller distance has more energy than a system with larger distance.

Now look at the two systems on the right of Figure 9.2B. The top system has less electric potential energy than the bottom system. The objects in both systems have opposite charges, but the objects are separated by different distances. These systems illustrate that when the electrical force is attractive between objects, electric potential energy increases as the distance between the objects increases.

Figure 9.2B

Electric potential energy depends on the sign of the charges on the objects in a system and the distance between the charges. Whether the electric force between objects is attractive or repulsive, the distance between the objects determines the amount of electric potential energy in the system.

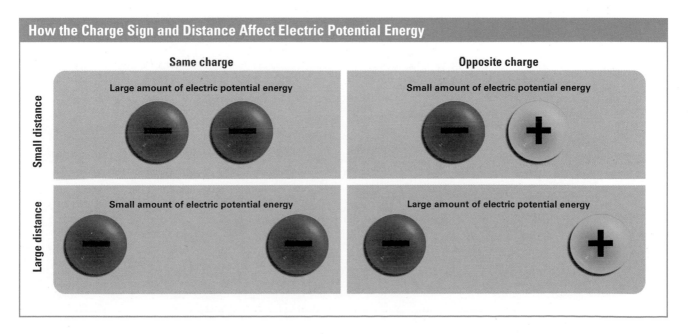

How the Charge Sign and Distance Affect Electric Potential Energy

Same charge | Opposite charge

Small distance

Large amount of electric potential energy | Small amount of electric potential energy

Large distance

Small amount of electric potential energy | Large amount of electric potential energy

3. Magnetic Potential Energy

Think about experimenting with two bar magnets. You can hold them so that the magnetic force pulls them together. You can also hold them so that the force pushes them apart. Both the magnetic force and the electric force can be either attractive or repulsive. Like the electric force, the magnetic force can cause a system to have potential energy. How is the potential energy caused by the magnetic force similar to the potential energy caused by the electric force?

A system has **magnetic potential energy** when potential energy is stored in a system of objects interacting by magnetic forces. The amount of magnetic potential energy stored in a system depends on three factors. One factor is the strength of the magnets. The other two factors are the orientation and the distance between the magnets.

If all other factors are equal, the amount of magnetic potential energy stored in a system increases as the strength of the magnets increases. This relationship is similar to the relationship between the amount of electric potential energy and the amount of charge.

The amount of magnetic potential energy depends on the orientation and distance between magnets. This is similar to the way that electric potential energy depends on the sign and distance between charged objects. If the magnets in a system are oriented so that the magnetic force is attractive, magnetic potential energy increases as the distance between the objects increases. On the other hand, if the magnets in a system are oriented so that the magnetic force is repulsive, magnetic potential energy decreases as the distance between the objects increases. These relationships are modeled in the systems shown in Figure 9.3.

Figure 9.3

Magnetic potential energy depends on the orientation of magnets in the system and the distance between the magnets. Whether the magnetic force between magnets is attractive or repulsive, the distance between the magnets determines the amount of magnetic potential energy in the system.

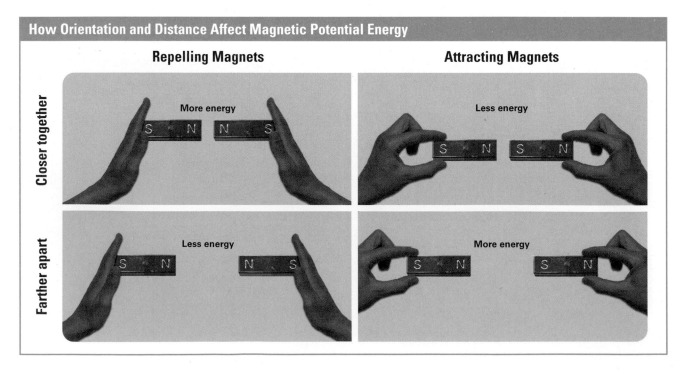

How Orientation and Distance Affect Magnetic Potential Energy

	Repelling Magnets	**Attracting Magnets**
Closer together	More energy	Less energy
Farther apart	Less energy	More energy

4. Other Types of Potential Energy

What do you do when you want to shoot a rubber band across the room? You might hold one end of the rubber band with one finger and stretch the other end using your other hand. The stretched rubber band has potential energy, which later converts to kinetic energy. What type of potential energy does it have?

A stretched rubber band has elastic potential energy. **Elastic potential energy** results from elastic forces, which are forces that pull an object back to its original shape. Systems that have elastic potential energy are shown on the left of Figure 9.4. Elastic potential energy results from interactions between particles of matter. It is a combination of kinetic energy, electric potential energy, and magnetic potential energy. However, thinking about the elastic forces of an entire object is easier to model than thinking about all the interactions between the particles that make up the object. So, elastic potential energy is used to more easily describe the energy stored in a system in which an object is stretched or compressed.

Batteries, food, and fuel such as those shown on the right of Figure 9.4 have another type of potential energy. They have **chemical potential energy,** which is energy stored in the chemical bonds that hold atoms and molecules together. Like elastic potential energy, chemical potential energy is a combination of kinetic energy, electric potential energy, and magnetic potential energy. Chemical potential energy can be released when bonds holding matter together are broken. For example, the food that you eat stores chemical potential energy. When you digest the food, the chemical bonds are broken and the chemical potential energy is released. Your body then uses the released energy to move.

Figure 9.4

Systems in which objects are stretched or compressed may store elastic potential energy. Any system containing matter stores chemical potential energy in the chemical bonds that hold the matter together.

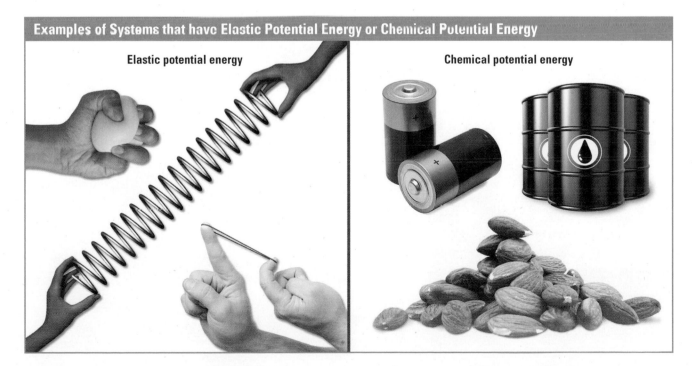

Examples of Systems that have Elastic Potential Energy or Chemical Potential Energy

Elastic potential energy

Chemical potential energy

Potential Energy in a Rube Goldberg Machine

Rube Goldberg was a cartoonist who became famous for drawing silly machines that do simple tasks in complicated ways. Today, such machines are called Rube Goldberg machines. The parts of this Rube Goldberg machine make up a system, each component of which stores potential energy. When one component of the system releases its energy, it transfers that energy to the next component.

Elastic Potential Energy

The first component of the system is a compressed spring, which stores elastic potential energy. When the spring is released, the potential energy causes the spring to stretch out, pushing the boxing glove forward. The spring's elastic potential energy becomes kinetic energy of the moving glove, which is then transferred to the bowling ball.

Gravitational Potential Energy

When the boxing glove hits the bowling ball, the kinetic energy of the glove is transferred to the ball. The ball rolls off the ledge and falls. As it falls, its gravitational potential energy is converted to kinetic energy, which is transferred to the match.

Chemical Potential Energy

When the bowling ball transfers energy to the match, the match swings up and is lit. The burning of the match converts the match's chemical potential energy into thermal energy of the flame.

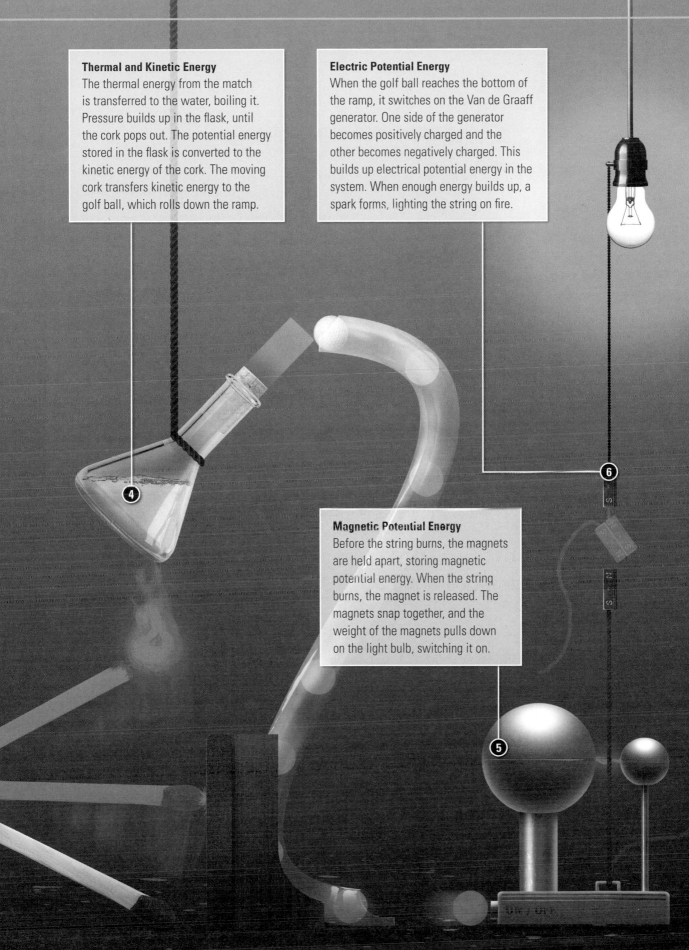

Thermal and Kinetic Energy
The thermal energy from the match is transferred to the water, boiling it. Pressure builds up in the flask, until the cork pops out. The potential energy stored in the flask is converted to the kinetic energy of the cork. The moving cork transfers kinetic energy to the golf ball, which rolls down the ramp.

Electric Potential Energy
When the golf ball reaches the bottom of the ramp, it switches on the Van de Graaff generator. One side of the generator becomes positively charged and the other becomes negatively charged. This builds up electrical potential energy in the system. When enough energy builds up, a spark forms, lighting the string on fire.

Magnetic Potential Energy
Before the string burns, the magnets are held apart, storing magnetic potential energy. When the string burns, the magnet is released. The magnets snap together, and the weight of the magnets pulls down on the light bulb, switching it on.

Three Types of Movable Bridges

Swing Bridge

Lift Bridge

Bascule Bridge

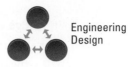

5. Evaluating Bridge Designs

Suppose that you are a city planner for a coastal city. The city has a river that splits the city in half. The mayor of the city wants to build a bridge near the mouth of the river to improve transportation between the two sides of the city. However, business owners whose factories are located along the river are worried that a bridge will prevent supply ships from moving goods to and from their factories.

You suggest that the city constructs a new bridge. One criterion for the bridge is that it should be movable, with a roadway that moves to allow tall ships to pass by. Another criterion is that the bridge should be attractive. Some of the constraints for the bridge are that it cannot go over budget, and that it should not interfere with nearby businesses. City engineers can now present the three bridge designs shown in Figure 9.5 to be systematically evaluated.

The first bridge presented is a swing bridge. The roadway of a swing bridge spins on a pillar located in the middle of the river. The mayor likes this design because the bridge will not interfere with ocean views from the city. But the business people who own the property right next to the proposed bridge location will have to tear down their docks to accommodate the movable bridge. Furthermore, the business people worry that the pillar in the middle will limit the size of ships that can travel up the river. Environmental groups believe the heavy roadway will require too much energy. The environmentalists think that the city should be looking for ways to reduce energy usage. Because of all the objections, the swing bridge design is rejected.

Figure 9.5

The roadways of movable bridges move to allow ships to pass through. How the roadway moves depends on the bridge design. A systematic evaluation of the designs determines the advantages and disadvantages of each design.

Next, engineers propose a lift bridge. A lift bridge raises the roadway straight up between two towers. The counterweights are attached to the roadway by a cable. When the roadway is down, the counterweights are at the top of the towers. When the roadway needs to be raised, the counterweights are lowered, and gravitational potential energy is converted into kinetic energy to move the roadway. Then when the roadway is lowered again, gravitational potential energy is converted into kinetic energy to raise the counterweights back up.

The property owners next to the bridge site like this design because it would not require them to tear down their docks. The environmental groups also like this design because the counterweights reduce energy usage. However, business owners complain that the low height of the roadway in the up position will prevent tall ships from entering the river.

The engineers have one more design to present: a bascule bridge. The roadway of a bascule bridge pivots on one end to move from its horizontal position to a nearly vertical position. A bascule bridge would not interfere with property next to the bridge. The design also uses counterweights and gravitational potential energy to move the bridge, thereby saving energy. But the greatest benefit of the bascule bridge is that it opens the river to ships of any size. The economic benefits are also an important factor in favor of the design.

With the city government and the citizen groups in agreement, you approve the bascule bridge design. You also tell the engineers to begin working on more detailed plans for the bridge's construction.

Bascule bridges, like the one shown here, use gravitational potential energy and counterweights to move the bridge.

LESSON SUMMARY

Potential Energy in Systems

Gravitational Potential Energy A system has gravitational potential energy when potential energy is stored in a system of objects interacting by gravitational forces.

Electric Potential Energy A system has electric potential energy when potential energy is stored in a system of objects interacting by electric forces.

Magnetic Potential Energy A system has magnetic potential energy when potential energy is stored in a system of objects interacting by magnetic forces.

Other Types of Potential Energy Elastic potential energy and chemical potential energy are combinations of other types of energy.

Evaluating Bridge Designs Engineers and other people interested in solving a problem evaluate design choices based on criteria and constraints.

Fuel Up with Food

It's the morning of the big game, and you're excited because your basketball team is competing in the league championship this afternoon. Your coach sends the team a text message, "Be sure to eat a good breakfast this morning—you're going to need the energy!" What does breakfast have to do with having energy?

Your breakfast, like all food, stores potential energy, and you need energy from food for playing basketball, and much more. Think about what has to happen in your body for you to live. Your heart has to beat, and your lungs have to expand and contract. Your brain has to tell your heart and lungs and the rest of your body what to do. All these functions require energy, and you also need energy to move around and to take in information using your senses. Your body is a complex collection of systems that requires a regular supply of energy from food.

Of course, humans aren't unique in needing a source of energy. Almost all living things—from the tiniest bacterium to the largest whale—need energy, and most animals, like humans, get energy from eating food. Plants also need food for energy. They are able to make their own food through photosynthesis, a process that uses energy from the sun and matter from the environment to produce sugars that store energy in chemical bonds.

Living things are able to use the energy stored in food because of processes that break down the substances that make up food. In your body, the process of digestion, part of which takes place in your stomach and intestines, breaks down food so it can later be "burned." When food is burned, energy stored in the chemical bonds in the food is released and can be used by your body.

Playing basketball requires a lot of energy, but so does daily living! Your body gets energy to live, move around, and play basketball from the food that you eat.

Consuming Calories

You have learned that the S.I. unit of energy is the Joule, but there is another unit of energy that people talk about every day: the Calorie. In the United States, the Calorie is a common way to measure the energy stored in food. The more Calories a sample of food has, the more energy is released when you "burn" it.

The food you eat is made up of nutrients, three of which provide the energy your body uses. These nutrients are proteins, carbohydrates, and fats, which store different amounts of energy. Both proteins and carbohydrates store four Calories per gram, while fats store nine Calories per gram. These numbers may make you think that you should eat fats if you want more energy, but you should eat some of each nutrient to stay healthy.

Different foods are sources of different nutrients, and some foods contain more than one nutrient. For example, fish and chicken contain both proteins and fats. Fruits and vegetables are good sources of carbohydrates, and some vegetables, such as beans, are also good sources of protein.

The energy in food is measured in Calories. Different foods have different amounts of calories and different kinds of nutrients, such as protein, fat, and carbohydrates.

Burning and Bombing

Suppose that you want to know how many Calories are in the food that you are eating. The easiest way to find out is to look at the label on the package that the food came in. Or if you don't have a label, you could weigh or measure the food and then look online to find out how many Calories are in each gram of that particular food. Where do the values come from?

The values tell you how much energy is released when your body "burns" the food. The original method scientists used to find out how many Calories food has was to actually burn the food! The food was burned in a device called a *bomb calorimeter*. The word "bomb" is in the name because the food is burned quickly, similar to an explosion.

A bomb calorimeter is made of a sealed inner container, which is inside another sealed and insulated container that is full of water. A measured amount of food is placed in the inner container and is ignited with an electric current. The food burns and gives off thermal energy. The thermal energy is transferred through the walls of the inner container to the water surrounding it. The thermal energy causes the temperature of the water to rise, and the change in temperature is measured with a thermometer. The mass of the water in the container and how much the temperature of that water changed is used to calculate the amount of energy given off by the burning food.

Bomb calorimeters do a good job determining the amount of energy contained in food, but using them is time consuming. So today, most of the Calorie values you see are calculated by estimation. First, scientists determine the masses of protein, carbohydrates, and fats in a sample of food. Then they multiply those masses by four Calories per gram for proteins and carbohydrates or by nine Calories per gram for fats. This method is accurate, but is not as exciting as exploding the food.

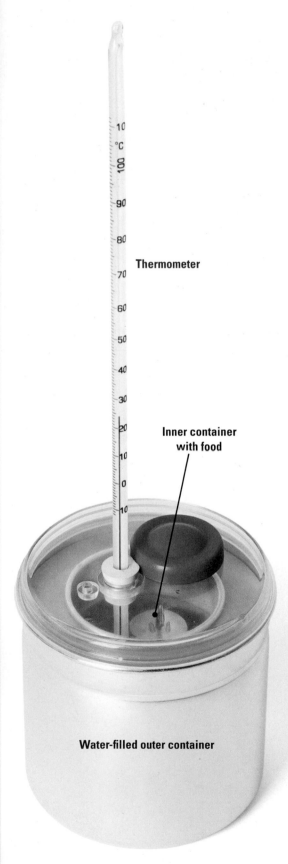

Thermometer

Inner container with food

Water-filled outer container

The energy contained in food can be found by using a bomb calorimeter. Food is burned inside the inner container, and the energy released increases the temperature of the water in the outer container.

Nutrition Facts
Serving Size 1/6 package (60g)
Servings Per Container 6

Amount Per Serving	Mix	Prepared
Calories	260	360
Calories from Fat	80	150
	% Daily Value*	
Total Fat 9g*	14%	26%
Saturated Fat 3.5g	18%	30%
Cholesterol 0mg	0%	1%
Sodium 360mg	15%	20%
Total Carbohydrate 46g	15%	16%
Dietary Fiber 1g	4%	4%
Sugars 28g		

All packaged foods have Nutrition Facts labels. These labels tell you serving sizes, how many Calories the food provides, and how much of certain nutrients are in the food.

Eating for Energy

Have you ever noticed the labels on the sides of food packages in the grocery store? Now you know how the information on that label is calculated. How can you use the information on those Nutrition Facts labels?

The first thing you should read on a Nutrition Facts label is the serving size. This tells you how much of the food you should eat to get the nutrients listed on the rest of the label. Remember that the serving size is not always the same as the package size! A package may contain two fruit and nut bars, but a serving size may be only one fruit and nut bar.

Next, you should check the Calorie content of the food. Eating more Calories than you "burn" can cause you to gain weight. Notice that the label also tells you how many of the Calories come from fats. Although you do need to eat some fat to stay healthy, eating too much fat can put you at risk for diseases such as cancer and heart disease.

The rest of the label lists various important nutrients. The first three—total fat, cholesterol, and sodium—are nutrients that you should limit. Dietary fiber, protein, and the vitamins and minerals listed under the black bar are all nutrients that you should get enough of each day to be healthy.

The next time you grab breakfast, check the labels on the food packaging. Make sure the food contains lots of the good nutrients and not too much of the nutrients and minerals you should eat in limited quantities. A good breakfast will help provide the energy you need to play basketball or any other activity that you like. ◆

Thermal Energy

OVERVIEW

The rabbit you see here has extremely long ears. Did you know that its ears allow it to survive extremely high temperatures? In this unit, you will investigate different phenomena related to temperature and heat. You will also learn about how energy, heat, and matter are related. Then you will create a device that can withstand extreme temperatures.

Phenomenon-Based Storyline
Temperatures in the desert vary greatly between daytime highs and nighttime lows. How do people and other animals minimize or maximize thermal energy transfer to survive these temperature swings?

Investigations Plan and carry out an investigation to determine how temperature change depends on the masses and types of matter involved. Design posters to explain conduction, convection, and radiation.

Investigations Investigate thermal conductivity and analyze data about temperature changes of ice. Compare the heat capacities of sand and water.

Performance Assessment Design and test a device that either minimizes or maximizes thermal energy transfer, to be used in a desert situation.

UNIT 4

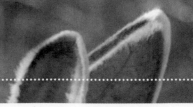

Performance Expectations

MS-PS3-3. Apply scientific principles to design, construct, and test a device that either minimizes or maximizes thermal energy transfer.

MS-PS3-4. Plan an investigation to determine the relationships among the energy transferred, the type of matter, the mass, and the change in the average kinetic energy of the particles as measured by the temperature of the sample.

MS-PS3-5. Construct, use, and present arguments to support the claim that when the kinetic energy of an object changes, energy is transferred to or from the object.

MS-ETS1-3. Analyze data from tests to determine similarities and differences among several design solutions to identify the best characteristics of each that can be combined into a new solution to better meet the criteria for success.

Science and Engineering Practices

Planning and Carrying Out Investigations
Plan an investigation individually and collaboratively, and in the design: identify independent and dependent variables and controls, what tools are needed to do the gathering, how measurements will be recorded, and how many data are needed to support a claim.

Constructing Explanations and Designing Solutions
Apply scientific ideas or principles to design, construct, and test a design of an object, tool, process or system.

Analyzing and Interpreting Data
Analyze and interpret data to determine similarities and differences in findings.

Connections to Nature of Science: Scientific Knowledge is Based on Empirical Evidence
Science knowledge is based upon logical and conceptual connections between evidence and explanations.

Crosscutting Concepts

Scale, Proportion, and Quantity
Proportional relationships (e.g., speed as the ratio of distance traveled to time taken) among different types of quantities provide information about the magnitude of properties and processes.

Energy and Matter
• Energy may take different forms (e.g., energy in fields, thermal energy, energy of motion).
• The transfer of energy can be tracked as energy flows through a designed or natural system.

Cause and Effect
Cause and effect relationships may be used to predict phenomena in natural or designed systems.

Disciplinary Core Ideas

PS3.A: Definitions of Energy
Temperature is a measure of the average kinetic energy of particles of matter. The relationship between the temperature and the total energy of a system depends on the types, states, and amounts of matter present.

PS3.B: Conservation of Energy and Energy Transfer
• When the motion energy of an object changes, there is inevitably some other change in energy at the same time. • The amount of energy transfer needed to change the temperature of a matter sample by a given amount depends on the nature of the matter, the size of the sample, and the environment. • Energy is spontaneously transferred out of hotter regions or objects and into colder ones.

ETS1.B: Developing Possible Solutions
• There are systematic processes for evaluating solutions with respect to how well they meet the criteria and constraints of a problem. • Sometimes parts of different solutions can be combined to create a solution that is better than any of its predecessors.

ETS1.C: Optimizing the Design Solution
Although one design may not perform the best across all tests, identifying the characteristics of the design that performed the best in each test can provide useful information for the redesign process—that is, some of those characteristics may be incorporated into the new design.

Connect Your Learning

Before you get dressed in the morning, you might look at the weather to check the temperature. But what is meant by the word *temperature*? It is more than just a measure of how hot or cold it is outside. It is also a good indicator of how much energy an object has. There are many ways you can use terms like temperature and heat to describe and measure more phenomena than the outside temperature.

Marathon runners wrap themselves in what looks like foil to keep their body temperatures at a safe level. How can the technology of a "space blanket" keep people warm and use light to act as a sail in outer space?

Thermal Energy

A firefighter's suit protects them from high heat while also keeping the firefighter comfortable. How are suits designed to allow a person to stand up to a fire and not get burned?

What looks like a piece of ice is protecting a delicate flower from a flame. But it is not ice! It is an insulating material called an aerogel. How do scientists and engineers use what they know about insulators to create special materials that can stand up to heat?

Thermal Energy and Heat

How does energy affect temperature?

Introduction

The slices of meat and vegetables on these kabobs are being grilled. Heat from the red-hot pieces of charcoal beneath the food cooks them. Energy is needed to warm and cook food and make meat safe to eat. What is the relationship between heat and energy? How does adding energy to something make it hot?

You may have never cooked food on a charcoal grill or on a campfire. However, you do have experience with heat and energy. For example, you know that pavement can get very hot on sunny summer days. You also know that water will boil when you put it on the stove and that cookies will bake in a hot oven. In each of those examples, energy was added to something to make it hot.

This lesson starts by discussing temperature. Temperature is often thought of as a measure of how hot or cold something is. However, you will learn that temperature is also related to the kinetic energy of particles in matter. You will also learn that the thermal energy of a substance depends on its temperature, its mass, and its state of matter. Finally, you will read that heat is a flow of thermal energy and that heat can flow by three different methods.

Vocabulary

temperature a measure of the average kinetic energy of particles of matter

thermal energy includes the kinetic energy of the particles that make up a system and the potential energy stored in the system because of the interactions between the particles

heat thermal energy that is transferred from one region or substance to another

thermal equilibrium the condition in which objects that are touching have the same temperature

conduction heat transfer caused by the collisions of particles of matter that are in direct contact

convection the transfer of energy caused by the circulation of matter due to differences in density

radiation the transfer of energy by light waves

Next Generation Science Standards

Performance Expectations

MS-PS3-4. Plan an investigation to determine the relationships among the energy transferred, the type of matter, the mass, and the change in the average kinetic energy of the particles as measured by the temperature of the sample.

MS-PS3-5. Construct, use, and present arguments to support the claim that when the kinetic energy of an object changes, energy is transferred to or from the object.

Science and Engineering Practices

Planning and Carrying Out Investigations Plan an investigation individually and collaboratively, and in the design: identify independent and dependent variables and controls, what tools are needed to do the gathering, how measurements will be recorded, and how many data are needed to support a claim.

Crosscutting Concepts

Scale, Proportion, and Quantity Proportional relationships (e.g. speed as the ratio of distance traveled to time taken) among different types of quantities provide information about the magnitude of properties and processes.

Energy and Matter • Energy may take different forms (e.g. energy in fields, thermal energy, energy of motion). • The transfer of energy can be tracked as energy flows through a designed or natural system.

Disciplinary Core Ideas

PS3.A. Temperature is a measure of the average kinetic energy of particles of matter. The relationship between the temperature and the total energy of a system depends on the types, states, and amounts of matter present.

PS3.B. • When the motion energy of an object changes, there is inevitably some other change in energy at the same time. • The amount of energy transfer needed to change the temperature of a matter sample by a given amount depends on the nature of the matter, the size of the sample, and the environment. • Energy is spontaneously transferred out of hotter regions or objects and into colder ones.

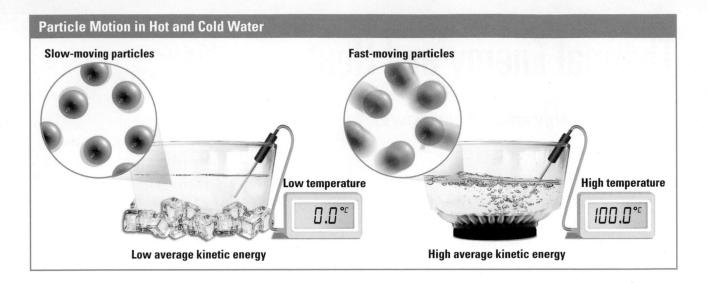

Slow-moving particles

Fast-moving particles

Low temperature

0.0 °C

Low average kinetic energy

High temperature

100.0 °C

High average kinetic energy

Figure 10.1

The temperature of an object is a measure of the average kinetic energy of its particles. Average kinetic energy, and therefore the temperature, depends on the speeds of the particles. The water in the ice bath has a lower temperature than the water over the Bunsen burner. The particles in the water in the ice bath move slowly while the particles in the water over the Bunsen burner move quickly; each sample has different kinetic energies.

1. Temperature

On a hot summer day, you head to the pool to cool off. Afterward, you grab a cold drink and put some leftover pizza in the microwave to warm up. Every day you encounter hot things and cold things. What causes objects to have different temperatures?

All matter is made of tiny particles, atoms and molecules, which move at various speeds in all directions. In hot objects, these particles move faster, and in cold objects, they move slower. Because each particle is moving, each particle has a certain amount of kinetic energy. **Temperature** is a measure of the average kinetic energy of particles of matter.

The temperature of an object can change. For example, a cookie sheet changes temperature when you make sugar cookies. When you place the cookies on the sheet, it has a temperature of 20°C. You put the sheet with the cookies into the refrigerator to chill the dough before baking. The average kinetic energy of the particles in the sheet decreases, and its temperature drops to 2°C. Then you put the sheet and cookies into the oven to bake. The average kinetic energy of the sheet's particles increases rapidly, and its temperature rises to 190°C. Recall that kinetic energy depends on speed and mass. The particles that make up water have about the same mass, so differences in kinetic energy are due to differences in their speed. One sample of water in Figure 10.1 is on ice. Those water particles move slowly, and their average kinetic energy is low. As a result, the water has a low temperature. The other sample of water in Figure 10.1 is warmed by a Bunsen burner. Its particles move quickly, and their average kinetic energy is high. So, the water has a high temperature.

Differences in particle mass also affect temperature. The mass of an oxygen gas particle is about twice the mass of a water particle. Suppose that the particles in samples of oxygen and water are moving at about the same speed. The oxygen gas has a higher temperature because its particles have more mass and thus more kinetic energy.

2. Thermal Energy

Which has more energy: a giant iceberg or a cup of hot water? You know that the cup of water has a higher temperature and a higher average kinetic energy, but it does not have more energy. What is the relationship between the energy in a system and its temperature?

When deciding which system has more energy, you must consider the systems' thermal energy. The **thermal energy** of a system includes the kinetic energy of the particles that make up the system and the potential energy stored in the system due to interactions between the particles. A system's thermal energy depends on three factors: the mass of the system, its state of matter, and the substance it is made of.

Mass and Thermal Energy The first factor that affects thermal energy is the mass of the matter present. Thermal energy increases as the mass increases, as shown in Figure 10.2A. A large pot of boiling water at 100°C has more thermal energy than a small pot of boiling water at 100°C. Both systems have the same temperature, but the large pot has a greater thermal energy because it contains more water particles. A giant iceberg has more thermal energy than a cup of boiling water for a similar reason. Even though each individual particle in the iceberg has on average less kinetic energy than the particles in the cup of boiling water, there are so many more water particles in the iceberg that when you add them together, they have more energy.

States of Matter and Thermal Energy The second factor that affects thermal energy is the state that the matter is in. In a solid, the particles do not have enough energy to break away from other particles. So, particles in a solid can only vibrate in place. In a liquid of the same substance, particles have enough energy to slide past each other, but are mostly held close together. Finally, in a gas, particles have so much energy that they break free from the other particles and move freely.

Figure 10.2A

The thermal energy of a system depends on the amount of matter present. A large pot of boiling water at 100°C has more thermal energy than a small pot of boiling water at 100°C.

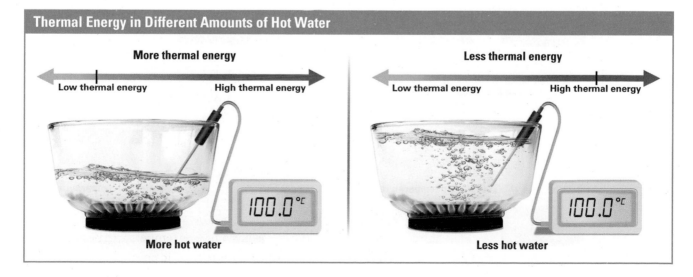

Thermal Energy in Different Amounts of Hot Water

More thermal energy

Low thermal energy   High thermal energy

More hot water

Less thermal energy

Low thermal energy   High thermal energy

Less hot water

Ice, liquid water, and water vapor are the same substance (water) in three different states. If you have 100 g of ice at 0°C and 100 g of liquid water at 0°C, the two systems have the same average kinetic energy and the same number of particles. But the ice is in a lower energy state. A lot of energy has to be added to the ice to change it to liquid water at the same temperature. So, the system with the liquid water has more thermal energy.

Similarly, 100 g of liquid water at 100°C and 100 g of water vapor at 100°C have the same average kinetic energy and number of particles. However, a lot of energy has to be added to liquid water to change it into a vapor. So, the water vapor has more thermal energy.

Types of Matter and Thermal Energy The third factor that affects thermal energy is the type of matter present. Figure 10.2B shows two systems at the same temperature: 1 kg of water and 1 kg of mercury. Suppose you heat the systems to increase their temperatures by 1°C. The water will require more thermal energy to raise its temperature. Some of the thermal energy that goes into the systems is used to break the attractions between particles, increasing their potential energy. Water requires more thermal energy to rearrange its particles. After heating, more thermal energy is in the water than in the mercury because water stores more potential energy between its particles. In general, some types of matter have more thermal energy than others at the same temperature.

Figure 10.2B

The thermal energy of a system depends partly on the type of matter in the system. When the temperatures of identical masses of water and mercury are increased by the same amount, water stores more potential energy, so the water's thermal energy increases more than the mercury's thermal energy.

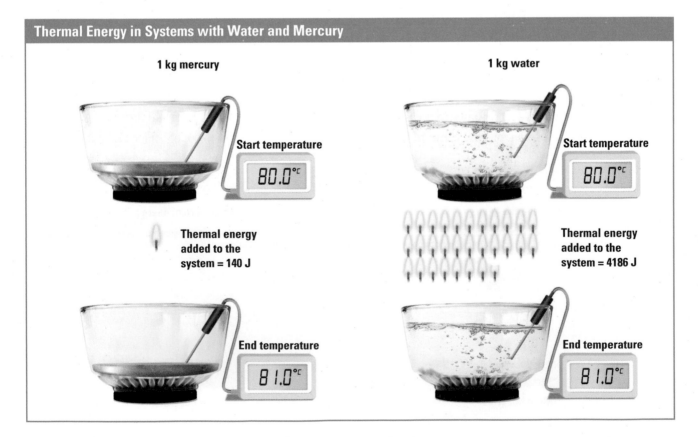

Thermal Energy in Systems with Water and Mercury

1 kg mercury

1 kg water

Start temperature

80.0 °C

Start temperature

80.0 °C

Thermal energy added to the system = 140 J

Thermal energy added to the system = 4186 J

End temperature

81.0 °C

End temperature

81.0 °C

Factors that Affect Thermal Energy

Temperature and thermal energy are different measures of the energy of a system. However, they are related because thermal energy depends on temperature. The thermal energy of a system also depends on types of matter, states of matter, and amounts of matter.

Thermal Energy and Temperature

The thermal energy of a system increases as its temperature increases.

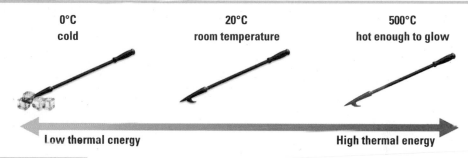

0°C cold	20°C room temperature	500°C hot enough to glow

Low thermal energy   High thermal energy

Thermal energy and Amounts of Matter

The thermal energy of a system increases as the mass of the system increases.

100°C a little water	100°C medium water	100°C a lot of water

Low thermal energy   High thermal energy

Thermal Energy and States of Matter

A system gains or loses energy when the matter that makes up the system changes state, so thermal energy depends on the state that the matter is in.

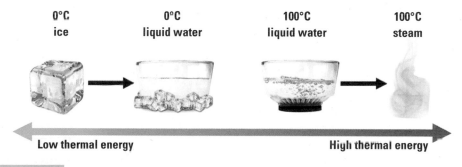

0°C ice	0°C liquid water	100°C liquid water	100°C steam

Low thermal energy   High thermal energy

Thermal Energy and Types of Matter

Thermal energy of a system depends on the type of matter in the system because different substances store varied amounts of thermal energy.

20°C 1 kg mercury	20°C 1 kg acetone	20°C 1 kg water

Low thermal energy   High thermal energy

The pot is hotter than the air, so heat flows from the contents of the pot to the air.

The fire is hotter than the pot, so heat flows from the fire to the pot.

Figure 10.3A

Thermal energy is transferred as heat from higher temperature regions to lower temperature regions. For example, the fire has a higher temperature relative to the pot, so thermal energy is transferred from the fire to the pot. Similarly, the pot has a higher temperature relative to the surrounding air, so thermal energy is transferred from the pot to the air.

3. Heat

The word *heat* is used in everyday language. When you heat up something, you increase its temperature. But in science, "heat" has a precise meaning. What is heat to a scientist?

Heat is thermal energy that is transferred from one region to another. Scientists track energy flowing into and out of regions as heat. A region can be an object or part of an object. A bowl of soup is a region that is an object. A spoon placed in the soup can be divided into two regions: the part in the soup and the part above the soup.

For heat to flow between two regions, the regions have to be at different temperatures. Heat always flows from higher temperature regions to lower temperature regions, as shown in Figure 10.3A. When heat flows between two regions and no energy is added to the system, the temperature of both regions changes. The temperature and the average kinetic energy of the hotter region drops, and the temperature and the particles' average kinetic energy of the colder region rises.

How quickly heat flows depends on the difference in temperature and the substances involved. The rate that heat flows between regions is proportional to the temperature difference between them. Recall that "proportional" means that the ratio between two variables is constant. Because heat flow is proportional to the temperature difference, the greater the temperature difference between two regions is, the faster heat flows between them. The substances involved also affect heat flow. Heat flows quickly between certain substances and slowly between other substances. For example, heat flows quickly to and from metals but flows slowly to and from air and other gases.

Thermal energy can be transferred as heat by the collision of particles. Figure 10.3B shows a system made up of a room-temperature spoon placed into a cup of hot liquid. Recall that, like all matter, the spoon and the liquid are made of tiny particles that are too small to see. These particles are in constant motion.

In this spoon and liquid system, the particles in the two regions collide at the surface where the spoon and the liquid touch. The particles in the higher temperature region (the liquid) move faster and have more kinetic energy than the particles in the lower temperature region (the spoon). When a liquid particle collides with a spoon particle, some kinetic energy from the liquid particle is transferred to the spoon particle. The spoon particle gains kinetic energy and starts moving faster. The liquid particle loses kinetic energy and moves more slowly.

Collisions between liquid particles and spoon particles happen all over the surface of the spoon that is under the liquid. Because the particles are very small, the number of particles colliding each moment is huge. Furthermore, each particle can collide with other particles many times each second. During each collision, energy transfers from a faster-moving particle to a slower-moving particle.

As a result of these many collisions, the average speed of the fast-moving liquid particles decreases. Also, the average speed of the slow-moving spoon particles increases. So, the average kinetic energy of the liquid particles decreases, and the liquid's temperature decreases. At the same time, the average kinetic energy of the spoon particles increases, and the spoon's temperature increases.

Figure 10.3B

Thermal energy is transferred between regions at different temperatures through the collision of particles of matter. When a spoon is placed into a cup of hot liquid, collisions between liquid particles and spoon particles transfer energy to the spoon.

Particle Motion in Heat Transfer

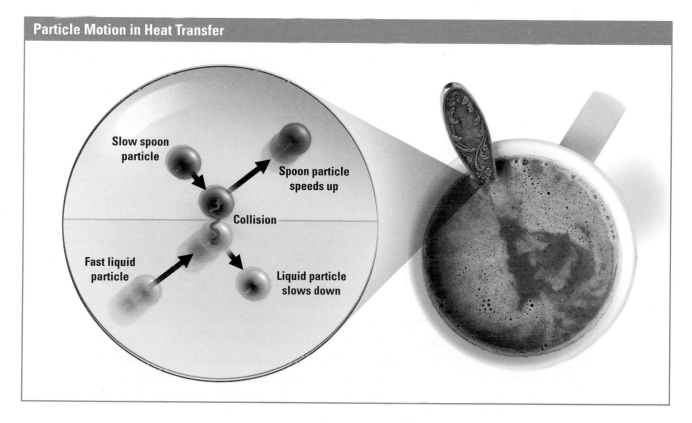

Slow spoon particle

Spoon particle speeds up

Collision

Fast liquid particle

Liquid particle slows down

**Same increase in thermal energy
Small increase in temperature**

**Same increase in thermal energy
Large increase in temperature.**

Figure 10.4

How much the temperature of a substance changes depends on the mass of the substance and how much thermal energy is transferred to the substance. If the same amount of thermal energy is transferred to different masses of the same substance, the temperature of the smaller mass will increase more than the temperature of the larger mass.

4. Heat and Conservation of Energy

If you eat at a buffet, you might notice small burning cans underneath pans of food such as the ones shown in Figure 10.4. These cans contain fuel that is burned to keep the food above it warm. Suppose that you see one can under a large container of soup and another can under a small container of soup. Which container of soup is hotter if both soups started at the same temperature and have been on the buffet for the same length of time?

You might think that both containers of soup would have the same temperature, but that is not what happens. Instead, the smaller container of soup will have a higher temperature. When the two cans of fuel burn, the same amount of heat flows to the two soup containers. So, the thermal energy of both soup containers increases by the same amount. However, remember that the relationship between thermal energy and temperature depends on the mass. When the thermal energy of both containers increases by the same amount, the temperature of the small container rises more because it has less mass.

In order for temperature to change, energy must transfer into or out of an object. When the temperature of the soup (or any object) increases, the energy it gains comes from somewhere. In the case of the soup, the energy came from the burning fuel. When the temperature of an object decreases, the energy it loses goes somewhere. If the burning fuel is extinguished, the temperature of the soup will drop because it loses energy to the surrounding air. When thermal energy is lost to the air, the temperature of the soup decreases. However, in both situations, the energy is merely transferred between different parts of the system of the burners, soup, and air. In both situations, the total amount of energy is conserved.

The thermal energy of a region or object can change. The thermal energy of the containers of soup changed when they were placed over the burning fuel. Whenever the thermal energy of a region or object changes, another change in energy has to happen because of the conservation of energy. In the case of the soup and the fuel, potential energy stored in the fuel was converted into thermal energy when the fuel was burned.

Another example of the conservation of energy and temperature change happens when you rub your hands together to warm them. When you move your hands back and forth, you cause friction between their surfaces. This friction causes particles in your hands to move, so the kinetic energy of the particles increases. As a result, your hands' temperature rises and their thermal energy increases.

Friction can be used to start a campfire for cooking. If you rub two pieces of wood together very fast, friction increases the average kinetic energy of the wood particles. It increases so much that the temperature of the wood rises high enough to burn. Once the wood is burning, a chemical reaction converts potential energy stored in the wood into thermal energy. This thermal energy can then be transferred to other objects, such as a pot of water. The thermal energy increases the average kinetic energy of the objects' particles and raises the objects' temperatures.

Energy is conserved whenever an object or region gains thermal energy. When wood burns, potential energy stored in the wood is converted into thermal energy. This thermal energy transfers to the air and any nearby objects.

Friction can be used to increase thermal energy and temperature. Rubbing your hands together causes friction, and friction causes the average kinetic energy of your hand particles to increase. So, your hands become warmer.

A

Large temperature difference
Heat flows quickly

B

Small temperature difference
Heat flows slowly

C

No temperature difference
Heat does not flow

5. Thermal Equilibrium

If you've ever taken a hot bath you know that the bath water does not stay hot for long. The water temperature drops because thermal energy is transferred away from the water. But, no matter how long you let the bath water sit, it will not get colder than room temperature. Why does the water eventually stop changing temperature?

When objects are touching, heat can flow between the objects as shown in Figure 10.4. If the objects are at different temperatures, heat will flow from the higher temperature object to the lower temperature object. The hot tea water and the spoon are touching, so heat flows from the tea water to the spoon.

Heat keeps flowing from the hotter water to the spoon until the substances reach the same temperature. When objects that are touching have the same temperature, the objects are in **thermal equilibrium**. Objects in a system that are in thermal equilibrium will stay at the same temperature assuming that no energy is added to or removed from the system. That's why the spoon does not get warmer than the tea water. The two objects are in thermal equilibrium.

Although objects in thermal equilibrium do not change temperature, this does not mean that there is no energy transfer between them. The particles of the objects still collide where the objects touch, and the particles still transfer energy to one another. However, the amount of energy transferred away from one object is equal to the amount of energy transferred to the object. This is because there is an equal number of collisions that transfer energy into the object as transfer energy out of the object. So overall, the thermal energy and temperature of both objects in the system stays the same.

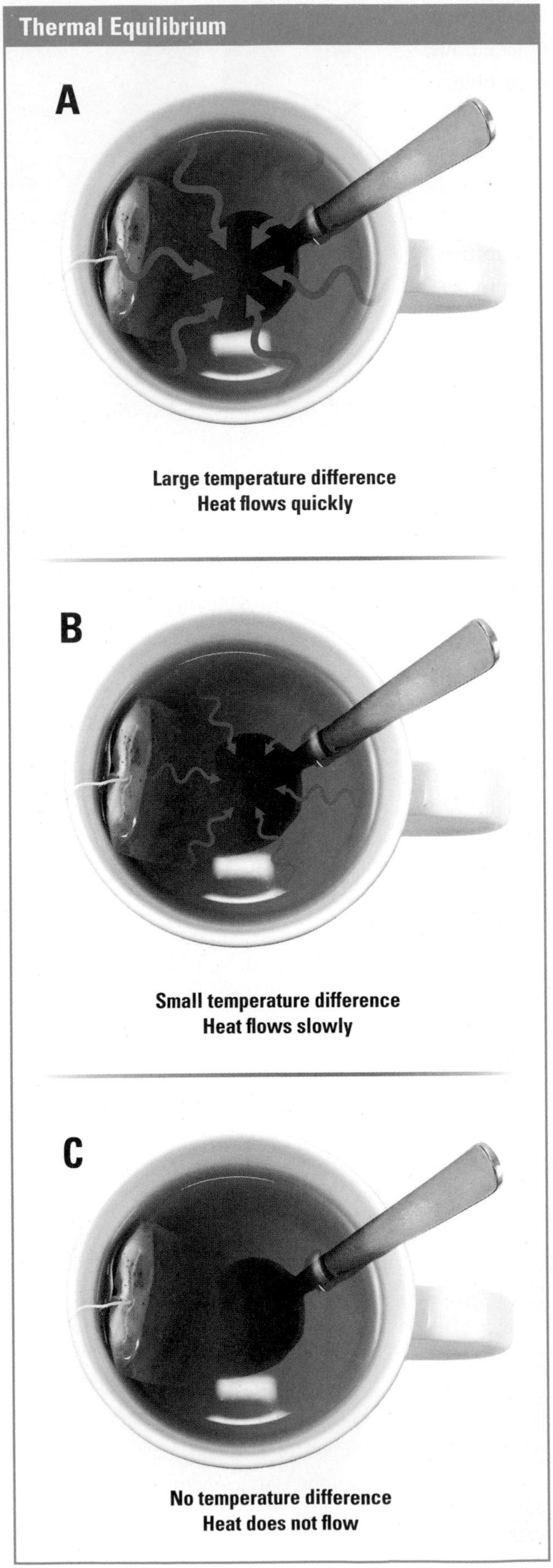

Figure 10.5

Heat flows between objects when the objects are touching and are at different temperatures. Heat flows quickly in *A* because the spoon and the tea water are touching. In *B*, heat flows more slowly from the hotter tea water to the cooler spoon. In *C*, no heat flows because the objects have the same temperature and are therefore in thermal equilibrium.

Transfer of Thermal Energy

The transfer of energy can be tracked as it flows through a system. A solar cooker is a system that uses energy from the sun to cook food.

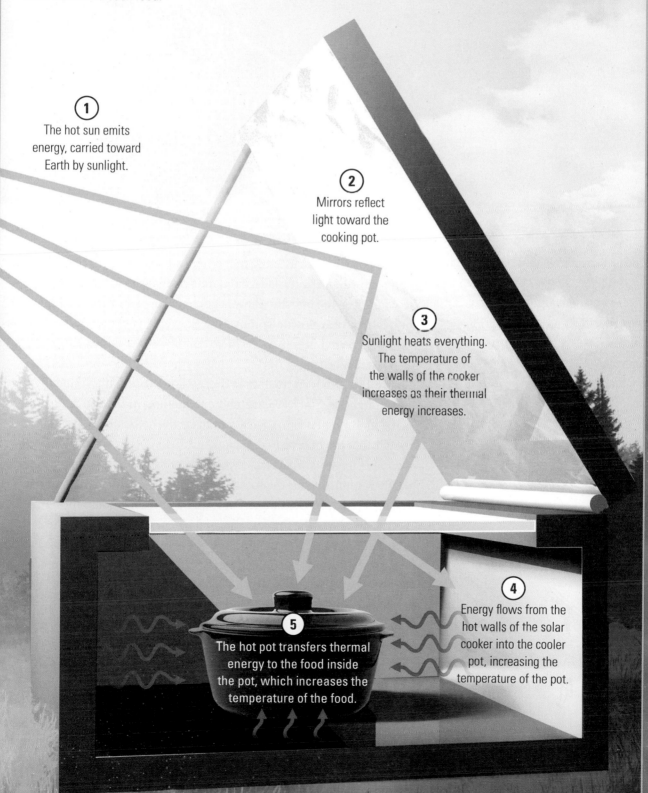

1 The hot sun emits energy, carried toward Earth by sunlight.

2 Mirrors reflect light toward the cooking pot.

3 Sunlight heats everything. The temperature of the walls of the cooker increases as their thermal energy increases.

4 Energy flows from the hot walls of the solar cooker into the cooler pot, increasing the temperature of the pot.

5 The hot pot transfers thermal energy to the food inside the pot, which increases the temperature of the food.

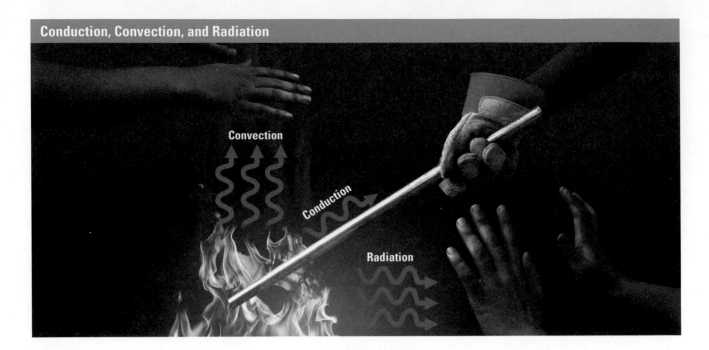

Figure 10.6

Conduction, convection, and radiation are the three methods of heat transfer. Conduction transfers heat from a fire to a metal skewer through direct contact. Convection warms the air above a fire though the motion of the air. Radiation transfers energy away as light waves in all directions.

6. The Three Methods of Heat Transfer

Suppose you are toasting marshmallows on a skewer over a fire. As you wait, you feel your face and hands being warmed by the fire. In a few minutes, the marshmallow is golden brown and ready to eat. You pull it off and accidentally touch the skewer. *Ouch!* that burns. How is heat transferred in this scenario?

Heat can be transferred by three methods, which are shown in Figure 10.5. You can track how energy flows through a system by the three methods. You learned about one method in Section 3. **Conduction** is the method of heat transfer caused by the collisions of particles of matter that are in direct contact. Conduction between the hot skewer and your finger is what makes your finger hurt. Conduction is also partly responsible for the toasted marshmallow. The marshmallow was warmed partly by conduction between it and the hot air above the fire.

The air above the fire was warmed by another method of heat transfer. **Convection** is the transfer of energy caused by the circulation of matter due to differences in density. Unlike conduction, convection is not a transfer of energy between objects. Instead, energy is carried from one place to another by the movement of gases or liquids. Convection happens because of density differences between warm gases (or liquids) and cool gases (or liquids). The air next to the hot logs of the fire is warmed by conduction. Warm air is less dense than cool air, so it rises up through the cool air above the fire.

As the warm air rises, the cool air around the fire sinks. This cold air ends up next to the logs, is warmed by conduction, and rises. But as the now warm air rises, it starts to cool off because it has moved away from the hot logs. What results is a circular pattern of air movement that is called a *convection current*.

When you sit next to the fire, your face and hands are warmed by yet another method of heat transfer. **Radiation** is the transfer of energy by light waves. Recall that light is made of waves that can travel through matter and empty space. All objects give off some light waves. Most objects give off infrared light waves, which are low-energy waves that people cannot see. The light waves given off carry energy away from objects. Very hot objects, such as burning logs in a fire, glow and give off visible light, too. All light waves coming off the burning logs carries energy away from the logs. The waves strike you and transfer energy to your body, which is a transfer of energy by radiation.

You experience heat transfer by radiation all the time. Energy from the sun, which is necessary for all life on Earth, is transferred to Earth by radiation. Radiation is also useful for a more delicious reason. Toasters warm up slices of bread using radiation. When you turn on a toaster, the wires inside it warm up and begin to glow. Radiation from the glowing wires dries out the bread and makes it crunchy. Radiation is also important when toasting marshmallows.

In a given situation, one method may transfer the most heat, but the other methods may also contribute. Radiation transfers the most heat in a toaster, but convection warms the air above the toaster and conduction may make the outside of the toaster hot.

More than one method of heat transfer may happen in a given situation. All three methods of heat transfer happen when you use a toaster. Radiation transfers the most heat to the bread and the surrounding air, while convection transfers heat to the air, and conduction transfers heat to the toaster body.

LESSON SUMMARY

Thermal Energy and Heat

Temperature Temperature tells you how hot or cold an object is and is a measure of the average kinetic energy of particles of matter.

Thermal Energy The thermal energy of a system depends on temperature, the mass of a system, the system's state of matter, and the substance the system is made of.

Heat Heat is thermal energy that is transferred from a region with higher temperature to a region with a lower temperature.

Heat and Conservation of Energy Energy is conserved when heat flows from one object to another.

Thermal Equilibrium When objects are in thermal equilibrium, they are at the same temperature and stay at the same temperature if no energy enters or leaves the system.

The Three Methods of Heat Transfer Heat can be transferred by conduction, convection, or radiation.

Solved with a Space Blanket

You're walking through a park when you see shiny objects on the sidewalk far ahead of you. "It looks like a robot army," you chuckle to yourself. When they get closer, you notice they are people wearing tights and what look like silver sheets as capes. "Now they look like futuristic superheroes," you laugh. Then someone tells you they are marathon runners wearing space blankets. Why do the runners need blankets?

People's body temperatures rise when they exercise, so runners tend to wear thin clothes when running a marathon because they don't want to get too hot during the race. But when they stop running, their body temperatures drop, and they need a blanket to stay warm.

Marathon organizers hand out a special kind of blanket to runners after the race. These blankets are very thin and lightweight and have a shiny coating that makes the blankets look futuristic. But the futuristic look of these blankets is not the reason why they are commonly called *space blankets*.

Marathon runners wrap themselves in space blankets to keep warm after a race. Space blankets are made of a thin, lightweight material.

Made for Outer Space

Space blankets got their name because the material that they are made from was used by NASA for various space missions. The material is a thin plastic film that is coated with aluminum and has some surprising properties.

The plastic film was originally developed in 1952 as an additional product by a company that was producing a new kind of polyester fabric. The company realized that the plastic film had properties that might make it useful in a wide range of applications. The company made a short movie to show off the properties to manufacturers. In the movie, a man jumps on a trampoline made of the film to show its strength. Then, a woman swings on a trapeze hung from the film to show its resistance to tearing. It also shows a bowling ball thrown at a frozen sheet of film and at a steam-heated sheet of film to show that the film's properties are not affected by extreme temperatures. The movie also notes that, when the film is coated with a metal, it is a very good thermal insulator.

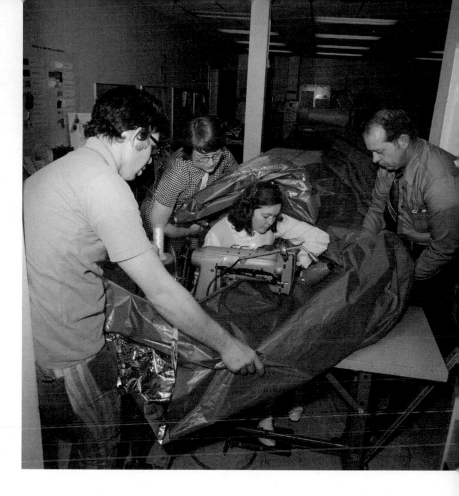

The properties of a new plastic film were ideal for use in many of NASA's space programs. NASA engineers built an emergency heat shield for Skylab using the aluminum-coated plastic film.

NASA engineers found out about the properties of the plastic film and became very interested. When building a spacecraft, weight is always a constraint, and the ability to withstand both extremely hot and extremely cold temperatures is important. The thin, lightweight plastic film fit the criteria for materials they could use to make spacecraft. NASA engineers took the plastic film, coated it with aluminum and other metals, and began finding many ways to use it.

NASA used the material to build balloon-like satellites in 1960 and to cover the Apollo moon landers in the late 1960s and early 1970s. The material has been used to insulate spacesuits since the 1960s. NASA also used the material as part of an emergency heat shield for Skylab, NASA's first space station. Skylab's original heat shield was ripped off during its unmanned mission launched on May 14, 1973. When astronauts arrived at the space station on May 25, one of their first jobs was to install the new shield to protect the station and themselves when they went to live inside it.

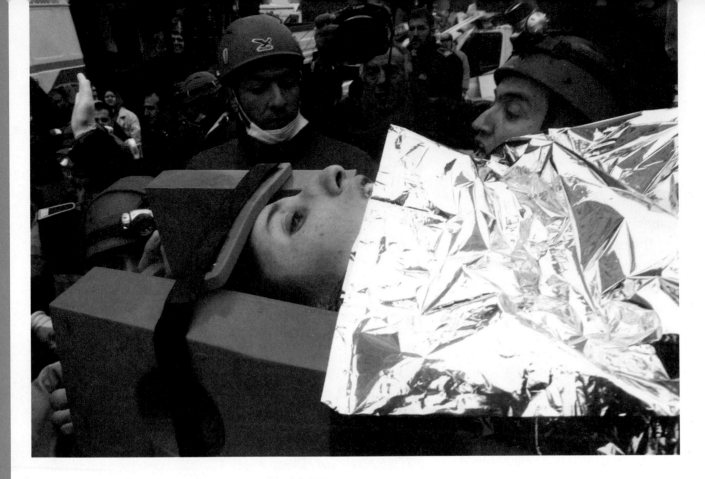

The plastic film has many applications on Earth. First responders often use space blankets when helping victims of natural disasters or accidents. This person is kept warm with a space blanket after being rescued from earthquake debris.

Down-to-Earth Uses

Some of the same properties of the plastic film that appealed to NASA engineers also appealed to people making products for use on Earth. Today, people use space blankets and products made from space blanket materials in a variety of ways.

Besides covering marathon runners, the most common use of space blankets is in emergency situations. Because space blankets are so thin and lightweight, a large blanket can be folded up into a small package that is easily carried and distributed. First responders can easily store and hand out hundreds or thousands of space blankets to victims of natural disasters or accidents.

The insulating properties of the plastic film come in very handy in several products. For example, clothes lined with the plastic film keep people warm in extremely cold situations. Dog-sled mushers who need to stay outside for hours or even days can wear space-blanket-lined coats and mittens during their races.

The flexibility and insulating properties of space blanket material are also useful in medicine. A nurse in Boston designed a special hat made from space blanket material to keep babies warm after surgery. The flexibility of the material allows the hat, which is made of three flaps, to be folded around a baby's head. It can easily be unfolded if the baby gets too hot or if a doctor needs access to the baby's head.

Super-Sized Space Blankets

Only a small piece of space blanket is needed to make a baby hat. But size is not a constraint when using space blanket material. Because the plastic film is so strong and resistant to tears, it can be formed into huge sheets. Of course, unless you are gift wrapping a car, you and most people do not have a use for a giant sheet of space blanket. However, NASA engineers find that super-sized space blankets are perfect for some of their needs.

One of the newest ways NASA is using space blanket material is to make solar sails out of it. A solar sail on a spacecraft works similarly to a sail on a boat. Wind pushes on a boat's sail, and the force from the wind on the sail makes the boat move. A solar sail has sunlight pushing on it instead of wind. Because the sail is in space, it will always be hit by sunlight. Light exerts force on the sail. The force from each ray is tiny, so a solar sail must be huge to catch enough rays to move a spacecraft.

In 2014, NASA built a solar sail made of four huge, triangular pieces of space blanket material. The four pieces formed a square that was 38 m on each side—that's about ¼ the size of a football field! This sail never made it into space, but NASA engineers continue to refine their design. A successfully designed solar sail can assist NASA in completing future missions, such as carrying a probe to an asteroid. The success of missions like these is thanks in part to an out-of-this-world space blanket. ◆

Solar sails are made of huge pieces of space blanket material and can be used to push a spacecraft through space. This solar sail is 38 m on each side and is made of just four pieces of material. The ripples in the material show where supports are holding the material up.

Thermal Properties of Matter

How does heat affect matter?

Introduction

Suppose that you are a firefighter. Before you approach a fire, you have to put on your gear. A helmet protects your head, and a facemask protects your face. You also wear a suit like the one shown. How does this suit protect you? Why does it cover almost all of your body?

When battling fires, firefighters work in areas that get very hot. Fires heat the air around them, and the thermal energy can transfer to people. If people are not protected from the thermal energy transfer, they can be burned. A firefighter's suit is made of material designed to slow the transfer of thermal energy from the outside of the suit to the inside.

In this lesson, you will learn about the thermal properties of substances. These properties determine whether objects feel hot or cold and how quickly objects change temperature. You will also learn about energy changes during changes of state. Finally, you will read how engineers optimized a substance called *aerogel* by overcoming its brittleness to take advantage of its unique thermal property.

Vocabulary

thermal conductivity a property of a substance that describes how quickly thermal energy can spread through the substance

thermal conductor a substance that has a high thermal conductivity

thermal insulator a substance that has a low thermal conductivity

heat capacity a property of a substance that describes how much thermal energy is needed to change the temperature of the substance

---

Next Generation Science Standards

Performance Expectations

MS-PS3-3. Apply scientific principles to design, construct, and test a device that either minimizes or maximizes thermal energy transfer.

MS-PS3-4. Plan an investigation to determine the relationships among the energy transferred, the type of matter, the mass, and the change in the average kinetic energy of the particles as measured by the temperature of the sample.

MS-ETS1-3. Analyze data from tests to determine similarities and differences among several design solutions to identify the best characteristics of each that can be combined into a new solution to better meet the criteria for success.

Science and Engineering Practices

Planning and Carrying Out Investigations Plan an investigation individually and collaboratively, and in the design: identify independent and dependent variables and controls, what tools are needed to do the gathering, how measurements will be recorded, and how many data are needed to support a claim.

Constructing Explanations and Designing Solutions Apply scientific ideas or principles to design, construct, and test a design of an object, tool, process or system.

Analyzing and Interpreting Data Analyze and interpret data to determine similarities and differences in findings.

Scientific Knowledge is Based on Empirical Evidence

Crosscutting Concepts

Scale, Proportion, and Quantity Proportional relationships (e.g. speed as the ratio of distance traveled to time taken) among different types of quantities provide information about the magnitude of properties and processes.

Energy and Matter The transfer of energy can be tracked as energy flows through a designed or natural system.

Cause and Effect Cause and effect relationships may be used to predict phenomena in natural or designed systems.

Disciplinary Core Ideas

PS3.A. Temperature is a measure of the average kinetic energy of particles of matter. The relationship between the temperature and the total energy of a system depends on the types, states, and amounts of matter present.

PS3.B. • The amount of energy transfer needed to change the temperature of a matter sample by a given amount depends on the nature of the matter, the size of the sample, and the environment. • Energy is spontaneously transferred out of hotter regions or objects and into colder ones.

ETS1.B. • There are systematic processes for evaluating solutions with respect to how well they meet the criteria and constraints of a problem. • Sometimes parts of different solutions can be combined to create a solution that is better than any of its predecessors.

ETS1.C. Although one design may not perform the best across all tests, identifying the characteristics of the design that performed the best in each test can provide useful information for the redesign process—that is, some of those characteristics may be incorporated into the new design.

1. Thermal Conductivity

You can test whether a cake is finished baking by poking it with your finger. The cake springs back if it is finished. You can safely touch the cake with your finger, but if you touch the metal cake pan, you'll get burned quickly. The cake and the pan are at the same temperature in the oven. Why can you touch one but not the other?

The reason a hot metal pan causes a burn and a hot cake does not has to do with how quickly energy transfers to or from each material. **Thermal conductivity** is a property of a substance that describes how quickly thermal energy spreads through the substance. Substances that have high thermal conductivities transfer thermal energy faster than substances that have low thermal conductivities. Figure 11.1A shows the thermal conductivities of some common substances.

Substances that have high thermal conductivities are called **thermal conductors**. Recall that thermal energy flows from higher-temperature objects to lower-temperature objects. So, when a thermal conductor touches a higher-temperature object, thermal energy from the object quickly transfers to the thermal conductor. The transfer of energy makes the object's temperature quickly drop. This process explains why you will be burned when you touch a hot metal cake pan. Most metals have high thermal conductivities. When you touch the hot metal, thermal energy quickly transfers from the pan. As a result, the temperature of your finger quickly rises and you get a burn.

Figure 11.1A

Thermal conductivity is a property of matter that describes how quickly thermal energy spreads through a substance. The units of thermal conductivity are Watts per meter-Kelvin, which describes how much energy is transferred over time, distance, and difference in temperature. Metals generally have high thermal conductivity, while air and wood have low thermal conductivities.

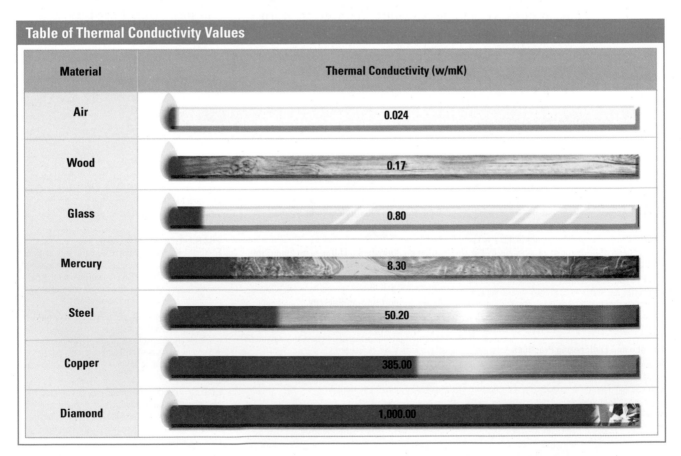

Table of Thermal Conductivity Values

Material	Thermal Conductivity (w/mK)
Air	0.024
Wood	0.17
Glass	0.80
Mercury	8.30
Steel	50.20
Copper	385.00
Diamond	1,000.00

Substances that have low thermal conductivities are known as **thermal insulators**. Thermal energy does not transfer quickly to or from thermal insulators. Firefighters' clothes are protective because they are made of thermal insulators. Thermal energy from the fire transfers very slowly to the clothes and then transfers very slowly to the firefighters' bodies. So, firefighters can be in a fire for sometimes several moments without getting burned. Similarly, when you touch a hot cake in the oven, your finger does not get burned. The cake and your finger form a system through which the flow of energy can be tracked. This is because the cake is transferring thermal energy to your finger very slowly. So, the cake must be a thermal insulator.

Thermal conductivity partly determines whether objects feel hot or cold to you. Suppose that the hallway in your home has a wood floor and the bathroom has a tile floor. The floors throughout your home are at room temperature (about 23°C). When you step on the floor, your feet and the floor form a system through which energy flows. Your feet have a temperature of around 37°C. Because your feet are at a higher temperature, thermal energy is transferred from your feet to the floor.

Wood is an insulator, so the transfer of thermal energy to the wood floor is slow, as shown in Figure 11.1B. You do not perceive a particularly hot or cold sensation when you walk on the wood floor in the hallway. But when you step on the tile floor in the bathroom, it feels much colder. Tile is also an insulator, but it has a higher thermal conductivity than wood, as seen in Figure 11.1B. Energy transfers from your feet to the tile floor at a medium rate, and the sensation you feel from the tile floor feels cooler than the sensation from the wood floor. If a room floor was made of copper, how would the floor feel?

Remember that the wood floor, the tile floor, and copper floor are at the same temperature. They only *feel* like they have different temperatures because their different thermal conductivities draw thermal energy from your feet at different rates.

Figure 11.1B

How warm or cold an object feels is partially caused by differences in thermal conductivity. Objects that have high thermal conductivities draw thermal energy away from your feet quickly and feel cold to you. Objects that have low thermal conductivities draw thermal energy away more slowly and feel warm to you.

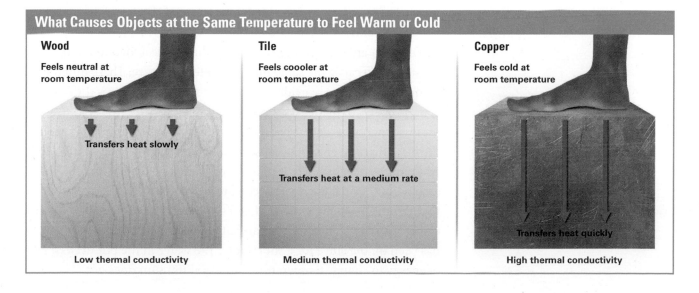

What Causes Objects at the Same Temperature to Feel Warm or Cold

Wood

Feels neutral at room temperature

Transfers heat slowly

Low thermal conductivity

Tile

Feels coooler at room temperature

Transfers heat at a medium rate

Medium thermal conductivity

Copper

Feels cold at room temperature

Transfers heat quickly

High thermal conductivity

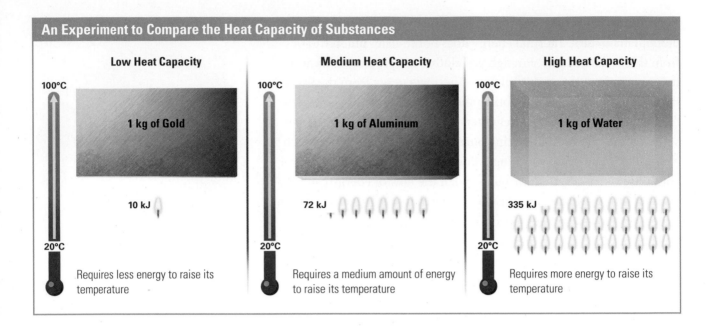

An Experiment to Compare the Heat Capacity of Substances

Low Heat Capacity

100°C

1 kg of Gold

10 kJ

20°C

Requires less energy to raise its temperature

Medium Heat Capacity

100°C

1 kg of Aluminum

72 kJ

20°C

Requires a medium amount of energy to raise its temperature

High Heat Capacity

100°C

1 kg of Water

335 kJ

20°C

Requires more energy to raise its temperature

Figure 11.2A

An experiment provides evidence about heat capacities. The experiment shows that different substances require different amounts of thermal energy to increase their temperatures by the same amount. This evidence leads to the explanation that different substances have different heat capacities and that those heat capacities can be measured.

2. Heat Capacity

Suppose that you are cooking spaghetti. You put cool water in a large aluminum pot on the stove and turn the stove on. After two or three minutes, you know that the pot will be hot enough to burn your hand. But you could still safely dip your fingers into the water. The water might be warm, but not hot. Why do the pot and the water warm up at different rates?

The pot and the water warm up at different rates because of another property of matter. **Heat capacity** is the property of a substance that describes how much thermal energy is needed to change its temperature.

The thought experiment illustrated in Figure 11.2A can help you understand heat capacity. Suppose that you have 1 kg of gold, 1 kg of aluminum, and 1 kg of water, all of which are at 20°C. You place each substance over a heat source and measure how much energy is needed to raise the temperature of the substances to 100°C. You find that you need 10 kJ of energy to raise the temperature of the gold, 72 kJ for the aluminum, and 335 kJ for the water.

Different amounts of thermal energy had to be added to the three substances to cause the same increase in temperature. These different amounts of energy are evidence that these three substances differ in some property of matter. That property is heat capacity. The gold needed the least energy because it has the lowest heat capacity. The water needed the most thermal energy because it has a very high heat capacity. Aluminum's heat capacity is in between that of gold and water, so the amount of thermal energy it needed to reach 100°C was in between the amounts needed by the gold and the water. The differences in heat capacity also explain why you can put your hand in a pot of water that has been on the stove for a short time. The water in the pot needs a lot of energy to change temperature, but the aluminum does not.

Heat capacity can explain some phenomena in nature. For example, if you visit the beach at sunrise and walk on the sand and in the water with bare feet, both the sand and the water will feel cool. If you visit the same beach at noon, the sand will feel much warmer than before, but the water will not feel much different. But how can you confirm that this will be the case?

You can design an experiment to collect evidence about the differences in the heat capacities of sand and water. In this experiment, illustrated in Figure 11.2B, you measure the temperature of the water and the sand at sunrise and at noon. Your data show that the sand's temperature increased more than the water's temperature.

The increase in temperatures of the sand and the water is evidence that thermal energy was transferred to both substances. You can use the following arguments to support the ideas about the thermal energy transferred to the sand and water. The longer the sun shines on the sand and water, the more thermal energy is transferred to the substances. Because the sand and water at the beach are at essentially the same spot on Earth, the same amount of thermal energy is transferred to each in a given amount of time.

However, the data also show that the temperature of the sand increased more than the temperature of the water. From this evidence you can conclude that sand has a lower heat capacity. The evidence supports this explanation because the sand's temperature increased more than the water's did after the substances absorbed the same amount of thermal energy.

Figure 11.2B

Differences in heat capacity explain why sand and water change temperature at different rates. Sand has a low heat capacity, so its temperature increases quickly during the day. Water has a high heat capacity, so its temperature changes more slowly.

The Effects of Heat Capacity of Sand and Water

Sunrise
0 hours of sunlight heating water and sand

Cold water   Cold sand

Noon
5 hours of sunlight heating water and sand

Cool water   Hot sand

Choosing Materials Based on Their Properties

Is high thermal conductivity a good property for matter to have, or is it a bad property? What about high heat capacity? A material's thermal conductivity and heat capacity are not inherently good or bad, but they can determine if the material is good to use in specific situations.

Problem
What materials are useful for insulating a building?

Criteria
Insulating a building means to keep heat from flowing out of the building in the winter and keep heat from flowing into the building in the summer.

Solution
A material that has low thermal conductivity, such as fiberglass, is best for insulating a building. Low thermal conductivity keeps heat from flowing through a substance very quickly.

Problem
What materials are useful for quickly browning the outside of salmon?

Criteria
To quickly brown salmon, heat has to be transferred quickly to the fish.

Solution
A material that has high thermal conductivity, such as copper, is best for quickly browning salmon. High thermal conductivity allows the substance to get hot quickly and to transfer heat to the salmon quickly.

Problem
What material would be most useful for cooling a power plant?

Criteria
When cooling a power plant, a large amount of thermal energy must be absorbed.

Solution
A material that has a high heat capacity, such as water, is best for cooling a power plant. High heat capacity means that a substance can absorb a large amount of thermal energy without its temperature increasing very much.

Problem
What material would be most useful when making a curling iron?

Criteria
A curling iron should require little energy to heat up but should also store little energy so that it cools off quickly after use.

Solution
A material that has a low heat capacity, such as stainless steel, is best for a curling iron. Low heat capacity means that a substance does not need to absorb much thermal energy to increase in temperature.

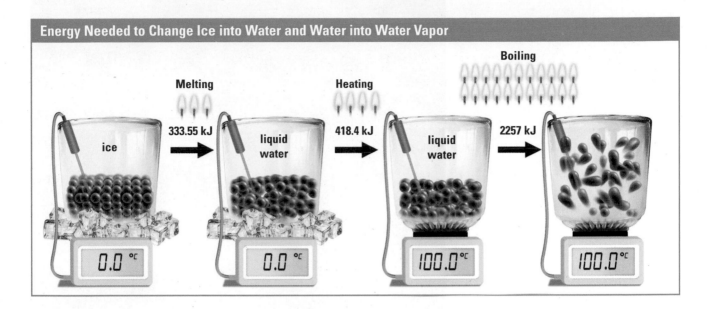

Energy Needed to Change Ice into Water and Water into Water Vapor

Melting

333.55 kJ

ice — liquid water

0.0 °C — 0.0 °C

Heating

418.4 kJ

liquid water

100.0 °C

Boiling

2257 kJ

liquid water

100.0 °C

3. Energy in State Changes

You've probably heard the phrase, "A watched pot never boils." This saying means that something that you are eagerly waiting for seems to take a long time to happen. It is based on the fact that, relatively speaking, a lot of time is needed to boil a pot of water. Why is water so hard to boil?

Recall that the different states of matter have different amounts of energy. A substance has more energy in its gas state than it does in its liquid state, and a substance in its liquid state has more energy than in its solid state. So, for a substance to change from one state to another it has to either gain or lose energy. Thermal energy is absorbed when a solid changes into a liquid or when a liquid changes into a gas. On the other hand, thermal energy is released when a gas changes into a liquid or when a liquid changes into a solid.

The change in energy needed to change the state of a substance is much greater than the change in energy needed to change the temperature of the substance in a given state. Look at Figure 11.3. The amount of energy needed to increase the temperature of 1 kg of water from 0°C to 100°C is about 420 kJ. But the amount of energy to change 1 kg of water at 100°C to water vapor at 100°C is almost 2260 kJ!

Why is so much more energy needed to change state? When thermal energy is added to increase the temperature of a substance, that energy increases the average kinetic energy of the particles in the substance by making the particles move faster. But when thermal energy is added to change the state from solid to liquid or liquid to gas, that energy goes into overcoming the attractions between the particles.

During any change of state, the temperature of the substance does not change even as thermal energy is added or removed. So, a pot of boiling water stays at 100°C even if you keep the stove on. The water does not change temperature because all the added energy is carried away by the particles that transitioned into the gas state.

Figure 11.3

An experiment provides evidence that energy changes happen during changes of state. Water absorbs a lot of energy when it changes from solid to liquid and when it changes from liquid to gas. The absorption of energy is explained by the energy needed to overcome the attractions between particles of matter.

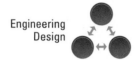

Aerogels are materials that have extremely low thermal conductivities. This flower is sitting on a piece of aerogel above a hot flame. The flower does not burn because the low thermal conductivity of the aerogel keeps thermal energy from being transferred to the flower.

Engineering Design

4. Optimizing Materials

Some winter days are so cold that you can't seem to get warm no matter how many thick layers of clothes you have on. However, someday, you might have a thin coat made with a material that is such a good insulator that you may not have to wear any layers at all and can still be toasty warm. The material is such a good insulator that the first coats made with it were actually too warm! What is this magical insulator?

The insulator is a type of material called an *aerogel*. Aerogels are not natural materials. They were invented by scientists in the 1920s. After their invention, scientists collected data to analyze the properties of aerogels. They interpreted the data and determined that aerogels had two very useful properties and some possibly undesirable properties.

Aerogels' useful properties were that they had extremely low densities and extremely low thermal conductivities. These properties can be very important for certain applications. However, they also found that aerogels did not stand up well to stretching, bending, or compressing forces. Aerogels are brittle and break easily. The ability to withstand forces without breaking is a very useful property. If an object is made from a material that cannot withstand forces, it can break easily during use.

To make aerogels more useful, scientists compared them with another group of materials called *polymers*. Some polymers are natural materials, but many polymers are human made. Nylon is an example of a human-made polymer. Their analysis of the two types of materials showed that polymers stood up well to being stretched and compressed, but did not have very low thermal conductivities.

Beginning in the early 1990s, scientists and engineers worked on optimizing aerogels to combine the convenient properties of aerogels with the convenient properties of polymers. They wanted an aerogel that had a very low thermal conductivity but was also flexible and strong. The engineers first made aerogel blankets, which were fabric-like fiber webs filled with bits of aerogel. These blankets could be wrapped around objects that needed to be insulated.

Engineers continued to look for ways to make flexible aerogels. In 2012, they announced two new kinds of flexible aerogels. One kind was made by coating thin layers of aerogel with polymers. The polymers strengthened the aerogel and the resulting material could be bent and folded. The other new kind of aerogel was made by making aerogels out of polymers. Originally, aerogels were made using a substance called *silica*. Silica is brittle, so the resulting aerogels were brittle. By making aerogels out of polymers, the engineers were able to make a material that was flexible and very strong. A small block of this new aerogel is strong enough to hold up a car!

The new aerogels may be used to make spacesuits and new types of spacecraft. But people on Earth can also use the new aerogels. They can be used to make warm winter coats and provide insulation for refrigerators and freezers. The aerogels might even be used to make lightweight, heat-resistant clothing for firefighters.

The first aerogels were very brittle. They would shatter if compressed, bent, or stretched, which limited their use to applications where no forces would be applied to them.

LESSON SUMMARY

Thermal Properties of Matter

Thermal Conductivity Thermal conductivity describes how quickly thermal energy spreads through a substance. Thermal conductors have high thermal conductivities and thermal insulators have low thermal conductivities.

Heat Capacity Heat capacity describes how much thermal energy is needed to change the temperature of a substance.

Energy in State Changes A substance gains or loses energy when it changes from one state into another.

Optimizing Materials Scientists and engineers developed materials that combined the low thermal conductivities of aerogels with the flexibility of polymers.

Fighting Fire with Science

Help Wanted: Volunteer firefighter. Must be brave, physically fit, and able to work well with others and make quick decisions. Knowledge of CPR (cardiopulmonary resuscitation) and first aid is a plus. All applicants will be required to pass a fire science test to be considered for the job. Study materials for this test are available.

Firefighters often work in dangerous situations where knowledge of science is important. Knowing fire science helps firefighters predict what might happen during a fire.

What is fire science, and why do firefighters need to pass a test in it? Fire science is the study of the physics and chemistry of fire, and it covers topics such as how fires burn and why different methods are used to put out fires. Many volunteer firefighters are required to pass a test in fire science, and full-time firefighters often need a certificate or a college degree in fire science.

Education in fire science is important for firefighters because knowledge of physics and chemistry can help predict what may happen inside a burning building. For example, whether a building will collapse during a fire partly depends on the thermal properties of the building materials.

Most matter expands when heated, but how much the matter expands varies from substance to substance. Steel is a good conductor, and its temperature increases quickly in a fire. Steel beams inside a building can expand so much that they push on walls and weaken them. Brick, on the other hand, is a poor thermal conductor. Thermal energy transfers slowly from one side of a brick to the other, and as a result, the side of the bricks next to the fire expand more than the side of the bricks away from the fire. The uneven expansion causes the wall to lean and possibly collapse. Knowing how building materials respond to heat can help firefighters predict when and how a building may collapse.

Combustion Chemistry

When a building is burning, many different substances can be on fire at once. When substances burn, they are undergoing a chemical reaction called *combustion*. During a chemical reaction, substances (called *reactants*) combine to form new substances, including ash and carbon dioxide. In combustion reactions, one reactant is the substance being burned (such as wood or paper) and the other reactant is always oxygen. Combustion reactions are exothermic, which means they give off energy. This energy is given off as light and thermal energy, which you see as flames and feel as heat.

Not all substances burn, but those that do will combust (that is, light on fire) when they reach a high enough temperature in the presence of oxygen. During a fire, thermal energy given off by already-burning objects can increase the temperature of objects that are not yet burning. If the temperature of the objects that are not burning increases enough, those objects will catch fire. One of the goals of firefighting is to keep objects that are not on fire from catching fire. Firefighters can do that by keeping the temperature down, limiting the supply of oxygen, or both. How? They use water.

You learned that water has a high heat capacity, which means that water needs to absorb a lot of thermal energy for its temperature to increase. When firefighters douse an unburning object with water, the water absorbs thermal energy from the object, which lowers the object's temperature. Meanwhile, the water temperature does not increase very much because of its high heat capacity. If the water keeps the object's temperature low enough, it will not catch fire.

If a fire is not yet too hot, coating objects in water also limits the supply of oxygen to the objects. If an object is covered in water, oxygen cannot reach its surface and combustion cannot start because there is no reactant.

The flames and heat from a fire are energy released by the chemical reaction of combustion. Water prevents the combustion of an object by keeping the object's temperature down and by limiting the supply of oxygen.

Smothering with Water Vapor

Using water to put out a fire probably sounds obvious to you because you know that wet objects do not burn. However, if the temperature of a burning object is high enough, water sprayed on it does not make it wet because the water quickly evaporates. But firefighters keep spraying water because they know that the evaporation of water also helps to prevent and stop combustion.

The evaporation of water prevents combustion reactions by keeping air temperatures down. Every change of state involves a transfer of energy. A lot of energy must be transferred to liquid water to change it into water vapor. So, when the liquid water sprayed by firefighters changes to water vapor, energy is transferred from the air around it, which keeps the air temperature down. If the air temperature is lower, the temperatures of the objects in the room do not increase as much and they may not begin to combust.

The water evaporation can also stop combustion by smothering a fire. Water vapor, like all gases, is matter and takes up space. The water vapor produced when liquid water evaporates takes up a lot more space than liquid water. In a burning room, water vapor can displace, or push away, the air from the room. When the air is pushed away from a fire, the fire's oxygen supply is cut off, and the combustion reaction stops.

Some of the water that firefighters spray into a fire is turned into water vapor, which stops a fire in two ways. The evaporation of the liquid water lowers the air temperature, and the water vapor displaces air and smothers the fire.

Dressed for Success

Firefighters may often be in stressful situations and need to make quick decisions based on their knowledge of fire science. Since there can be a lot for the firefighters to think about, it helps that they do not have to contemplate the science behind the equipment that they wear.

Engineers with knowledge of fire science have developed specialized gear to keep firefighters safe. The gear has two main functions: it needs to keep firefighters from getting burned, and it needs to allow body heat to escape so that the firefighter does not overheat. Today, firefighter gear is constructed of three layers, which work together to protect and keep a firefighter comfortable.

The outer layer of the gear is made of a tough, fire-resistant material that protects both the firefighter and the other layers. The next layer is the moisture barrier, which keeps water and other liquids from soaking into the equipment. This layer is made of a breathable material that allows body heat to escape. The innermost layer is the thermal liner, which is made of a material that is a thermal insulator. The thermal liner keeps the fire's thermal energy from being transferred to a firefighter. It is also breathable and absorbs sweat to keep the firefighter comfortable.

If you ever want to become a firefighter, remember that there's a lot more to the job than spraying water on a burning building. You need to know some important science—science that can save your life and the lives of others! ◆

Firefighters wear gear that protects them from getting burned and keeps them from overheating. The gear was engineered with knowledge of fire science.

Learning Resources

The whole Earth and everything beyond it is the subject of science. This set of learning resources includes some essential thinking tools you need in order to explore, investigate, and explain how the world works.

Laboratory Safety

To think like a scientist, you have to act like one. This means making observations, experimenting, and carrying out other types of investigations. The same goes for solving engineering problems. You have to propose, build, test, and improve your designed solutions. All of these things are fun and interesting, but there can be risks involved in handling equipment and materials. What do you have to be aware of to stay safe when practicing science and engineering?

Your teacher may ask you to sign a Science Safety Contract and discuss it with your parents. This is an important first step towards science safety. Before working in the science lab, review these rules.

☑ Understand the hazards and rules for a particular investigation before you begin.

☑ Make sure your personal clothing is safe for the lab. Do not wear loose clothing, especially long sleeves.

☑ Wear closed shoes to protect your feet.

☑ If you have long hair, tie it back.

☑ Wear safety goggles, protective aprons, and gloves when required by your teacher.

☑ Transport and handle all equipment and chemicals as directed by your teacher.

☑ Report breaks, spills, or other accidents to your teacher right away.

☑ Report injuries to your teacher right away, and follow your school's first aid procedures.

☑ Know where safety equipment is in the lab you use and when or how to use it.

☑ Dispose of materials in the designated containers at the end of the investigation.

☑ Clean up your work area and wash your hands at the conclusion of the investigation.

☑ Know what to do in case of a hazardous event such as a power failure, earthquake, or emergency evacuation.

☑ Be aware of safety for everyone in your group.

Planning Investigations

Designing your own investigations is a chance to act like a real scientist—and that includes keeping yourself and others safe.

☑ Choose equipment and materials that your teacher tells you are safe to use.

☑ Plan how you will handle the materials safely, including how you will dispose of materials that cannot be used again.

☑ Include safety steps when writing your procedure.

☑ Always obtain permission from your teacher before carrying out your investigation plan.

Field Trip Safety

Some of the most important thigs you can do to stay safe on a field trip is to be prepared in advance.

☑ Return a signed parental permission form to your teacher before a field trip.

☑ Check the weather forecast so that you can choose appropriate clothing. If there is any possibility of severe weather, make sure there is a plan for taking shelter.

☑ No matter the weather, wear footwear that encloses and protects your feet.

☑ Wear clothing, hats, or sunscreen to protect yourself from sunburn. Remember, you can get burned on a cloudy day as well as on a sunny one.

☑ Learn in advance the types of organisms you may encounter that are dangerous and should be avoided.

☑ During the field trip, don't touch plants unless instructed by your teacher or guide.

☑ Know how to get first aid for poisonous plants and animal stings and bites.

☑ Never eat or put in your mouth anything you find outdoors without permission.

☑ Wash up carefully after an outdoor science activity.

☑ If the area you visited has ticks, inspect your clothing and body for ticks at the end of the field trip.

Safety for Living Things in the Classroom

When you investigate living things, you can't just think about yourself. You have to think about the organisms in your care, too.

☑ Understand appropriate and humane treatment of animals. This includes selecting a suitable container to house the animals and making sure the temperature is within the proper range for that species.

☑ Help make sure that animals kept in the science classroom are provided with adequate water, food, and that their containers are kept clean.

☑ Keep handling of animals to a minimum and never disturb sleeping animals.

☑ Plan for appropriate care of living things over weekends, holidays, and vacations.

☑ Don't bring personal pets or unknown plants or animals into school, as they may be poisonous, venomous, or negatively affect the other living things in your science classroom.

☑ Never carry out investigations that will cause discomfort, pain, or disease to animals.

☑ Return native wild species to their natural environment.

☑ Never release non-native species into the natural environment.

☑ Wash your hands and surfaces after handling living things.

Asking Questions

Asking questions is central to science. Scientists learn about the natural world by asking questions and trying to answer them. As scientists learn about the natural world, they come up with more questions to answer. What kinds of questions do scientists ask, and how can you learn to ask them?

Questions drive the scientific process. Scientists ask testable questions to guide their research and gain scientific knowledge. This knowledge can lead to new questions to be answered.

Questions Scientists ask questions about the natural world and about current scientific ideas. The types of questions scientists might ask include: What causes a particular phenomenon? How do different factors affect observations? Why did an event occur?

Testability Science can only answer questions that are testable, which means that a scientist must be able to gather evidence to answer the question. To determine if a question is testable, ask yourself: How can the answer to this question be determined? Would the answer be a fact or an opinion? Can I design an investigation to answer this question?

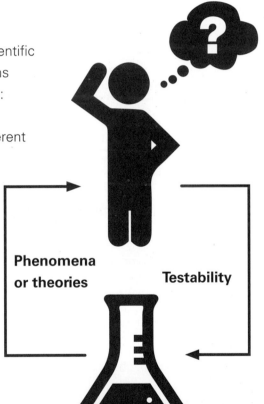

Phenomena or theories

Testability

Science Testable questions can lead to new scientific knowledge, which can lead to new questions. Ask yourself: How can I gather data to answer this question? How well does this data support the answer? Are there other possible answers that this data could support?

Phenomena and Theories Scientists ask questions based on observed phenomena and scientific theories. The questions may be asked to clarify ideas or to introduce new ideas. Ask yourself: What other questions does this new understanding raise? How does this explanation relate to other scientific ideas or theories?

If you go to cities around the world, you will probably see a couple of pigeons or maybe a couple of hundreds of pigeons. Unlike many other wild animals, pigeons do not seem to mind living around people. How might you research pigeons to find out why that is?

Asking Questions You can start your research by asking questions. These questions might include: Why are pigeons more common in cities than other species of birds? What birds lived in an area before an area was developed? How does the diet of a city pigeon compare with the diet of a pigeon living in the country?

You can ask testable questions to learn about the natural environment. For example, if you are studying pigeons, you might ask questions to compare the diet of city pigeons with the diet of country pigeons.

Determining Testability After scientists come up with questions, they pick at least one question to investigate further. Suppose that you wanted to find the answer to the question "How does the diet of a city pigeon compare with the diet of a pigeon living in the country?" The question you are trying to answer must be testable. To determine this, you might ask: What kind of investigation will help answer the question? What evidence do I have to gather to answer the question?

Conducting Science You may want to start your investigation on pigeon diets by reviewing research done by other scientists. Some questions you may consider are: What other research has been done on pigeon diets? What methods did other scientists use? How will my investigation differ or improve on previous investigations?

Coming Up with Phenomena and Theories While investigating pigeon diets, you may try to connect your observations with known phenomena and theories. Ask yourself: What do my observations say about pigeon nutrition? How does a pigeon's diet compare with that of other species of birds? How do my results relate to phenomena like the adaptation of pigeons to their environment?

The fact that asking questions in science often leads to new questions may seem frustrating, but it is actually a good thing. The cycle of questions leading to more questions means that science will always grow and improve.

Defining Problems

Before engineers can begin designing a solution, they have to define the problem they are trying to solve. By thoroughly defining the problem, engineers know exactly what qualities the solution must have and what obstacles they may need to work around to achieve the solution. What do engineers have to do to define a problem?

Defining problems involves clearly identifying the problem, the boundaries and components of the problem, and the criteria and constraints of the problem's solution.

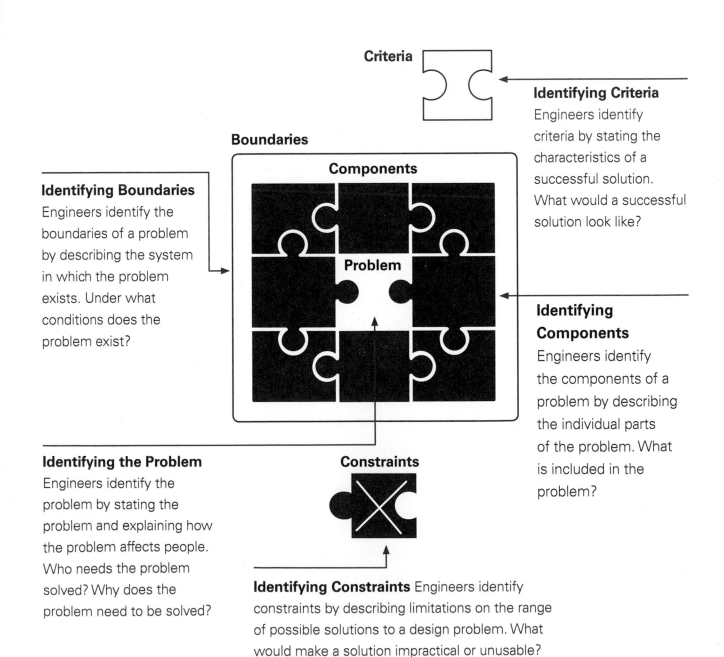

Criteria

Identifying Criteria
Engineers identify criteria by stating the characteristics of a successful solution. What would a successful solution look like?

Boundaries

Components

Identifying Boundaries
Engineers identify the boundaries of a problem by describing the system in which the problem exists. Under what conditions does the problem exist?

Problem

Identifying Components
Engineers identify the components of a problem by describing the individual parts of the problem. What is included in the problem?

Identifying the Problem
Engineers identify the problem by stating the problem and explaining how the problem affects people. Who needs the problem solved? Why does the problem need to be solved?

Constraints

Identifying Constraints Engineers identify constraints by describing limitations on the range of possible solutions to a design problem. What would make a solution impractical or unusable?

Defining a problem by identifying boundaries, components, criteria, and constraints is the first step in finding a good solution. Making healthy lunches that students will eat is a problem that many schools struggle with.

If you could buy anything to eat at your school cafeteria, what would you get? You probably want foods like pizza and cake. But pizza, cake, and other popular foods tend not to be healthy. What can school cafeterias do to encourage students to eat better foods?

Identifying the Problem Kids across the country eat most of their lunches at school. School cafeterias try to provide nutritious meals, but often the healthy parts of the meals end up in the trash. So, the problem is providing healthy foods that students will eat.

Identifying the Boundaries and Components The boundaries of this problem surround the school and the people in it. The components of the problem include the food, the students, school kitchen, kitchen staff, and administrators. The students eat the food that is prepared by the kitchen staff, while the administrators purchase the food and approve the meals. However, many things are not important to the problem, such as the color of the walls and whether lunch tables have chairs or benches to sit on.

Identifying Criteria and Constraints The criteria and constraints of a successful solution can be organized in a table.

Criteria	Constraints
• meals are nutritious	• budget (need to afford food)
• at least 85% of students eat the meal	• kitchen (need right equipment to prepare food)
• meal plan has variety	• time to prepare food

Solving the problem of serving healthy school lunches is not easy, but understanding the problem will help find a solution. If the solution is successful, it will be good and delicious.

Developing and Using Models

Scientists use models to explain and understand natural phenomena. Scientific models can be physical models such as a globe or a drawing of a cell. Scientific models can also be conceptual models, which means that they are collections of related ideas. For example, the big bang theory is a conceptual model to describe how the universe began. How can you learn to develop models the way a scientist would?

When scientists develop a model, they identify the components of the model, describe the relationship between the components, and explain the connections between the model and the real world.

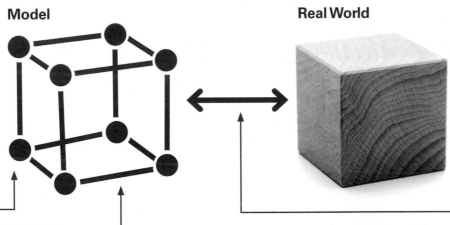

Model

Real World

Components Components are the parts that make up the model. Each component represents something in the real world. When you develop a model, you have to decide which parts of the real word are important to represent and which are not.

Relationships The relationships in a model describe how the components interact. When you develop a model, the relationships you describe help you understand how the components of the model work together and make predictions about the model.

Connections The connections between a model and the natural phenomenon it represents make the model useful. Models simplify the phenomenon to make it easier to observe, understand, predict, or quantify.

Scientists develop some models by combining what they have learned about a particular phenomenon. However, sometimes scientists use a simple, common object as a model to help explain something in nature. For example, lasagna could be used as a model for sedimentary rock. The common object used as a model has some similar features to the phenomenon it is modeling, but it generally cannot explain everything about the phenomenon. How is lasagna a good model for sedimentary rock formation, and how does it fall short?

Components The layers of lasagna represent the layers of rock in sedimentary rock. The different layers in lasagna—noodle, cheese, and meat—can represent different kinds of rock.

Relationships Lasagna layers are distinct, so you can see each layer. One relationship in this model is the order of the layers. Using this relationship, you can see how the lasagna was built even if you did not see it being assembled. You know the lasagna was built up so that the first layer is at the bottom and the last layer is at the top.

Scientists develop models to explain or describe natural phenomena. Lasagna is a useful model for describing the structure and formation of sedimentary rock, but it cannot compare in terms of timescale.

Connections The structure of the lasagna and the way it was built are similar to the structure and the formation of sedimentary rock. The layers in sedimentary rock are distinct and easy to see. Sedimentary rock is also built up with the oldest rock layers at the bottom and the newest rock layers at the top.

However, lasagna and sedimentary rock have important differences. A person can build a lasagna in about 15 minutes, but sedimentary rock may take millions of years to build up. Studying the layers in sedimentary rock can tell you about the environments in which the layers formed. Studying lasagna layers cannot tell you much of anything, except for which layer you like the best!

Planning and Carrying Out Investigations

Scientific research involves conducting investigations. Scientists use many different methods for planning investigations, but every method has common elements. One method is outlined here. The elements in this method are common to other methods that a scientist might use. What things should you consider when planning an investigation, and what might happen when carrying out an investigation?

The steps in planning and carrying out an investigation can happen in any order and can be repeated multiple times.

Identifying Evidence Identify what evidence you need to answer your question; only some evidence will be useful. If you were investigating why birds sing in the morning, you might observe birds in the morning and also at other times of the day to see what else they do.

Identifying the Phenomenon

The subject of your investigation might be a phenomenon to be explained, a question to be answered, or a design to be tested. You might try to answer the question, "Why do birds sing in the morning?"

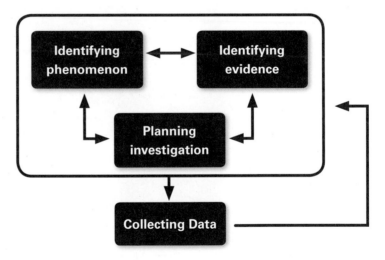

Planning the Investigation

Describe how you will gather data that will serve as evidence toward a claim. Create a specific list of steps to follow. For example, you could set up a camera in a park. Then, you could watch the video, marking down bird activity such as singing, feeding, and flying.

Collecting Data Collect your data by following the steps outlined in your investigation plan. Be sure to keep your data organized. For an investigation about birds singing, you could make a table with rows marked with time of day and columns marked with various bird behaviors.

Refining the Plan Refining your investigation plan means making changes to improve it. Ask yourself questions such as: Was the data accurately and precisely collected? Does the data support a claim about the phenomenon that I am investigating? If the answers are "no," then you need to change the investigation's plan.

Your science class is having a toy car race to investigate forces and motion. Each team of students is given a kit with which to build a toy car, but the design of each car is up to the team members. What plan do you come up with for your investigation?

Identifying the Phenomenon Together your class brainstorms factors that may affect the speed of a toy car. The class decides to investigate how a car's shape affects the car's speed.

Identifying Evidence Your class identifies the data to collect: which car shape wins each race. These data can then be analyzed to find evidence for which shape is best for a fast car.

Specifying the Steps The class comes up with the following steps:

1. Each of the 15 teams will make a car, and each car will have a different shape.

2. Cars will race on a track that has five lanes.

3. In preliminary rounds, five cars will race at least two times. The first car to win twice will advance to the final round.

4. In the final round, the preliminary round winners will race. The first car to win twice will be declared the best shape.

Collecting Data The winners of the preliminary rounds include your wedge-shaped car, a minivan-shaped car, and a car shaped like a cone. However, you notice that the car in the leftmost lane always finishes last.

Refining the Plan Because the leftmost car always loses, the answer to the question, "Were the data accurately collected?" is "no." The class runs trial races, which show that cars run slower in the outside lanes. The class revises the investigation plan. Instead of racing five cars, you race three cars using only the center lanes. Then you will have two semifinal rounds and one final round.

Your wedge-shaped car wins its preliminary round and its semifinal before barely losing to the cone-shaped car in the final round. The race is so close that some classmates think the investigation may need more revision to be sure of the winning design. What other revisions could you make?

Scientists plan and carry out investigations to gather evidence to support their explanations. You can gather evidence about which toy car design is fastest by holding a series of races and recording which design wins each race.

Analyzing and Interpreting Data

Scientists and engineers collect data in many different ways. In order to connect data to their investigation, scientists and engineers have to analyze and interpret the data. How can you think like a scientist or an engineer to make sense of data you collect?

Analyzing and interpreting data involves organizing the data, identifying relationships within the data, and then interpreting the data based on the relationships found.

Organizing Data Scientists and engineers organize their data in tables or graphs to help them make sense of it. Data that include written descriptions might be organized in data tables, while data that show changes over time might be organized in a line graph, bar graph, or pie chart.

Identifying Relationships Scientists and engineers identify relationships by looking for patterns in the organized data. They ask themselves questions such as: What parts of the data show changes? Are there data that change in regular ways? Do two different kinds of data change in similar ways?

Interpreting Data Scientists and engineers interpret data by drawing conclusions from the relationships identified. They may ask: What could be causing the patterns in the data? What could happen if the patterns continue? Could the patterns have more than one explanation?

Your science class is studying a nearby lake. You collect measurements of air and water temperature at the same place at the same time every day for a year.

Organizing Data You divide the measurements into air temperatures and water temperatures for each month. Then you find the average air temperature and water temperature for each month. Finally, you organize the average temperatures into a data table.

Both air temperature and water temperature change throughout the year. But you are not sure how the temperature changes are related. So, you graph the temperatures over time.

Identifying Relationships You can see a relationship between air and water temperature in the graph. The changes in temperatures follow similar patterns, but the patterns do not line up. The water graph is about a month behind the air graph. The air graph reaches its highest temperature in July, but the water graph does not reach its highest temperature until August.

Interpreting Data After studying your graph, you propose an explanation for why air and water temperatures follow a similar pattern. You propose that the changing air temperatures cause changes in water temperature. That is why the temperature changes follow similar patterns. Furthermore, you suggest the patterns do not line up because water changes temperature slower than air does.

The data in this table are organized using a line graph. You can see a relationship in the data on the graph; the changes in air and water temperature follow a similar pattern. How would you interpret this relationship?

Average Lake Air and Water Temperatures

Month	Air Temp. (°C)	Water Temp. (°C)
Jan (1)	-5.6	6.1
Feb (2)	-4.4	3.3
Mar (3)	-1.1	1.7
Apr (4)	7.2	2.2
May (5)	12.2	3.3
June (6)	18.3	6.7
July (7)	21.1	10.0
Aug (8)	17.8	16.7
Sept (9)	12.8	15.6
Oct (10)	4.4	13.9
Nov (11)	-0.6	10.0
Dec (12)	-2.2	7.8

Using Mathematical and Computational Thinking

Scientists use mathematical and computational thinking in many ways. They might use math to analyze data, make predictions, or build scientific models. Furthermore, some scientific laws and principles can be expressed as equations. For example, Newton's second law of motion can be expressed as force = mass × acceleration. In each of these situations, scientists use math to represent observed systems. How can you use math to represent systems you encounter in science and your everyday life?

When scientists use math to describe a system, they state what parts of the system are represented, describe how numbers and symbols are used to model the system, and then use math to analyze the system.

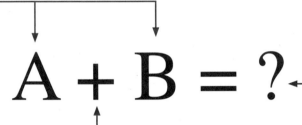

Representation In math, representation means to use symbols (such as letters) to stand in for variables in a system. For example, Newton's law describes the relationship between three variables: force, mass, and acceleration. These variables are represented by the letters F, m, and a, respectively.

Mathematical Modeling Mathematical modeling means to find how the variables in a system are related mathematically. For example, the relationship between the variables in Newton's second law is represented mathematically by the equation $F = m \times a$. You could use graphs to find relationships or you could see if the variables are related by an equation. Scientists sometimes build computer simulations that connect many different variables.

Analysis Analyzing a mathematical system means to find patterns in the system. The pattern can be used to make predictions or support claims. Analyzing a system might involve solving equations, finding trends in graphs, or using a computer simulation. For example, you can use the equation for Newton's second law to analyze how a change in force affects acceleration. If a force on an object is doubled, the acceleration of the object will also double.

The equation for Newton's second law of motion, like many equations in science, can be applied in many situations. However, scientists sometimes develop equations that describe only the situation that they are studying. How can you develop an equation to describe the change in a rabbit population in an ecosystem?

Representation The first step in developing a rabbit population equation is to identify and represent the variables in the system. You might pick the following variables and representations:

- b represents the number of rabbits born

- e represents the number of rabbits eaten by predators

- d represents the number of rabbits that died of natural causes

- Δp represents the change in rabbit population (The Greek letter delta (Δ) often means "change in," so Δp means change in p, the rabbit population.)

Mathematical Modeling To mathematically model the change in rabbit population, you have to decide how each variable affects the population. Does the variable increase or decrease the population? What mathematical operations are the equivalents to increasing and decreasing a value? An increase in population would add to the population, and a decrease would subtract from the population. Births increase the population and deaths decrease the population. So an equation for the change in population would be:

$$\Delta p = b - e - d$$

Scientists often use math to represent the systems they are studying. An equation can be used to find the change in a rabbit population in an ecosystem. The equation can be analyzed to predict how the rabbit population might change under various conditions.

Analysis To analyze the accuracy of your equation, you might solve the equation to see how the number of rabbits changes each month. Then you might draw conclusions, such as the rabbit population increases in the summer months due to a rise in births. You could also analyze the equation by using it to make predictions. What would happen if the predators in the ecosystem died? What would happen if a disease spread throughout the rabbit population?

Constructing Explanations

As they work, scientists construct explanations of phenomena. Constructing explanations is similar to engaging in argument from evidence but has key differences. When scientists engage in argument, they are using evidence to defend an idea. When scientists construct explanations, they are using evidence and reasoning to build an idea. How can you learn to think like a scientist when constructing explanations for the phenomena you experience?

Scientists construct explanations by using reasoning to describe the connections between phenomena and evidence.

Phenomenon When scientists construct explanations, the phenomenon is the event or observation that they are explaining. For example, scientists might try to explain why honeybees are dying off.

Arguments for the Explanation Scientists use arguments to support their explanation. An argument is made up of a claim, evidence for that claim, and reasons why the evidence supports the claim. For example, scientists might claim that more flowering plants are sprayed with pesticides now than ever before. Evidence supporting that claim may include data about historic and present day sales of pesticides.

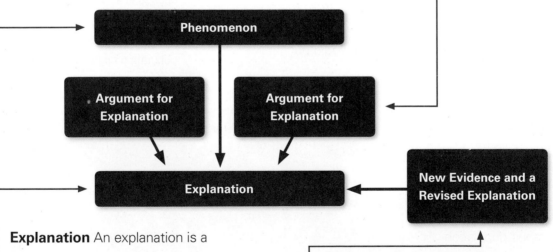

Explanation An explanation is a statement composed of one or more arguments that describe how or why the phenomenon happens. An example explanation might be: Honeybees are dying off because of the use of pesticides on flowering plants.

New Evidence and a Revised Explanation After scientists have proposed an explanation, new evidence may arise that makes the scientists change their explanation. Perhaps scientists studying honeybees learn that a disease is spreading throughout honeybee populations. They may revise their explanation to include the disease as a reason why the bees are dying off.

You can construct explanations for phenomena that you observe in your everyday life. For example, suppose you have a banana bread recipe that you make successfully all the time. Your friend who lives in Denver, Colorado tries to make the bread, but the batter overflows and the bread is gummy. What causes the differences?

Phenomenon Your friend says that he followed your recipe exactly. You determine that the only variable that changed between your loaf and his loaf was where the loaves were made. So, the phenomenon that you are trying to explain is why the same recipe produces a nice loaf at your home but makes a mess at your friend's.

Explanation You and your friend talk to figure out the differences between your homes. You know some differences, such as the number of bedrooms in the homes, will not cause changes in how bread bakes. You rule out those differences as factors. Eventually, you come up with an explanation. The recipe failed because your friend in Denver lives at a higher altitude than you do.

Scientists construct explanations of phenomena and use arguments to support their explanations. An explanation as to why a banana bread recipe fails in Denver is that the city is at a higher altitude. Therefore, Denver has a lower air pressure.

Arguments for the Explanation The main argument for your explanation is that the higher altitude in Denver causes the banana bread batter to rise too much during the baking process. You learned that the air pressure at higher altitudes is lower. When the air pressure that is pushing down on the batter is lower, the air bubbles produced by the baking soda in the batter can get bigger. The bigger bubbles cause the batter to rise too much and overflow the pan.

New Evidence and a Revised Explanation You tell your friend your explanation, and he has another idea. He explains that the lower pressure in Denver allows liquids to evaporate more quickly. This new evidence causes you to rethink your explanation.

Your explanation is not completely wrong, but it needs to be improved. Your explanation accounts for the batter overflowing but does not explain why the loaf was gummy. You cut yourself a piece of banana bread while you think about how quicker evaporation of liquid in the batter might affect the bread's texture. Hopefully, the snack will help you come up with a more complete explanation!

Designing Solutions

An engineer's primary job is to design solutions to problems. You use these solutions all the time. For example, an engineer designed the calculator you use in math class. Engineers have also designed bus routes, airplane seats, and water treatment plants. How do engineers come up with their solutions? And how do they know which solution is best?

Engineers generate a lot of ideas for solutions. They then narrow down those solutions to find the best one to a given problem.

Possible Solutions Engineers think of many different solutions to a single problem. All the possible solutions should be based on scientific knowledge. They may ask themselves: What scientific ideas are related to the problem? What scientific ideas will help or hinder finding a solution to this problem?

Evaluating Solutions Evaluating solutions is the process of comparing the solutions to the criteria and the constraints. In this step, engineers determine how well each solution meets the criteria and fits within the constraints.

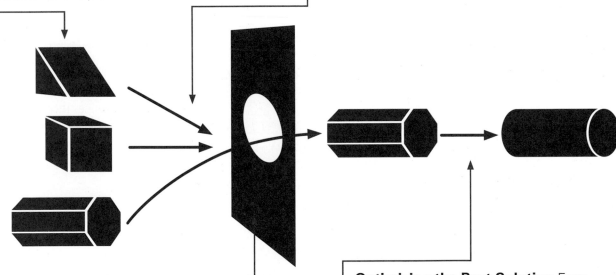

Criteria and Constraints Criteria are the requirements that must be met for an engineering solution to be successful. Constraints are limitations on an engineering solution. Criteria and constraints describe which possible solutions are good and which are not as good. Criteria and constraints may be redefined based on things learned during the designing process.

Optimizing the Best Solution Even after picking the best solution to a problem, engineers need to refine the solution. During this step, engineers test their solution and make changes based on the results of the tests. The solution may need to go through several iterations to make it the best possible solution.

Suppose that your class is having a fundraiser, and the class decides to sell cookie cutters in the shape of the school's logo. Before you can sell the cutters, you have to make them. And before you make the cutters, you have to decide what material to use.

Criteria and Constraints The criteria for the material include that it has to have the ability to be shaped in the form of your school's logo, and it has to hold its shape. Other criteria are that the material has to be able to cut cookie dough and last a long time.

Some of the constraints for the material are that the students in your class have to be able to make the cutter from the material and that the material is not too expensive.

Possible Solutions Science can help you come up with possible materials to use for the cookie cutters. Copper is a possible material because it is a malleable metal. It can be bent into the right shape. Stainless steel is another malleable metal.

Evaluating Solutions You use the criteria and constraints to evaluate the solutions. Copper fits the following criteria: It can be shaped, it can hold its shape, and it will last a long time. It fits the constraint that students can shape it, but it is relatively expensive. So, it does not fit within the inexpensive constraint. Stainless steel fits the following criteria: It can be shaped, it can hold its shape, and it will last a long time. It fits within the constraints that students can shape it, and it is inexpensive. You decide to use stainless steel.

Optimizing the Best Solution Using stainless steel, you make a prototype cookie cutter. The prototype is made out of a 1-cm wide strip of steel. You make cookies using the prototype and find that it does not hold its shape. The narrow strip bends too easily.

You make a second prototype that is made out of a 2.5-cm wide strip of steel. You test the second prototype and find that it holds its shape well. This prototype is determined to have the best design.

You and your classmates make 200 cookie cutters that are identical to the second prototype. You sell the cutters and raise enough money for a field trip to a science museum.

Engineers compare solutions to the criteria and constraints to determine which solution is most likely to solve the problem. The best solution is then optimized through testing and refining. You can use a similar process when designing your own solutions.

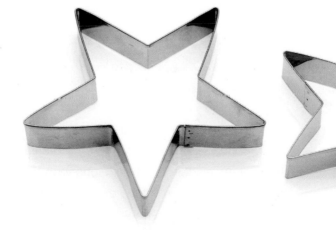

Engaging in Argument from Evidence

Engaging in argument is a key element of scientific practice. However, the arguments that scientists and engineers have with each other are not like typical arguments. They are not trying just to prove each other wrong. Rather, they are trying to collaboratively find the best explanation or model, or design the best solution. What kinds of thinking and statements are needed for a strong argument?

Strong scientific arguments have three key components—a claim, evidence for that claim, and reasoning as to why the evidence supports the claim.

Claim The claim is the statement that the argument is attempting to convince people to believe. Scientists might make claims about an explanation of a phenomenon, such as why snowflakes are always symmetrical. Or, they may make claims about a model, such as a food web. Engineers might make claims about which material is best for their design.

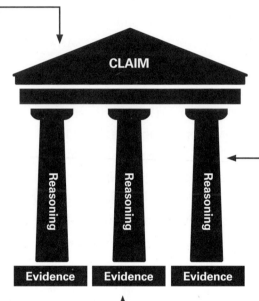

Reasoning Evidence alone is not enough to convince people of a claim. Reasoning shows how the evidence is connected to the claim, using logic or scientific concepts. The reasoning might, for example, explain why a diagram of the structure of water molecules supports the claim that all snowflakes are symmetric.

Evidence Evidence is the data or observations that support a claim. Relevant measurements, tables, and graphs can often be used as strong evidence for a claim. Generally, the more evidence there is for a claim, the stronger the argument is.

Refutation Of course, no argument is one sided. There is often an opportunity for someone to refute an argument. A refutation provides new evidence, which, along with reasoning, shows that the claim is incorrect. A refutation may also provide a different interpretation of the evidence, showing that it does not support the original claim.

Your friend Jerome sent you a photo with his phone. "Check out this great rainbow!" Look at Jerome's photo, and make an argument about the weather Jerome is experiencing. Try asking yourself questions as you develop your argument.

To make your claim, ask yourself, "What kind of weather is in this photo?" Next, identify your evidence by asking, "What specific things do I see in this photo that support my claim?" Then develop your reasoning by asking, "How do the things I pointed out as evidence support my claim?" Your argument might look something like this:

Your friend sends you a photo of a rainbow. You can develop an argument of what the weather was like at the moment the photo was taken by asking yourself a set of questions.

Claim Jerome took the photo while weather was clearing up after a rainstorm.

Evidence There are no visible raindrops in the photo, and the ground does not look wet. However, there is a rainbow in the sky. There are also dark clouds on the right side of the sky, but not on the left side of the sky.

Reasoning Since there are no visible raindrops in the photo and the ground does not look wet, it was probably not raining right when the photo was taken. However, rainbows only form when there are water drops in the sky, and usually form immediately after it has been raining. Also, dark clouds like the ones in the photo usually produce rain. But since the clouds only cover half of the sky in the photograph, the storm seems to be moving away from the place the photograph was taken.

Do you agree with this argument? If not, come up with a refutation. Then, the next time you make a claim, do it like a scientist or engineer—back it up with evidence and reasoning.

Obtaining, Evaluating, and Communicating Information

Scientists spend a lot of time obtaining, evaluating, and communicating information. In fact, most people use this process every day. For example, when you read, you are obtaining information. You then evaluate the information you read by determining if it is accurate and important. You also might communicate this information by talking about it with a friend. How does obtaining, evaluating, and communicating information help scientists do their work?

A scientist may obtain, evaluate, and communicate information during any point in an investigation.

Obtaining Information
When scientists gather information, they may ask: Where can we find information about this topic? What different kinds of information are available?

Evaluating Information
Scientists evaluate information by asking questions like these: What does this information mean? Is this information reliable? Is this information relevant?

Communicating Information Before scientists share information, they must decide how to communicate it. They may ask themselves: What is the best way to communicate this information? Should we give lectures, or should we write about it? Should we make a video? Or will a graph, photo, or mathematical equation better communicate the information?

Although scientific research is generally thought of as being a good thing, it can be controversial. One controversial topic in astronomy is the placement of telescopes on a dormant volcano in Hawaii named Mauna Kea. Some of the world's best telescopes are already on Mauna Kea. Astronomers consider the volcano to be one of the best places in the world for telescopes, and they would like to build additional ones there. However, some Hawaiians consider the volcano to be sacred and do not want any more telescopes built on it. Do you think astronomers should put more telescopes on Mauna Kea? How would you decide?

Obtaining Information *Where can you find information about this topic?* Probably the easiest place for you to get information is the Internet. You can also check specialized resources at the library. *What different kinds of information are available?* Scientists, the Hawaiian government, and Hawaiian residents are some of the groups that provide information on this topic.

Evaluating Information *What does this information mean?* Some information will tell you why Mauna Kea is such a great place for telescopes, while other information will explain the negative impact of telescopes on the volcano. *Is this information reliable?* Consider where the information is from. Websites from universities, the government, and major media outlets tend to be reliable sources. *Is this information relevant?* Once you have information from reliable sources, think about whether the information supports either side of the Mauna Kea controversy. If the information does not help one side or the other, the information is probably not relevant.

Communicating Information *What is the best way to communicate this information?* If you are communicating your opinion about telescopes on Mauna Kea to your class, you might make a poster or explain your reasoning in a class discussion. But if you are a Hawaiian citizen, you might want to write a letter to the state governor that could influence the future of Mauna Kea.

People obtain, evaluate, and communicate information all the time. Scientists and the public need to obtain and evaluate reliable information when making decisions on controversial topics, such as the placement of telescopes on Mauna Kea.

Patterns

Patterns play a key role in many scientific investigations. Scientists make sense of data they have collected by trying to recognize and analyze patterns. Often, noticing a pattern in nature will spark a series of questions. All patterns have an underlying cause, which can be uncovered by a scientific investigation. What patterns can you recognize in the following natural phenomena?

How can the different patterns in finches' beaks help you understand how a species can adapt to its environment? When Charles Darwin discovered different species of finches on the Galapagos Islands, he noticed that each species had a beak that was well-suited to its diet. The differently shaped beaks led Darwin to discover the pattern that exists between the shape of a finch's beak and its individual diet. This pattern seemed to point to a species' ability to adapt to its environment.

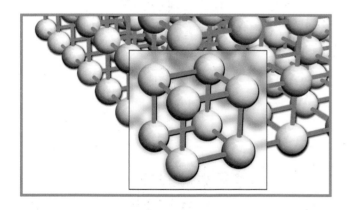

How is the microscopic pattern of table salt related to the macroscopic, or easily visible, shape of a salt crystal? You can see that each individual crystal has a cube-like structure. On the atomic level, sodium and chlorine atoms are arranged in a regular, repeating pattern that is shaped like a cube. The way a substance appears to the human eye is often determined by its atomic level structure.

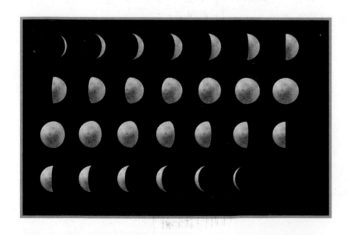

How can understanding patterns help you predict the different shapes of lunar phases? The apparent shape of the moon from Earth is determined by the positions of Earth, the moon, and the sun. Over the course of about a month, the moon transitions from a new moon to a full moon and back to a new moon in a repeating pattern. Because the apparent change in the moon's shape always follows the same pattern, you can predict when the next full moon will take place!

Cause and Effect

Looking for cause-and-effect relationships can help immensely when you are designing experiments to answer scientific questions or testing engineering solutions. Think about these three questions from different areas of science. What experiments might people design to test them?

Do magnetic fields cause compass needles to rotate? Suppose you measure the direction a compass needle points under normal conditions. Then you could add a magnetic field and look at the change in the behavior of the needle. Identifying cause-and-effect relationships allows you to make predictions about related situations. You could predict that a compass needle will always point north because Earth's magnetic field prompts the needle to point in a consistent direction.

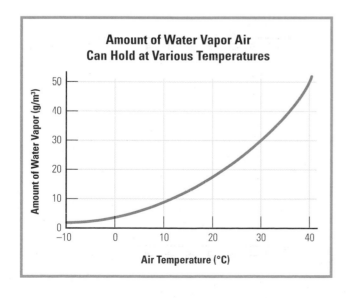

Does the introduction of wolves cause elk populations to decrease? Biologists might measure the size of the elk population before and after wolves settled in an area. While cause-and-effect relationships may seem obvious, they are not always true. For example, climate change could have resulted in the loss of nutrient rich grasses for elk to eat, leading to a decrease in the elk population.

Amount of Water Vapor Air Can Hold at Various Temperatures

Amount of Water Vapor (g/m³) vs. Air Temperature (°C)

Does an increase in temperature indoors cause humidity to rise? First, you could measure the current humidity in a room. Then you could increase the air temperature of the room and measure if there was a change in humidity. It is important to only change the air temperature so there is only one cause to observe the effects of.

Scale, Proportion, and Quantity

Systems occur at different measures of size, time, and energy. Part of science is recognizing that different objects and situations occur at different scales, in different proportions, and in different amounts. Something that can be observed at one scale may not be observable at another scale. How can scale, proportion, and quantity help you understand phenomena in science?

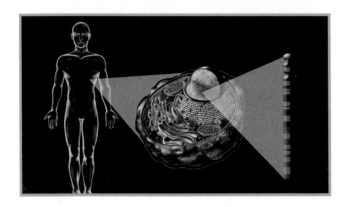

How can you describe the functions of the human body at different scales? Your whole body functions to eat, breathe, and move. At a smaller scale, cells, which can only be seen with a microscope, are the building parts for tissues and organs. Inside these cells is a nucleus, which contains chromosomes on an even smaller scale. Chromosomes are structures that contain instructions for how your body should grow.

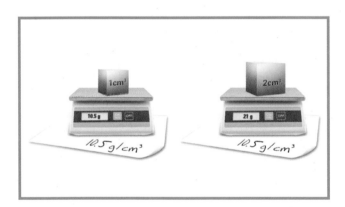

How can proportions be used to identify materials? Density is a proportion that can be used to identify materials. Here, there are two different cubes on a scale. The mass of each cube is different, just as the volume of each cube is different. However, the density of the two cubes is the same. Though the cubes are a different mass and volume, their density allows you to identify them as the same material.

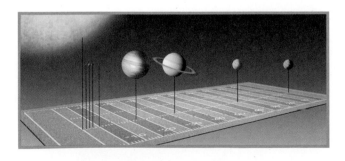

Why are different measurement units used to measure quantities in space? Within the solar system, scientists use astronomical units (AU) in which 1 AU is the average distance between the sun and Earth. However, the distances between stars are so far apart that scientists use a different unit of measurement—light years.

Systems and System Models

Systems occur in the natural world and in objects that are engineered by humans. Many systems interact with other ones, are parts of a larger complex one, or have subsystems of their own. How can you use the concept of systems to understand different phenomena such as the human body, a motor, and the motion of planets in the solar system?

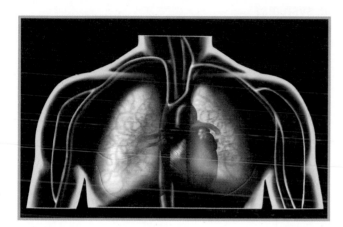

How do subsystems interact within the human body? Your whole body is composed of subsystems that work together to allow you to function. As your respiratory system draws in oxygen through your lungs, it sends oxygen to your bloodstream that is then carried through your body by the circulatory system. Both of these systems work together to help fulfill the body's needs. This is an example of two naturally occurring subsystems interacting as part of a complex whole.

How does a model of a motor represent the way energy and matter flow through a system? This model of an electric motor shows that there is an energy input into the system from the battery. The energy is transferred to electrically charged particles in the motor's wires. The particles begin to flow, forming an electric current that flows past a magnet. The forces between the wires and the magnet cause the motor's shaft to spin, outputting energy.

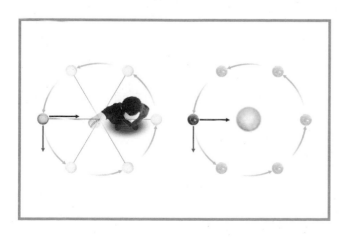

How can you use a model to represent the Earth-sun system? Suppose you swing a ball tied to a string around your head, causing it to move in a circle around your head. The string exerts a force on the ball, but the ball is moving fast enough to keep it from falling back into your hand. In this model, the string represents the gravitational force between the sun and Earth. Using a model allows you to understand how gravitational force functions in the Earth-sun system.

Energy and Matter

Systems can be described in term of energy and matter. Matter is anything that has mass and volume. Energy is the ability to cause motion or change. Energy takes two forms—kinetic energy, which is energy due to motion, and potential energy, which is stored energy. If you can track the energy in a system, you can use it to explain or predict motion and other changes. How does the transfer of energy drive motion or changes in each of the following systems?

How does a food web describe the transfer of energy and matter in an ecosystem? Energy can come from different places and is introduced into the food web when producers, such as plants, absorb energy from sunlight. Other organisms, called consumers, eat producers and other consumers to obtain their energy. Organisms use the energy they obtain to do things like move and stay warm. When they use this energy, they transfer energy to the environment.

Matter follows a path similar to energy in the food web. A consumer will eat an organism lower in the food web, consuming that organism's matter. However, unlike other organisms in the food web, producers get their matter from a different place than where they get their energy. Producers get matter from air, soil, and water, rather than sunlight. The matter from the air, soil, and water comes from decomposers that get their matter from the dead matter and wastes left behind by other organisms in the food web.

Matter and energy follow similar, but different paths. Matter is constantly being cycled through the ecosystem, while energy will flow in one direction.

How does a snowboarder transform potential energy into kinetic energy? Suppose a snowboarder was at the top of a hill, waiting to glide down to the bottom. A chairlift used energy from electricity to lift her up the mountain. That energy is stored by the snowboarder as potential energy. Since the mountain is so tall, she has a large amount of potential energy stored up.

Once the snowboarder tips over the ledge and glides down the hill, her potential energy begins to transform into kinetic energy. Kinetic energy is the energy an object has due to its motion. As the snowboarder is moving down the hill, not only is she moving herself, she is also moving the snow beneath her board. So, she is transferring some of her energy to the snow, giving it kinetic energy.

After the snowboarder glides to the bottom of the hill, nearly all of her potential energy has become kinetic energy. In order to stop, she must transfer all of her kinetic energy to her surroundings. Her board slides across the snow, spraying some of the snow forward and heating it up.

How does the transfer of energy drive the motion of matter in the water cycle?
Water particles are always moving, so they always have some kinetic energy. Water particles near the surface of water with a lot of kinetic energy evaporate off of the surface. When they do, they carry energy away from the water.

Since the particles that escaped the surface of the water have a lot of kinetic energy, they also have a high temperature. Their high temperature causes them to rise into the atmosphere. As they rise, their kinetic energy is converted into potential energy. Since the particles are losing kinetic energy, they also cool.

High in the atmosphere, slow-moving particles condense to form water droplets and clouds. These droplets are held high in the atmosphere due to updrafts of air.

During the precipitation stage, the water particles become too heavy to be held in the atmosphere by updrafts. They begin to fall, and their potential energy is converted back into kinetic energy. Even after reaching the ground, they continue to convert potential energy into kinetic energy as water flows down rivers and into the ocean.

Structure and Function

The structure and properties of a natural or engineered material often determine how that material will function. If a scientist or engineer can understand the structure of that material, then they can also determine how it should function and what may cause it to function improperly. How can you use the concept of structure and function to understand the behavior of natural and engineered materials?

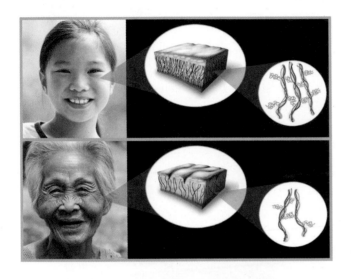

How do changes in the structure of skin tissue affect its function? Two of the proteins made by skin cells, collagen and elastin, help determine the skin's traits. When you are young, your skin continually replaces its collagen and elastin, which keeps your skin strong but flexible. Young skin is very good at protecting the underlying tissues of the body. Over time your body produces less of these proteins, resulting in more wrinkles and reduced protection, strength, and flexibility. The skin's functioning is directly related to the structural components that make it up.

How does the molecular structure of plastic affect its function? Plastics, such as the ones that make up water bottles, are polymers that are made of long flexible chains of molecules. Their structure allows them to retain their shape while remaining flexible. Biodegradable plastics are made of polymers that easily break down into smaller molecules over time. This allows the plastics to break down when buried in a landfill.

How do engineers use the properties of light and glass to design camera lenses? The structure and shape of the glass lens determines how well it functions as a medium for light waves. Glass can be shaped to refract the right amount of light, minimize absorption and reflection, and transmit light to the camera sensor. Once the structure is designed to be just right, the camera can get the perfect shot.

Stability and Change

Scientists can measure the behavior of systems by their stability, or resistance to change, and how they respond to change. Systems, whether small or large, will respond to any amount of change in different ways. How can you observe the way that systems respond when different amounts of change are introduced on different scales?

How can an ecosystem adjust to a change and reestablish its stability? When beavers construct a dam on a stream, they cause changes in the nonliving parts of the ecosystem. These changes in the nonliving parts of the ecosystem do not destroy the system but instead change which species can live there. The ecosystem adapts to changes over long time scales so that it is not completely disrupted. The ecosystem is able to reach a new state of stability.

How do stability and changes in your motion affect you when you ride in a car? If you are moving, you will continue moving at the same speed and in the same direction unless unbalanced forces are acting on you. In a car crash, this stable motion can be very dangerous. Unbalanced forces on the car cause the car to stop suddenly. If you are not wearing a seatbelt, there is no force pushing you back, so your motion will remain stable. You will keep moving forward.

How do different amounts of change over time effect the stability of Earth's system? The amount of carbon dioxide in Earth's atmosphere took millions of years to slowly reach a level that supports animal life on land. But starting about 150 years ago, people have been adding large amounts of carbon dioxide in the air. This fast change caused many destabilizing effects to Earth's system, which causes changes in stability to subsystems such as weather and climate systems.

Analyzing Text Structure

After watching a television program about space, you decide to do some reading about our solar system. You have already found a long online article and a couple of books at the library, but there is a lot of information to read through. How can you get the most out of your reading in the least amount of time?

Identifying the Purpose of the Text One way to make sense of a text is to identify the author's purpose. An author may be writing for many different purposes, including any one of these three:

- **Persuasive Argument** The author tries to convince the reader that his or her argument is correct.

- **Tell a Story** The author informs the reader about a process or explains why something came to be.

- **Explanation of Facts** The author informs or teaches the reader about a subject or topic.

Identifying Text Structures Another way to analyze text is to figure out how the information is organized, or structured. Authors may use many different text structures, including the following:

- **Cause and Effect Structure** The author attempts to answer a question about what causes something to happen.

- **Chronological Structure** The author explains a series of events in order.

- **Compare and Contrast Structure** The author compares two or more subjects to argue or clarify facts.

Reading scientific texts can seem like a difficult task, but when you identify the structure and organization of the text, it becomes much easier to understand the topic you are reading about.

Identifying Organizing Elements Look for specific features of the text that you can use to preview or review the text. A piece of text may have one or more of these organizing elements.

- **Table of Contents** The table of contents helps you identify where information is located in certain lessons or sections.

- **Introductions and Summaries** An introduction can provide previews of the text and explain the structure, while a summary can provide main ideas and a conclusion statement.

- **Headings** Reading headings provides information about the topic of a particular section of text.

- **Graphic Organizers** Visual aids organize large amounts of data into charts and graphs that are easy to understand.

Common Roots, Prefixes, and Suffixes in Science

While reading, you come across the word *exoskeleton*. You know what *skeleton* means, but you wonder what *exo-* means. Knowing common roots, prefixes, and suffixes, and how they combine, can make unfamiliar science words easier to understand! Here is a list of some of the common roots, prefixes, and suffixes you may encounter when you are reading science related texts:

Root, Prefix, or Suffix	Meaning	Examples
astro-	pertaining to stars or celestial bodies	astronaut, astrophysics
bio-	life	biofuel, biomass, biome, biosphere
chem-, chemo-	chemical	chemical, chemistry, chemotherapy
eco-	environment, nature	ecology, ecosystem
endo-	within, inside	endoskeleton, endothermic
exo-	without, outside	exoskeleton, exothermic
gene-	pertaining to heredity	genes, genetics, mutagen
geo-	the earth, pertaining to Earth	geography, geology, geosphere
hyper-	over, above	hyperthermia
hypo-	under, below	hypothermia, hypodermic
macro-	very large in scale, scope, or capability	macroscopic
micro-	extremely small	microscope, microscopic
-ology	a science or branch of knowledge, the study of something	archaeology, biology, geology
poly-	many, several, more than one	polymer
-sphere	spherical shape, supporting life	atmosphere, biosphere, hydrosphere
therm-, thermo-	heat, hot	hypothermia, thermodynamics, thermometer

If you can recognize a common root, prefix, or suffix, you can identify the meaning of unfamiliar words. Insects commonly have exoskeletons. The prefix *exo-* means "without" or "outside."

Writing Scientific Arguments and Explanations

After making observations and conducting an experiment, your teacher gives you an assignment to write a scientific argument about your experiment. It may sound simple, but where do you start?

Scientists do a lot of hands-on experimentation, but they also write arguments that convince people their claims are true. Writing is very important to the scientific process—well-written observations and notes will help you write a strong argument.

Claim The claim is where you introduce your hypothesis or the answer to a question you are trying to solve by gathering data. This is also where you would establish a formal style. You can do this by using full sentences and scientific terms you may have learned in class.

When writing scientific arguments, it is useful to organize your data into charts or graphs and ask a peer to review your work. Doing these simple things will help to make your argument stronger and more convincing.

Evidence Your evidence is specific scientific data that supports your claim. You can also use charts and graphs to communicate your findings. They make it easy to see and compare evidence, which can make your argument stronger.

Reasoning After providing your evidence, you need to convince the reader that the evidence supports the claim. If your classmates have different claims, you can point these out and use evidence to tell the reader why your claim is correct. You may also write a concluding statement to refresh the reader's memory and summarize the evidence and related reasoning.

Before you finish writing a scientific argument, read it for any spelling and grammatical errors. It also helps to have a peer read your argument. If your peer does not understand your argument, you may need to rewrite it until how you came to your conclusion is clearer.

Writing Investigation Procedures

The steps needed to carry out an investigation are called a procedure. Scientists write a procedure as part of the process of designing an investigation and use the procedure as a guide during the investigation. Scientists also record a procedure so that their fellow scientists can follow the investigation easily and confirm results. How can you write a good investigation procedure?

A good procedure organizes steps and data easily so you can complete your experiment without running into problems or danger. A procedure should also be written so anybody can repeat your experiment and obtain an identical result. Use this checklist as a guide when writing your procedure and to evaluate your writing when you are done:

- ☑ All of the necessary steps are included and clearly labeled.

- ☑ The tools and materials for each step are listed.

- ☑ Each step is clearly written using precise language and vocabulary so that a classmate or any stranger can follow it.

- ☑ The steps are in the correct order.

- ☑ Safety notes are included for any steps that require them.

- ☑ The type of data you will collect in each step is clearly described.

- ☑ If necessary, a data table is prepared to record data in.

- ☑ The language of the procedure is unbiased and something a fellow scientist would be comfortable reading.

Once your teacher has reviewed your procedure, you are ready to conduct your investigation!

When writing an investigation procedure, it is important that the steps are clearly written, are in the right order, include the materials needed, and have identified safety precautions.

Communicating with Graphic Organizers

Your teacher divides the class into teams and gives you all an assignment to build a protective structure for an egg out of simple materials. Afterwards, you work together as a class to create a graphic organizer to explain all the information and see why different teams got different results.

Scientists use graphic organizers to visually communicate complex ideas or large amounts of data. If you can read a graphic organizer, you can explain the results you see. When gathering data, it is useful to take the information you have and sketch a graphic organizer by hand. Once you decide how to present the information on paper, you can create your graphic organizer on the computer. Many software programs have the tools you need to create graphic organizers, like flow charts, Venn diagrams, and tables.

Flow Chart Flow charts are useful for displaying processes. In this case, the flowchart is explaining the process your team used to build your egg protector. You can add more detailed information to each box, but the chart should be a step-by-step explanation of each stage of your work. Computers have many applications that can be used to create flowcharts, including word processors or paint applications. The flowchart you see here is a good reference for the process you should follow when designing a solution to a problem.

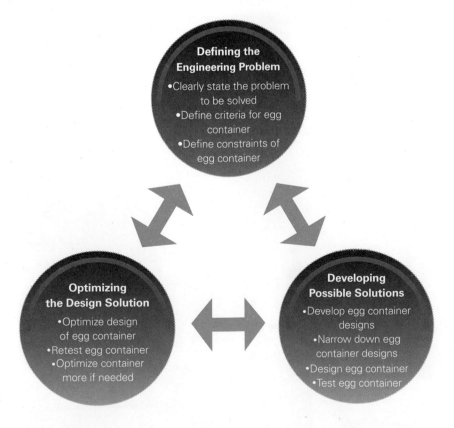

Defining the Engineering Problem
- Clearly state the problem to be solved
- Define criteria for egg container
- Define constraints of egg container

Developing Possible Solutions
- Develop egg container designs
- Narrow down egg container designs
- Design egg container
- Test egg container

Optimizing the Design Solution
- Optimize design of egg container
- Retest egg container
- Optimize container more if needed

Tables Tables group information into various categories by columns and rows and are useful for displaying large amounts of data. Scientists use tables to help them observe patterns in their data. In this case, the table displays the different materials used by the teams in your class to create their egg protectors. You can create a table by using spreadsheet software and inputting information into cells or by hand-drawing rows and columns on a sheet of paper. Look at the table below. Can you see any patterns in the materials used by the teams to create their egg protectors?

Team 1	Team 2	Team 3
Tissue Paper	Tissue Paper	Tissue Paper
Wooden sticks	Cotton Balls	Paper cup
Tape	Plastic Bag	Tape

Venn Diagram Like flowcharts, computers have applications that can be used to create Venn diagrams. Venn diagrams are used to show similarities and differences; each circle lists the traits of an object, and the overlap is used to list similarities. They are useful when comparing the traits of two or three different objects or ideas. Consider the Venn diagram below. Which material was used by all teams? Which materials were only used by one team? What conclusions would you be able to draw from this based on the results of the experiment?

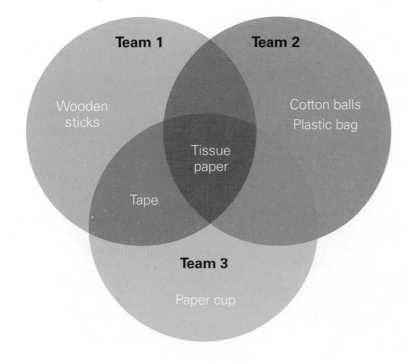

Research Project Tips

After reading about the periodic table, you decide you want to research it as a research project topic for your science class. One of the first things you need to do is find sources. With so many different places to look, including online and print sources, how do you even know where to begin?

How to Find Sources

- **First, go to the library.** The reference librarian will be able to point you in the right direction and teach you how to use the online catalog to find books, magazines, and journal subscriptions.

- **Find reliable sources.** Government and university websites, scientific magazines and journals, and other major magazines can be valuable sources of information that are easy to access.

- **Start general with search engines.** When using search engines, use words you would expect to find in your source. You do not need to worry about capitalization. Most search engines are able to understand what you are trying to find.

- **Try an advanced search tool.** Many search engines have a button for an "advanced search." Here, you can tell the search engine which kinds of websites you are looking for. If you want to find a government website, you can type "site:.gov" into one of the search fields.

The library is one of your best resources for research. Not only does it have books, it also has subscriptions for online magazines and journals that have current information on scientific advancements.

How to Evaluate Sources

- **Evaluate whether a source has bias.**
Consider whether the source has arguments
that are either supported by widely accepted
facts or available data. If you find information
on a website that is very different from
some of your other sources, you may want
to reconsider using that source.

- **Evaluate the source of your source.**
Unofficial websites that are not supported
by scientific, government, or academic
institutions are probably not good sources
to use. Check the URL for clues. Websites
that end in .gov or .edu tend to be more
reliable than general .com sites. You can also
read a source's "About" page to see what
their intention is for the information they
provide.

- **Evaluate the quality of your source.** One
source that has a lot of information about
one topic can be more useful than several
sources that have a little information about
one topic.

How to Cite Sources

- **Keep track of which sources you use.** Keep notes as to
which sources you use and where you use them in your own
work. It helps to use bookmarks that you can label to mark
which pages you draw information from. Another easy way to
keep track of your sources is to make a copy of the first page of
a book or article, or take a screenshot of a webpage. You may
also want to create a spreadsheet or document that keeps track
of the name of a source, its title or URL, and the information you
took from the site.

- **Use a style manual.** There are several guides that teach you
how to cite sources. The APA Style Manual, MLA Handbook,
and Chicago Manual of Style are good places to start.

- **Avoid plagiarism.** When you quote a source or use
information you got from a source, you need to give the source
credit. The style manuals will have instructions on how to give
credit for different kinds of sources.

As you gather information from
sources, it is very important to keep
track of which sources you use. Keep
organized notes for online sources by
creating a document or spreadsheet.
Label paper bookmarks or sticky notes
for print sources.

Positive and Negative Numbers

Positive and negative numbers are used together to describe quantities having opposite directions or values. Positive numbers represent values greater than zero, while negative numbers represent values less than zero. How can you use positive and negative numbers to describe changes in temperature?

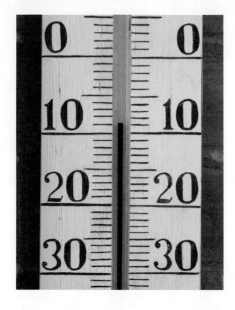

Thermometers display temperatures on a vertical number line. Numbers below zero on the number line are negative temperatures, while numbers above zero are positive temperatures.

A weather report says the temperature is –5°C. A negative number is a number that is less than zero. A number line represents numbers in relation to zero. On a horizontal number line, negative numbers are to the left of zero and positive numbers are to the right of zero. So, –5°C is five degrees below zero, which is five degrees to the left of zero. Likewise, 5°C would be five degrees above zero which is 5 degrees to the right of zero on a number line diagram.

During the afternoon, the temperature rises. The weather report says that the temperature increased by 7°C. What is the temperature now? To add a positive number, move right along the number line.

$$-5°C +7°C = 2°C$$

After sunset, the temperature drops, or decreases in value. The weather report says the temperature dropped 10°C after sunset. What is the temperature now? When you subtract a positive number, you move left along the number line.

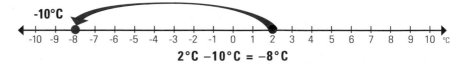

$$2°C -10°C = -8°C$$

What is the difference between the temperature in the morning (–5°C) and the temperature after sunset (–8°C)? To find the difference, subtract the morning temperature from the current temperature. To subtract a negative number means to add the positive of that number, so move right on the number line, just like adding a positive number.

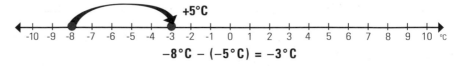

$$-8°C - (-5°C) = -3°C$$

Exponents and Scientific Notation

Scientists often need to represent very small numbers and very large numbers, which have many digits. These numbers can be so long that they are difficult to read. So, scientists developed a simpler method to represent these numbers, called scientific notation.

Scientific notation requires the use of exponents. An exponent is a number or symbol indicating how many times a base number should be multiplied by itself. For example, the "5" in 8^5 is an exponent, and 8^5 can also be expressed as "eight to the power of five" or $8 \times 8 \times 8 \times 8 \times 8$.

When you write numbers using scientific notation, 10 is the always the base number. Each time you multiply by 10, you move the decimal point one place to the right. So, multiplying by 10^6 moves the decimal point six places to the right. Scientific notation takes a number between 0 and 10 and multiplies it by a power of 10. This calculation moves the decimal point to the left or right the correct number of places.

Scientists use scientific notation to represent very small and very large numbers using powers of 10. Neptune is approximately 4,700,000,000 km from Earth, which can be written in scientific notation as 4.7×10^9 km.

Scientific notation is useful for writing very large numbers that represent distances in space. For example, engineers designing a probe to send to Neptune would often need to refer to the distance between Earth and Neptune, which is 4,700,000,000.0 kilometers. 4,700,000,000.0 can be expressed as 4.7 with the decimal point moved to the right nine places.

$$4.7 \times 10^9 \text{ km} = 4,700,000,000.0 \text{ km}$$

Very small numbers can also be written using scientific notation. For example, the diameter of a hydrogen atom is approximately 0.000000000106 meters. To write small numbers, you divide by 10 instead of multiplying by 10. You can represent this in scientific notation using negative exponents. 0.000000000106 meters is 1.06 meters with the decimal point moved to the left 10 times.

$$1.06 \times 10^{-10} \text{ m} = 0.0000000000106 \text{ m}$$

Dependent and Independent Variables

Scientists use dependent and independent variables to describe the relationships they measure in their investigations. Independent and dependent variables are used in equations to represent two different quantities that change in relationship to one another.

Equations, tables, and graphs are three ways to represent the relationship between an independent variable *x* and a dependent variable *y*. For a plane flying at 900 km/hr, the independent variable is flying time, and the dependent variable is distance traveled.

A commercial airplane has a cruising air speed for long-distance flights of 900 km/hr. In this relationship, the distance the plane travels depends on how long the plane has been flying. However, the time it has been flying does not depend on the distance it has traveled. So, time is the independent variable (*x*), and distance is the dependent variable (*y*). The relationship between kilometers traveled and the time in hours can be represented between two variables using an equation, a table, or a graph.

An equation that represents the relationship between the distance the airplane has traveled and how long it has traveled is:

$$y = 900x$$

The letter *x* represents the independent variable, which is the time the plane has been flying. The letter *y* is the dependent variable, which is the distance the plane has traveled.

The second way to represent the relationship between variables is with a table. The table on this page uses the equation $y = 900x$ to calculate the dependent *y* value that matches each independent *x* value in the table. It represents the relationship between *x* and *y*.

The third way to represent the relationship between two variables is with a graph. You can use either the equation or the table of values to represent the relationship in a graph. The graph both shows the equation and plots the points from the data table.

Airplane Distance Traveled Compared to Time

Time (hours) *x*	Distance (km) *y*
0	0
1	900
2	1,800
3	2,700
4	3,600

Chance and Probability

Some events scientists study involve things that definitely will happen or will not happen. However, most events might happen but will not happen for sure. How can understanding probability help predict how likely events are to happen?

Every year, sugar maple trees produce many seeds, which are carried away from the trees by wind. Many of the seeds germinate, or sprout into a seedling that can grow into a new tree, but not every seed does. A scientist decides to study how likely it is that a maple seed will sprout. That is, she will study the probability that a seed will germinate.

The scientist randomly collects a sample of 1,000 seeds from trees in a 1 km × 1 km area. She and her team plant the seeds in a large field. They return in the spring to determine how many of the seeds germinated into new maple trees. She might find that 910 of the seeds germinated. The proportion of seeds that germinated was $\frac{910}{1,000}$, or 91%.

Her team repeats the experiment several more times in different years and finds that in one year, 97% of the seeds germinated. In the second year, 94% germinated, and 95% germinated in the third year. From this data, she finds the average proportion of seeds that germinate and concludes that the chance of a maple seed germinating is about 95%.

Sugar maple trees produce many seeds, but some seeds do not germinate. By collecting data on how many seeds germinate, a scientist can estimate the probability that each individual seed will germinate.

A 95% probability means that each seed has a 95 in 100 chance of germinating. If you looked at 100 seeds, you would expect 95 of them to germinate. If you looked at 1,000 seeds, you would expect 950 to germinate. However, 950 seeds would not germinate every time. For example, sometimes 962 seeds would germinate, or 935 seeds, or 900 seeds, or even all 1,000 seeds. A probability describes the chance that something will happen, but it does not predict exactly what will happen every time.

Representing and Interpreting Data

Scientific investigations produce a lot of data, but it is often difficult to make sense of the data the way it is recorded during the investigation. Scientists carefully choose how they will represent data to make it easy to analyze, interpret, and communicate its meaning to others.

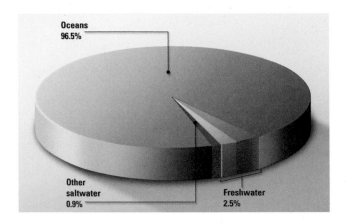

Pie Graphs A comparison between the amount of freshwater and saltwater on Earth is best represented using a pie graph. Scientists use pie graphs to display data with percentages. A pie graph, also known as a pie chart, divides a circle into sections to show the relative sizes of data and how a part relates to the whole. A pie graph can effectively show how one variable is divided between different categories. They often show the percentage of a variable in each category. For instance, the wedges on this pie graph show how the water on Earth is divided into three categories: water from oceans, fresh water, and other saltwater.

Scatter Plots Scientists use scatter plots to show repeated measurements of a similar phenomenon, such as the relationship between the waiting time between eruptions of the geyser Old Faithful and the length of the eruptions. Each measurement of an eruption is one point on the graph. The x coordinate of the point shows the duration of the eruption. The y coordinate shows the waiting time before the eruption. Scatter plots are effective for comparing two variables that do not fall into specific categories. There are many patterns in data that scatter plots can reveal.

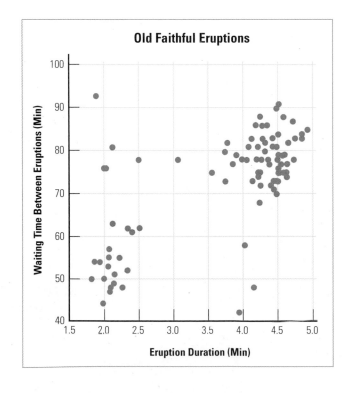

The scatter plot shows that Old Faithful eruptions fall into two main groups: a short wait between eruptions (45–60 minutes) followed by a short eruption (2 minutes), or a long wait between eruptions (70–90 minutes) followed by a long eruption (4–5 minutes).

A scatter plot that compares shoe size to height would probably form a line, indicating that people who are taller usually wear larger shoes.

Bar Graphs This bar graph of earthquakes in Oklahoma shows how many earthquakes occurred in Oklahoma in each year between 2000 and 2015. Scientists use bar graphs, or bar charts, to represent the relative sizes of data values in different categories, such as years, months, colors, or cities. They use horizontal or vertical bars to represent the size of the value in each category. Larger bars represent a higher value, and smaller bars represent a lower value. The bar graph of earthquakes in Oklahoma shows a huge increase in earthquakes in 2014 from previous years since the bar for 2014 is much larger than any of the previous bars.

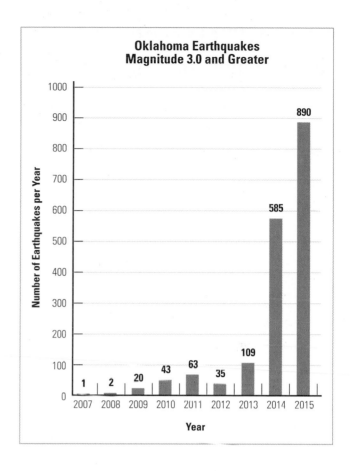

Line Graphs Scientists use line graphs to show how a dependent variable changes as an independent variable is increased. In many cases, the independent variable is a measure of time, so the graph shows how a dependent variable changes over time. For example, the average global temperature over time can be shown using a line graph. Like in a scatter plot, each data point has an x coordinate (time) and a y coordinate (average temperature). Unlike a scatter plot, each data point is connected to the last one with a straight line. Following the line shows how the average temperature changed over time.

This line graph shows many patterns about how the global average temperature changed between 1880 and 2000. The temperature was lowest between 1900 and 1920 and highest after 2000. What other patterns do you see in the graph?

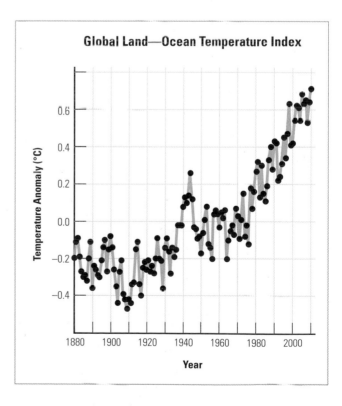

Ratios, Rates, Percents, and Proportional Relationships

When scientists collect data involving numbers, quantities are often compared. You can compare quantities using ratios, percentages, and unit rates. How are these mathematical concepts useful in understanding one of the most important scientific investigations related to changes in species?

Kettlewell released light and dark colored moths and then recaptured them to study how well each type of moth survived in polluted and unpolluted woods. He used the ratio of moths captured to moths released, expressed as a percentage, to support his findings.

Scientists have been observing and studying dark peppered moths near Manchester, England, since 1848. More than 70 species of moths in England have undergone a change from light to dark, with similar observations in the United States.

Expressing Ratios as Percentages To study this change, a scientist named Henry Bernard Davis Kettlewell released light and dark colored moths in polluted and unpolluted woods. He then recaptured as many of the moths as he could over the next week. In the unpolluted woods, he released 496 light colored moths and captured back 62 of them. So, the ratio of captured moths to released moths is 62:496. By finding an equivalent ratio with 100 as the number of moths released, you can find what percentage 62:496 equals.

$$62:496 = 12.5:100$$

Kettlewell recaptured 12.5% of the light moths he released. Similarly, he released 488 dark moths into the unpolluted woods and only recaptured 34. That is 34:488 as a ratio, or 7.0% as a percentage.

Using Unit Rates Scientists often compare quantities using unit rates. A unit rate is the number of one quantity there is for every one unit of another quantity. If Kettlewell wanted to know how many moths he needed to release in order to capture one moth, he would calculate the unit rate. He would do so by starting with the ratio of moths released to moths captured (496:62 for light colored moths). Then he would find an equivalent ratio where the number of moths captured is one. Unit rates are usually written as fractions.

$$\text{Unit rate} = \frac{8 \; moths \; released}{1 \; moth \; captured}$$

So, for every eight light colored moths Kettlewell released, he captured one light colored moth back.

Graphing and Interpreting Proportional Relationships

Scientists and engineers look for proportional relationships to better understand and predict how two variables are related. In a proportional relationship, the ratio of one variable to the other is always the same. How can using proportional reasoning make someone a better bowler?

An engineer wants to improve her bowling score, so she decides to study the relationship between the mass of the bowling ball she uses and the kinetic energy of the ball. She builds a machine that throws a bowling ball down the lane at exactly 8 m/s. Then she tests a variety of bowling balls. She makes a table of her data and finds the ratio of energy to mass of the balls. She sees that the ratio is the same for every ball moving at 8 m/s. She discovered a proportional relationship between the bowling ball's energy and mass.

She makes a graph of the data in her table and sees that the data points form a straight line. The line passes through the origin (0, 0). She calculates that the slope of the line is 32 J/kg. The line's slope is the same as the ratio of energy per unit mass in her table.

To make predictions, the engineer writes an equation to describe her data. The equation of a straight line is $y = mx + b$. The y-intercept (b) of her line is 0 J. The slope (m) of her line is 32 J/kg. So, the equation for her line is:

$$y = 32x$$

In this equation, y is energy of the ball, and x is mass of the ball. The engineer now knows how the energy of the ball depends on its mass. But she still has more questions. How does the energy depend on the speed of the ball? And how much energy should the ball have to knock down all the pins?

Mass versus Kinetic Energy With Constant Velocity

Mass (kg)	Energy (J)	Ratio: energy/mass (J/kg)
4	128	$\frac{128}{4} = 32$
5	160	$\frac{160}{5} = 32$
6	192	$\frac{192}{6} = 32$
7	224	$\frac{224}{7} = 32$

Angles, Perpendicular and Parallel Lines

Scientists use angles as well as parallel and perpendicular lines to describe how objects are oriented relative to each other. How can using these mathematical ideas help when explaining how light rays interact with a glass slide?

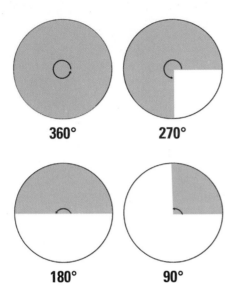

360°   270°

180°   90°

Angles Light travels in a straight line until it passes from one material, or medium, to another material. When a beam of light enters a glass slide, it bends. The amount that the beam bends depends on the angle between the slide and the beam of light. An angle is a shape formed by two rays that begin at the same endpoint, and the size of the angle can be changed by rotating the two rays. Angles are measured in degrees (°). Rotating 360° is rotating in a full circle, returning the object back to where it started. Rotating by 180° is rotating through half a circle, and rotating by 90° is rotating a quarter circle.

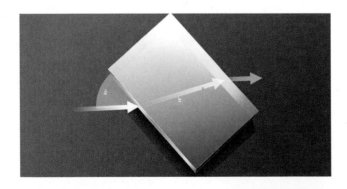

Parallel Lines The beam of light meets the glass at a 51° angle. As it enters the glass, it changes direction, turning 14° counterclockwise. When the beam of light leaves the glass, it rotates back, turning 14° clockwise. The beam of light leaving the glass is parallel to the beam of light entering the glass. Parallel lines are lines that, if you extend them out infinitely in both directions, will never cross.

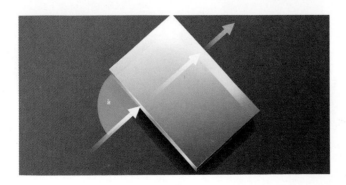

Perpendicular Lines A beam of light will not always bend when it enters a glass slide. If the beam of light is perpendicular to the edge of the slide, the light will pass straight through without bending. Two lines are perpendicular if they meet at a 90° angle.

Area, Surface Area, and Volume

Scientists use area, surface area, and volume to describe the sizes of various objects they study. Area describes the size of a two-dimensional surface. Surface area describes the total size of the surface of a three-dimensional object. Volume describes the amount of space a three-dimensional object takes up. How could a scientist who wanted to explain why cells are so small use the concepts of area, surface area, and volume? He investigates simple cube-shaped cells in the human body.

Area The scientist knows that for a cell to survive, enough nutrients have to pass through its cell membrane to supply the needs of the cell. The larger the area of the membrane, the more nutrients can pass through it. So, the scientist calculates the area of one square-shaped side of the cell.

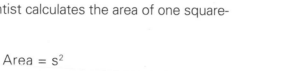

$$\text{Area} = s^2$$

Surface Area But the scientist knows that nutrients can pass through any side of the cube, not just one side. So, he needs to calculate the surface area of the cube. The surface area is the total area of the surface of the cube. The cube has six sides, so its surface area is six times the area of one side.

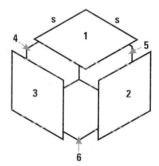

$$\text{Surface Area} = 6s^2$$

Volume However, the scientist knows that volume of the cube is important too. The volume is the total amount of space that the cube takes up. Generally, the larger the volume is, the more nutrients the cell needs to stay alive and the farther the nutrients have to go after entering the cell. The volume of a cube is the side length cubed.

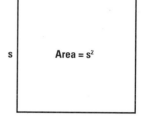

$$\text{Volume} = s^3$$

The scientist sees that as the cube gets larger, the volume grows much faster than the surface area grows. So, he decides that the cells he is studying are all very small because a large cell would not be able to take in enough nutrients through its membrane to support its volume. Cells need a large surface-area-to-volume ratio to survive.

Metric System Units

Throughout history, people around the world used different measurement units for trading goods and building objects and structures. Body parts were used to measure length. Grains of wheat were poured into containers to measure volume. Notches on a burning candle measured time. What problems did these customs cause, and how were they solved?

Traditional measurement units were awkward. It was difficult to compare one unit to another. Even when the same unit was used, there were often variations in how the unit was applied from place to place. In the late 1700s, that all changed. Scientists began to develop new units that were easy to use and accepted by scientists everywhere. Many of those units are part of the metric system.

The units you choose are determined by the goal of your investigation. If you want to measure the amount of matter in a rock, you would choose grams, a measure of mass, as your unit. If you want to measure how warm water is, you would use degrees Celsius. Other metric units are a combination of two units. For example, to describe the speed of a toy car rolling down a ramp, you would record the speed as meters per second.

Some Common Units of the Metric System

Measurement	Unit Name	Symbol
length	meter	m
mass	gram	g
time	second	s
temperature	degrees Celsius	°C
area	meter squared	m^2
frequency	hertz	Hz
force	newton	N
volume	meter cubed	m^3
density	kilogram per meter cubed	kg/m^3
speed, velocity	meter per second	m/s
acceleration	meter per second squared	m/s^2
energy	joule	J
power (energy per second)	watt	W
energy	watt hour	Wh
electric charge	coulomb	C

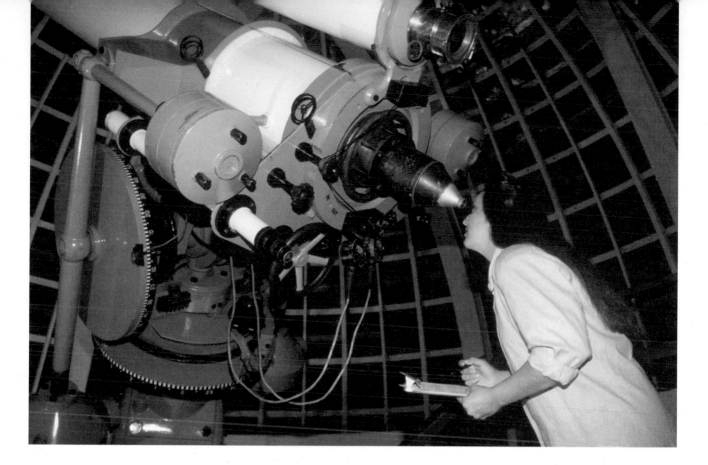

Some units were not developed as part of the metric system, but are still used by many scientists and engineers around the world. For example, if you want to compare distances of objects in the solar system, meters or even kilometers make the numbers difficult to communicate. Astronomers prefer to use astronomical units for this purpose. Similarly, when you need to describe distances between two stars or two galaxies, astronomical units are difficult. The distances are so great that astronomers use a unit called a light year, which is the distance that light travels in one Earth year.

Several measurement units are not part of the metric system, yet they are widely used by scientists and engineers. Two of these units, astronomical units and light years, are essential for communicating data to scientists such as this astronomer.

Some Common Units Outside the Metric System		
Measurement	**Unit Name**	**Symbol**
time	minute	min
time	hour	h
time	day	d
angle size	degree	°
liquid volume	liter	L
distances inside the solar system	astronomical unit	AU
distances between stars	light year	ly
energy	calorie	cal
digital information	byte	B

Metric System Prefixes

A base unit can be modified using prefixes that indicate different amounts of each unit. Let's say you are investigating plant species to determine how much variation there is among their flower sizes. Some plant species have flowers that are so tiny that they can only be seen with magnification. Others have flowers as wide as a human's arm length. How can understanding measurement prefixes help you?

This flower is produced by plants called *Rafflesia* and is about 1 m across. Most plants have flowers that are much smaller, so smaller units are more useful for describing them.

Using prefixes with base units allows you to choose the unit that is simplest to communicate. Adding a prefix to a base unit makes a new unit. The new unit is made larger or smaller than the base unit by multiplying the base unit by a certain factor of 10. Each prefix represents a different factor of 10.

Here is how it works when measuring length. Meters are the base unit for length and are suitable for describing the size of the largest flowers in the plant kingdom. Millimeters have the prefix *milli*, which is 0.001. So a millimeter is 0.001, or 1/1,000, times the amount of one meter. There are 1,000 millimeters in one meter. Millimeters is a suitable unit for measuring the smallest flowers in the world. Now, suppose you were to travel around the world touring exotic flowers. A larger unit for length would be helpful to describe the distance you traveled. There are 1,000 meters in a kilometer. The prefix *kilo* means 10^3, or 1,000. So a kilometer is 1,000 times the size of a meter.

Many base units can be changed to easier-to-use units by adding a prefix. Start by choosing a base unit. Move up to get larger units and move down to get smaller units.

Some Common Units of the Metric System				
Prefix	**Symbol**	**Word**	**Decimal**	**Factor of 10**
tera	T	trillion	1,000,000,000,000	10^{12}
giga	G	billion	1,000,000,000	10^{9}
mega	M	million	1,000,000	10^{6}
kilo	k	thousand	1,000	10^{3}
hecto	h	hundred	100	10^{2}
deka	da	ten	10	10^{1}
Choose a base unit.		one	1	10^{0}
deci	d	tenth	0.1	10^{-1}
centi	c	hundredth	0.01	10^{-2}
milli	m	thousandth	0.001	10^{-3}
micro	µ	millionth	0.000001	10^{-6}
nano	n	billionth	0.000000001	10^{-9}
pico	p	trillionth	0.000000000001	10^{-12}

Converting Measurement Units

You can also find equivalents of measurements that have the same base unit but different prefixes. One method is to divide or multiply by the number of one unit in the other unit. Another method is to use a metric "staircase" to decide how many places, and in what direction, to move the decimal point.

You can convert a larger unit to a smaller unit using multiplication. To do so, multiply the original measurement by the amount that the new unit differs from it. For example, to convert 9 kilometers to centimeters, you would multiply 9 (the number of kilometers) times 100,000 (the number of centimeters in one kilometer). So, 900,000 cm is equivalent to 9 km.

A smaller unit can be converted to a larger unit by using division. To do so, divide the original measurement by the amount that the new unit differs from it. For example, to use division to convert 900,000 centimeters to kilometers, divide 900,000 (the number of centimeters) by 100,000 (the number of centimeters in one kilometer). As before, 9 km is equivalent to 900,000 cm.

Another way to convert units is by picturing the metric "staircase" shown here to decide how many places to move the decimal point. For example, to convert 1 1 kilograms to milligrams, take six steps down the staircase and move the decimal point six places to the right. There are 1,100,000 milligrams in 1.1 kilograms.

In the United States, certain non-metric units are used in everyday situations. For this reason, you may sometimes need to convert non-metric units into metric units. Luckily, there are many websites and apps that will do conversions for you!

To convert to a larger unit, move the decimal point to the left for each step up the staircase. To convert to a smaller unit, move the decimal point to the right for each step you take down the staircase.

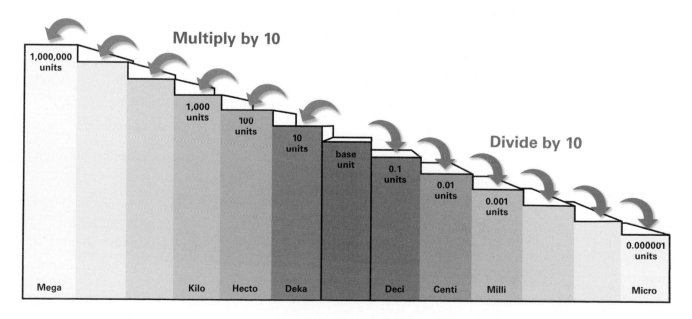

GLOSSARY

A

acceleration   the rate of change of an object's velocity; acceleration can be speeding up, slowing down, or changing direction

attractive   when referring to forces, pulling together

B

balanced forces   forces that have a net force equal to 0 N

C

chemical potential energy   potential energy stored in the chemical bonds that hold particles of matter together; chemical potential energy is a combination of different types of energy

conduction   heat transfer caused by the collisions of particles of matter that are in direct contact

constant   describes a value that does not change

constraints   limitations on an engineering solution

convection   the transfer of energy caused by the circulation of matter due to differences in density

criteria   the requirements that must be met for an engineering solution to be successful

E

elastic potential energy   potential energy resulting from elastic forces; elastic potential energy is a combination of different types of energy

electric charge   a property of matter that causes electrical phenomena

electric current   a flow of particles with electric charge

electric field   a force field surrounding an electrically charged object

electric forces   attractive or repulsive noncontact forces between charged particles

electric generator   a device that uses permanent magnets and electromagnets to produce electric current; an electric generator is an electric motor running backward

electric motor   a device that uses electric currents to produce motion using permanent magnets and electromagnets

electric potential energy   potential energy stored in a system of objects interacting by electric forces

electromagnet   a magnet made with a current-carrying wire whose strength can be varied and turned on and off

energy   the ability to cause motion or change

F

force   a push or a pull on an object

force field   a model that describes what the force on an object would be if the object were placed in any location in space; usually used to predict the strength and direction of noncontact forces

friction   a force that opposes motion between two surfaces that are touching

G

gravitational field   a map of a force field that can be used to predict which way gravitational forces will pull an object

gravitational forces always attractive, noncontact forces between objects that have mass

gravitational potential energy potential energy stored in a system of objects interacting due to gravitational forces

H

heat thermal energy that is transferred from one region or substance to another

heat capacity a property of a substance that describes how much thermal energy is needed to change the temperature of the substance

K

kinetic energy the energy an object has due to its motion

L

law of conservation of energy a scientific law that states that the total energy of an isolated system always remains the same

linear relationship a relationship between two variables when a graph of one variable versus the other is a straight line; it can be represented by the equation $y = mx + b$

M

magnetic field a force field created by a magnet

magnetic forces attractive or repulsive forces between magnets or attractive forces between a magnet and certain materials

magnetic poles the regions where the magnetic forces exerted by a magnet are the strongest

magnetic potential energy potential energy stored in a system of objects interacting by magnetic forces

mass the amount of matter in an object; mass is measured in kilograms

N

net force the sum of all forces acting on an object

newton a unit used to measure the strength of a force

Newton's first law of motion states that an object at rest stays at rest, and an object in motion stays in motion with a constant velocity unless acted on by unbalanced forces

Newton's second law of motion states that an object's acceleration is equal to the net force on the object divided by its mass

Newton's third law of motion states that when an object exerts a force on a second object, the second object exerts a force on the first object with equal strength, but in the opposite direction

nonlinear relationship a relationship between two variables when a graph of one variable versus the other is not a straight line

O

orbit the path that an object in space follows around another object due to gravitational forces between the objects

P

permanent magnet a magnet that is always surrounded by a magnetic field

phenomenon an observable fact or event

position   the distance and direction that an object is from a reference point

potential energy   the energy stored in a system due to the positions of objects in the system that are interacting at a distance

proportional relationship   the relationship between two variables when the ratio between the variables is constant; a graph of a proportional relationship is a straight line through the origin

prototype   a working model of a design solution that can be used for testing and refining the design

R

radiation   the transfer of energy by light waves

rate   an amount of something measured per unit of something else; many rates describe changes or events that happen over time

reference frame   a point of view on the speed and direction that objects are moving and what reference point they are moving relative to

reference point   an object or place you use to describe the locations of other objects

repulsive   when referring to forces, pushing apart

resistance   opposition to the flow of electric charge

S

scientific law   a set of verbal or mathematical rules to describe a natural phenomenon; unlike scientific theories, scientific laws do not explain the phenomenon

slope   the steepness of a line on a graph, calculated by dividing the change in the y-value by the change in the x-value for any two points on the line

speed   the rate that describes how far an object moves over time

temperature   a measure of the average kinetic energy of particles of matter

thermal conductivity   a property of a substance that describes how quickly thermal energy can spread through the substance

thermal conductor   a substance that has a high thermal conductivity

thermal energy   includes the kinetic energy of the particles that make up a system and the potential energy stored in the system because of the interactions between the particles

thermal equilibrium   the condition in which objects that are touching have the same temperature

thermal insulator   a substance that has a low thermal conductivity

U

unbalanced forces   forces that have a net force not equal to 0 N

V

velocity   an object's speed and direction of motion

W

weight   the amount of gravitational force on an object; weight is measured in newtons

*Page numbers in **bold** indicate definitions.*

during a roller coaster ride, 121

in Rube Goldberg machines, 151

and speed, 132–133, 134–135

transformation of, 120

L

laboratory safety, 196

Lake Maracaibo (Venezuela), 87, 88

law of conservation of energy, 115, **122**

least weasel's bite force, 52

lift, 35

lift bridge, 152, 153

lightning, 74, 75, 86–89

linear relationship(s), 129, **131**

line graphs, 241

lines

parallel, 244

perpendicular, 244

living things

animals. *See* animals

in the classroom, safety for, 199

humans. *See* humans

luggage carts, 42–43

M

magnetic field(s), 91, **94**–95

current-carrying wires moving in, 100

earth's, 95

magnetic field lines, 94

magnetic forces, 91, **92**–93

attractive, 92

and distance, 93

repulsive, 92

magnetic poles, 91, **92**–93

earth's, 95

magnetic potential energy, 143, **148**

and distance, 148

and orientation, 148

in Rube Goldberg machines, 151

magnetism and electromagnetism, 91–105

mantis shrimp, 20, 22

mass, 59, **68**

acceleration and, 47

gravitational forces and, 61, 64

gravitational potential energy and, 144, 145

gravity and, 69

and kinetic energy, 130–131, 134–135

thermal energy and, 165

materials

optimizing, 188–189

thermal conductivity of, 186

mathematical modeling, 210, 211

Mathematical Principles of Natural Philosophy (Newton), 27

mathematical representation, 210, 211

mathematical thinking, 210–211

matter

energy and, 224–225

thermal energy and, 165–166, 167

thermal properties of, 181–189

measurement units

converting, 249

metric system prefixes, 248

metric system units, 246–247

unit rates, 242

megalodon, 50, 51

meters per second (m/s), 9

metric system

prefixes, 248

units, 246–247

microphones, 109

miles per hour (mi/h or mph), 9

Milky Way, 63

model(s)

components of, 204, 205

connections with natural phenomenon, 204, 205

developing and using, 204–205

gravitational forces, 66

of gravitational forces, 66

mathematical modeling, 210, 211

prototypes, 75, 85

relationships in, 204, 205

systems models, 223

moon's orbit around earth, 63

motion

acceleration. *See* acceleration

describing, 7–19

energy and, 116–117

Newton's laws of. *See* Newton's laws of motion

position. *See* position

reference frame(s). *See* reference frame(s)

track racing, 128, 129

    racing bikes, 136–137

train reference frame, 13

transfer of energy, 224–225

trebuchets, 125

    tabletop, 126–127

Trip Around the Moon (Verne), 71

turbines, 103

    wind, 103, 104–105

Tyrannosaurus rex, 50, 51

U

unbalanced forces, 39, **42**

    on moving objects, 43

    Newton's laws of motion and, 48

unit rates, 242

V

Van de Graaff generators, 146

variable(s)

    dependent, 238

    independent, 238

velocity, 7, **10**

    acceleration, position, and, 16–17

    average, 10

    in different reference frames, 13

    negative, 10

    positive, 10

Venn diagrams, 233

Verne, Jules (science fiction author), 71, 72, 73

volleyball, 48

volume, 245

W

water into water vapor, 187

water vapor

    smothering fires with, 192

    water into, 187

weight, 35, 59, **68**

    gravity and, 68, 69

    in space, 68, 69

wind farms, 103

windmills, 103

wind turbines, 103, 104–105

wood floors, 183

CREDITS

Unit 3 Opener

110: Shutterstock 113TL: Thinkstock 113TR: Getty Images 113B: Klaus Thiemann/Dreamstime

Lesson 7

114: Thinkstock 116TL: Thinkstock 116TR: Thinkstock 116BL: Thinkstock 116BR: Thinkstock 117T: Thinkstock 117B: Miguel Angel Morales Hermo/Dreamstime 118: Thinkstock 118: Thinkstock 119T: Thinkstock 119B: Thinkstock 120: Shutterstock 121: Shutterstock 122: Shutterstock 122: Shutterstock 124: De Agostini Picture Library/G. Dagli Orti/Bridgeman Images 125: Colin Palmer Photography/Alamy

Lesson 8

128: Thinkstock 130: Shutterstock 130: Shutterstock 130: Shutterstock 131: Shutterstock 132: Shutterstock 133: Shutterstock 134: Shutterstock 134: Shutterstock 136: Getty Images 138: Getty Images 139: Getty Images 140: Getty Images 141T: Aflo Co., Ltd./Alamy 141B: Thinkstock

Lesson 9

142: Juice Images/Alamy 149LL: Getty Images 149LR: Thinkstock 149RTL: Getty Images 149RTR: Thinkstock 149RB: Getty Images 150: Getty Images 150: Thinkstock 150: Thinkstock 151: Getty Images 151: Thinkstock 151: Thinkstock 151: Thinkstock 152: Shutterstock 153: Klaus Thiemann/Dreamstime 154: Thinkstock 155: Thinkstock 156: Thinkstock 157: Anthony Berenyi/Dreamstime

Unit 4 Opener

158: Shutterstock 161TL: Shutterstock 161TR: Shutterstock 161B: Wikimedia

Lesson 10

162: Thinkstock 164: Thinkstock 164: Thinkstock 164: Thinkstock 164: Thinkstock 167: Shutterstock 167: Thinkstock 168: Shutterstock 169: Shutterstock 171T: Thinkstock 171B: Thinkstock 172: Getty Images 173: Shutterstock 175: Thinkstock 176: Shutterstock 177: NASA 178: ASSOCIATED PRESS 179: NASA

Lesson 11

180: Thinkstock 183T: Getty Images 183L: Thinkstock 183C: Getty Images 183R: Getty Images 185: Thinkstock 186T: Shutterstock 186TC: Shutterstock 186BC: Shutterstock 186B: Shutterstock 188: Wikimedia 189: LBNL/Science Source 190: Shutterstock 191: Shutterstock 192: Shutterstock 193: Shutterstock

Back Matter

194: Reto Stöckli, Nazmi El Saleous, and Marit Jentoft-Nilsen, NASA GSFC 196: Corbis Premium RF/Alamy 197: iStockphoto 198: Image Source Plus/Alamy 199: Thinkstock 201: Shutterstock 203: Shutterstock 204: Shutterstock 205T: Karin Hildebrand Lau/Alamy 205B: A.J.D. Foto Ltd./Alamy 207: Thinkstock 211: Shutterstock 213: Shutterstock 215: Thinkstock 217: Shutterstock 219: Shutterstock 220T: Wikimedia 221T: Thinkstock 221C: Thinkstock 225T: Thinkstock 225C: Thinkstock 226B: iStockphoto 227T: Thinkstock 227C: Getty Images 227B: NASA 228: Thinkstock 229: Borislav Toskov/Dreamstime 230: Image Source Plus/Alamy 231: Hero Images Inc./Alamy 234: Blend Images/Alamy 235: iStockphoto 236: Thinkstock 237: NASA/JPL 239: Thinkstock 242: Wikimedia 247: Ted Foxx/Alamy 248: iStockphoto